Y0-BQT-556

SEARCHING THE CHEMICAL LITERATURE

Revised and enlarged edition of Advances in Chemistry Series No. 4. Based on papers presented by the Division of Chemical Literature and the Division of Chemical Education of the American Chemical Society at national meetings from 1947 to 1956.

Number 30

ADVANCES IN CHEMISTRY SERIES

American Chemical Society

Washington, D. C.

1961

Library of Congress Catalog Card No. 61-11330
PRINTED IN THE UNITED STATES OF AMERICA

ADVANCES IN CHEMISTRY SERIES

Robert F. Gould, Editor

AMERICAN CHEMICAL SOCIETY APPLIED PUBLICATIONS

CONTENTS

Introduction

The first edition of "Searching the Chemical Literature" appeared as Number 4 in the ADVANCES IN CHEMISTRY SERIES. It was based on a symposium held by the Division of Chemical Literature of the American Chemical Society at the 117th national meeting in Detroit, April 16 to 20, 1950, and included four revised papers from the Symposium on the Preparation of Literature and Patent Surveys held by the Division of Chemical Education at the 111th ACS national meeting in Atlantic City, April 14 to 18, 1947. That edition was reprinted four times. As a result of this popularity, the late Dr. Walter J. Murphy suggested that a new symposium be held in order to bring the volume up to date. With the approval of the Executive and Program Committees of the Division of Chemical Literature, the new symposium was held at the 130th ACS national meeting in Atlantic City, September 16 to 21, 1956.

In view of the lapse of time since the latter meeting, the papers given there, as well as those from the first edition, were revised and brought up to date in 1960 and '61. Certain of the papers have been combined and/or revised by others because several of the original authors are no longer active in the field or have died.

The paper on the "Fiat Review of German Science" by Matthew W. Miller has been dropped from this edition with Dr. Miller's consent, since the subject is no longer of current interest. The paper on "Methods and Sources in Chemical Market Research" by John R. Skeen has been dropped with Mr. Skeen's consent because a whole symposium on this subject, arranged by Mr. Skeen, forms part of Number 10 in the ADVANCES IN CHEMISTRY SERIES, "Literature Resources for the Chemical Process Industries."

Papers are grouped by subject without regard to the original programs. This may emphasize the overlap that is difficult to avoid in symposia, particularly in collections of papers over so long a period. But it serves also to offer several points of view. While the treatment is not intended to be comprehensive, this volume offers surveys on the use of indexes and abstracts, on name, nomenclature, and language problems, on various types of literature sources, on government sources, on searching techniques, and on the facilities of four leading libraries.

It is hoped that this new and completely revised edition will prove helpful to those who use the chemical literature, a literature which has grown enormously in the decade since the first edition. To those just entering this field it may be a useful guide; to those who are experienced, it may bring new points of view.

T. E. R. SINGER

Literature and Patent Searching

CHARLOTTE M. SCHALER[1]
Sinclair Refining Co., New York, N. Y.

JULIAN F. SMITH
Lenoir Rhyne College, Hickory, N. C.

Planning and the use of basic searching principles produce better searches in less time. Defining the search problem, using available prior bibliographies, selecting the most appropriate key words, seeking sound, while avoiding unsound, short cuts, interpreting findings in the light of search goals, and knowing when to stop are major requirements. A patent department searcher should know enough about patent law to anticipate the patent attorney's problems. Planning the search involves careful organization of both technical and clerical steps for maximum efficiency. In bounding the search subject a set of questions to be answered in the search abstracts is usually devised. Employment of outside searchers depends partly on the regular staff's work load and partly on the company's location. Outside searchers may have access to large libraries far from the company's laboratory.

A search is made to secure information for a specific purpose. A study of the literature and patents stimulates thought and may lead to inventions, new research projects, new manufacturing plants, a lawsuit, or improvements in an old technique. Such improvements may even be made along known lines which nevertheless were unknown, or at least not thought of, by the scientists concerned until they read the search. Reading it, they may suddenly see possibilities leading to a novel material or a new use of a known chemical.

Like research itself, the records concerning research must be organized for maximum results with the least expenditure of time and money.

Searching grows more difficult with the increased quantity of available literature and more publication in foreign languages, including the Asiatic ones. Trans-

[1] Present address, Esso Research and Engineering Co., Linden, N. J.

lation programs are now concentrating on the Slavic, Japanese, and Chinese literature. The Office of Technical Services in Washington has appropriate records or can guide searchers to them. Sometimes the foreign language original has a summary in a familiar language.

In the systematic organization of its literature, chemistry is less advanced than law, with its annotated court decisions, but it is in a better position than physics, engineering, and biology. Medicine, despite efforts to improve its literature handling, can hardly run fast enough to keep up with current output. *Index Medicus* is an effort to help with mechanized production methods, but more help is needed.

Searchers in the chemical field have aids such as subject and formula indexes, classified abstracts, machine codes, and classification systems. Nevertheless trial-and-error prospecting is often necessary to find the shortest path to the goal. This search goal must be clearly conceived and matched with the allowable expenditure.

The Search Problem Must Be Clearly Defined. This means establishing the purpose, bounding the subject area, and setting limits on the time period to be covered.

Is a new plant to be built, and is the objective the collection of necessary information on processes, operating conditions, feeds, and possible products? Is an inventor hopeful of securing a patent? Does the company question the validity of a patent used by a competitor? To make an intelligent search, the searcher must know its purpose as well as its subject.

The subject area to be covered may be broad or extremely specific. It may, for instance, concern the use of solar energy for carrying out any chemical reaction. This would be a broad search. On the other hand, references to the use of a very specific drug for the treatment of a very specific disease may be sought. This subject might be further limited by the requirement that the drug be dissolved in a specific solvent and administered intravenously.

The precise subject limits must be ascertained not only to prevent needless work, but also to sharpen the final result. While it may seem self-evident that amorphous searches, rambling over unwanted territory, are inferior to those that bring out only essential points, unfortunately searches and especially bibliographies, made in lieu of searches, often err on this point.

In patent searching, the time period of interest relates to the purpose of the search. For example, an infringement search, made to determine whether something may be done commercially without infringing an unexpired U.S. patent, will go back only 17 years, the life of this country's patents. However, a search made to test a patent's validity will confine itself to references appearing before the application date of the patent.

Searches not made for a patent department may also have date boundaries, but here date limits are often dictated by the law of diminishing returns.

Use of Prior Bibliographies Saves Time and Effort. They not only supply pertinent references but they also generally indicate the names of the leaders in the field and the most profitable journal sources to be searched. They may list pamphlets, university brochures, theses, and out-of-the-way publications that might otherwise escape the searcher.

A professor and his collaborators may have done most of the work on the subject and published it in a series of obscure bulletins. This may become important when a subject of only borderline interest to the chemist suddenly assumes chemical significance due to some development. In such cases the chemical abstracting journals may not have reported the earlier work.

Sometimes consulting an expert will bring quick results. It may uncover the name of an authority writing in the field, a company with a staff of research workers specializing in it, or even an actual file of information on the subject that an expert is keeping.

File wrappers are important not only for validity and infringement investigations, but also as rich sources of pertinent bibliographic material.

It is usually not permissible for the searcher to substitute a few ready-made bibliographies for an actual search, unless those who have requested the search express complete satisfaction with the references found.

Selection of Key Words for Searching Indexes Must Fit Not Merely the Requirements of the Search but Also the Specific Journal Index Searched. For instance, many of the terms selected for searching the indexes of *Chemical Abstracts* will not be suitable for *Biological Abstracts* or for *Fuel Abstracts*.

The search ideas must be translated into the index language of each particular journal. This means that the searcher must familiarize himself with the indexing practices of the journal.

The searcher should ask himself: "If I had this search now as a finished product, and this editor published it, how would he index it for his readers?" The answer to this question will yield the key words to be looked up.

In searching foreign publications, the searcher should remember in selecting key words that British terms differ from American ones, that German terms underwent a change during the last war, and that most foreign languages have unique peculiarities.

To be on the safe side, the searcher should try every pertinent key word that he can think of, or that suggests itself to him in the course of the search.

A Patent Department Searcher Should Have or Gain a Grasp of Patent Fundamentals, as well as a technical knowledge of the art he is searching. He should not only be aware of the concept of novelty, as defined by the U.S. and foreign patent offices, but should also develop such a "feel" for this concept that he will be able to recognize both invention and patent anticipation.

If he does not know that processes, machines for carrying them out, articles of manufacture, compositions of matter, and improvements must be patented separately, not incorporated into a single patent, he will often be bewildered by the existence of patents that seem identical to him.

On the other hand, if he assumes that he need not know what is unpatentable because no patents will appear on such subjects, he is overlooking several important facts. His searches for the patent department must not be confined to patents, but should cover articles, books, etc., as well. He may cite inapplicable references even from among issued patents, if he does not understand the difference between the patentable and unpatentable.

To illustrate, if the searcher fails to realize that a principle or law of nature is unpatentable, he may imagine he has found an important anticipatory reference in the statement of a principle, which, it seems to him, makes the patented idea inevitable, not realizing that it is not a principle but a specific unusual application that is patentable. In fact, a patent will remain valid even if the principle on which it was supposed to be based is later proved false.

Again a searcher, ignorant of the fact that the transposition of the steps of a process is patentable only when the result attained thereby is both unexpected and useful, will have no criterion for dealing with such inversion. Therefore, in his searches he will either fail to cite any references with transposition or he will cite all such references without discrimination as to applicability to the case under consideration.

In dealing with a process, the searcher should break it down into its steps, and note the purposes of each one. He should evaluate equipment with reference to its use, not merely its specific structure.

A searcher in the patent field need not be an expert in patent law, but he should know enough about it to make intelligent searches for the use of patent attorneys. He should know why he is making the searches and what functions they are expected to serve.

As medium-sized and smaller companies generally do not have patent departments, their patent searchers in general require more familiarity with patent fundamentals than those working for larger firms, where searches are organized by supervisors in consultation with patent attorneys. In smaller firms the searcher usually has to define the search problem and the scope of the search for himself. Being left more to his own devices, he must inform himself on matters that are frequently outside the province of the searcher in a larger company.

A company is wise to have some patent searching done, because lack of information can be costly, sometimes resulting in infringement suits, anticipation invalidating the company's patents, and duplication of work, involving the waste of inventive talent. A state-of-the-art search, covering both patents and literature in all important countries, enables scientists to begin where the search stops.

The Procedure for Making a Search Depends on the Nature of the Information Sought and the Available Opportunities. The searcher should use the telephone, if he suspects possible short cuts through personal conversations. Living minds are the primary sources of information and a searcher should avail himself of all the help he can get.

While standard search procedures should usually be followed, the searcher need not be hidebound if an unusual type of search or some unexpected opportunity arises. He should keep an open mind as to sources and recognize the fact that he may not know all the possibilities.

When necessary, the searcher may break the rules. However, this should not be taken as a license to do so at whim. Searches vary in type, length, and requirements, so that occasionally one or more searching principles do not apply.

Searches in the market-research field break away from the usual rules. They involve much nonchemical and nontechnical information and depend on a knowledge of the field and sources of statistical information. The abstract journals are of little value in making such searches. However, those working in this field have their own techniques.

Internal Reports, Technical Correspondence, and Academic and Government Laboratory Records Should Not Be Overlooked. Government agencies are in much the same situation as the organizers of medical literature. They have difficulty in making their huge accumulation searchable; mechanization is helping, but not enough.

Accessible private records such as laboratory reports, technical correspondence, and test data are in some instances more useful than published literature. This is why most companies now index or classify in some way the information in their own research reports.

Searchers Should Be Interpretive, and highly so, in evaluating the importance of pertinent references for the search aim. The searcher may point out in what way two patents differ from each other or how close a literature reference comes to anticipating a patent.

Naturally the searcher cannot render the final legal decision on any question.

This is in the realm of the patent attorney. In any event, the Patent Office or a court will have the ultimate say in the matter.

When Reading Suggests a Potentially Useful Idea, beyond the Scope of the Search, the Searcher Should Pass It On for Investigation in the Laboratory. This may be a real contribution. The same idea may or may not occur to the investigators using the search. Searchers should identify themselves with their science or technology enough to make original thinking possible. This is easiest in a laboratory or company that makes the searcher a part of the research team, and encourages the rest of the team to recognize him as a member.

Sometimes original ideas which occur to the searcher are best routed into regular suggestion channels. Most laboratories have a more or less formalized setup for receiving and considering them. Another form of presentation is a recommendation in the search report or its introduction.

The free lance searcher, working for different clients, changing from one field of work to another, has the compensating advantage of wider reading, and at times the drastic variations in points of view and psychological approaches encountered in dealing with different companies and different branches of science and technology.

Reliability or Lack of It in Records Must at Times Be Dealt With. Sometimes it is important only to find what the literature says, not whether it is correct or false, especially if photostats must be submitted to courts or the Patent Office. Incorrect statements, especially in a patent being checked for validity, may on occasion be a patent attorney's ammunition.

An obvious error, let us say in a formula, may appear in a printed article. By checking the text, tables, or equations it can usually be corrected easily.

When the question of reliability of written records enters into a search, critical evaluation rests mainly with the investigators who use the search findings, particularly in patent searches. What may appear to the searcher as a mere oddity or even an error may be something truly new. Judgment on the matter is the prerogative of the subject-field expert.

Sloppy records arouse suspicion. The searcher should remember, however, that they may be authored by a genius who is one of the world's worst writers or by a busy scientist who failed to check a trusted typist's work.

Articles in a growing art, if written with little or no attention to prior literature, will be items to scrutinize with feelings of doubt. On the other hand, some of our best scientists are well read but lazy about compiling bibliographies.

It may pay to check errata lists where errors are suspected in connection with some important point. Sometimes a doubtful figure or statement can be dealt with only by a laboratory check.

A Search Should Be Stopped Either When It is Completed or When Further Efforts Fail to Produce Proportionate Results.

A search is completed when the goal is attained. For example, when several excellent references, proving the invalidity of a patent, have been found in a validity search, the search is complete. Patent attorneys are reluctant to base a contest of patent validity on a single reference, as the Patent Office may disagree with them. However, beyond a certain point the piling up of evidence adds mere quantity, without altering the result.

In a prior art or background search, completeness is not essential. When a comprehensive picture of the total situation has been attained, and when searching ceases to turn up more than a sprinkling of new references in return for much effort, the search may be stopped.

No Rule Can Take the Place of Imagination, Judgment, and Facility of the Searcher, on which the quality of the search depends as much as on the information available. If the searcher lacks imagination, he will fail to see connections between bits of information. If he lacks facility and judgment, he will not select the best key words for index searching, and he will not find certain pertinent information or, if he does, he may not recognize its value.

Planning the Search

Differences in the approach to searching in the various branches of science and technology lie not in searching principles but in (1) the nature of the material to be searched and the variations in the best methods of dealing with it, and (2) the objectives sought in making the search.

Though a search dealing with an organic compound may start with the formula index of *Chemical Abstracts,* while one on an industrial engineering problem may begin in the Engineering Societies Library in New York City, the same basic principle of searching is involved—namely, key terms are looked up in the most appropriate sources.

Routine Procedure. For a chemical search the usual procedure is to consult the indexes of *Chemical Abstracts,* plus the indexes of special journals in the field concerned, when these journals are not covered or not completely covered by *Chemical Abstracts.* For instance, if the search deals with a new vitamin preparation, *Chemical Abstracts* will not suffice.

Crane, Patterson, and Marr (7) list abstract journals and annual reviews in specific branches of chemistry and give excellent advice on how to use both subject and author indexes.

Common sense, a good knowledge of periodicals available in a branch of science or technology, and an intelligent use of periodical lists, such as the Union List of Serials in Libraries of the United States and Canada (59), enable the searcher to select the journals of most use for the search. As the Union List of Serials enumerates journals alphabetically by title, not subject, to find appropriate sources it is necessary to look up not only likely headings such as "Plastics," and "Textiles," but also terms like "Journal," "Annals," "British," and the like, which might form the first word of the journal title. After this, it is wise to scan the volume, opening it here and there in the hope of hitting upon other possibilities.

Background information and bibliographies may be obtained from books and annual reviews. Journal articles also yield bibliographies.

It saves time to file references that are to be abstracted by journal, then work through all the references in a single journal instead of hopping from one journal to another, especially if public libraries are used. This prevents constant shifting from room to room in large libraries, or even from one library to another.

Searching patents is an art in itself and cannot be discussed in detail here. Appropriate patent classes are usually searched at the Patent Office in Washington. *Chemical Abstracts* covers some patents. Searchers may consult the Uniterm Index of Chemical Patents and other aids. They will have difficulty with the Annual Patent Index of the *Official Gazette of the U. S. Patent Office,* because the entries are listed by title and inventors. As titles do not correspond to subjects, this index is not very useful.

Foreign patents sometimes have United States, British, or Canadian equivalents or near-equivalents. The Belgian patents, which appear rather soon after application, offer an excellent starting point for making connections. Kohnke and Lewenz (27) have described a procedure for doing this.

Practical Bounding of the Subject. A practical method of bounding the search subject is to make a list of questions which, if answered in the abstract of each item entered, fully cover the intended subject area and feed into the search objectives.

For a chemical reaction the questions may concern the starting materials, side reactions, main products, catalysts, and suitable reaction conditions.

Searches for patent departments usually cover specific date limits as well. Other searches usually cover the period when the main work was done or periods of special interest to the company.

Preliminary Estimate of Search Length. There may be a deadline for the completion of a search, especially when legal or financial considerations are involved. While no one can say precisely how long a search will take, some kind of estimate is usually essential.

Occasionally the literature holds surprises. A search may be swiftly concluded to everyone's astonishment by the uncovering of a few outstanding references giving the exact information desired. Such luck cannot be counted on. It may happen, though—even in a state-of-the-art search—by the discovery that someone else has made such a search and has published it. The book, "Alkylation of Alkanes. Vol. I. Patents," by Egloff and Hulla, is such a published search (*15*).

A novelty search is much more likely to be stopped suddenly when a few specific patents or articles are found that anticipate an idea that was to be submitted for patent application. On the other hand, what looked like a short search may drag to unexpected length.

The best way to make a calculated guess as to probable length is to set up a list of sources and do some spade work on the search. Familiarity with the field and acquaintance with the journals in it are top-ranking aids. From the list of journals abstracted by *Chemical Abstracts* and the Union List of Serials, a preliminary list of journals to be covered can be made up.

A glance at the number of references appearing under the selected main subject headings in the abstract journals gives an idea of whether the search will be very long, very short, or in between. For a more accurate answer, work on the search must actually be started.

Deciding Who Will Do the Work. Some large companies, especially those with well organized search departments, may do all their own searching. Others start a search and farm out parts of it. Still others search the literature and have attorneys in Washington search the Patent Office files. Some companies prefer having certain entire searches made within the company and other complete searches outside.

The time element enters the picture. Major questions are whether the search can be finished on time if done by company personnel, and whether such personnel can be spared from other searches or other work.

Search Department's Location. Is the source material readily available, or will it be necessary to search in another city? If the company is near a large city such as New York or Chicago, most sources will be within easy reach. If not, the company must choose between sending an employee to a distant city or hiring one or more outside searchers more favorably located.

A company with considerable search work may find it advantageous to hire a full-time outside searcher strategically located. If the company has insufficient work for this, a part-time searcher or a search bureau, such as the one connected with the Engineering Societies Library in New York City, may be selected.

Cost Plays a Role. As company employees are familiar with needs and the subject, it is usually economical for them to make short trips. However, if months of work are required, it may be wiser to hire an outside searcher even if a training period is involved.

Division of Work. As indexes are consulted, lists of references accumulate. Practically every company library has *Chemical Abstracts* indexes, though it will lack many of the original journals covered by *Chemical Abstracts*. Thus references can be collected, abstracts scanned, and preliminary work done in the company's search department, while original articles and patents may have to be tracked down elsewhere. This gives a clue to one way of dividing search work between company and outside searchers.

Outside searchers may also be asked to go through indexes of journals not covered by *Chemical Abstracts* and not available in the company's library.

More Accurate Estimate of Search Length. In the case of a state-of-the-art or general information (background) search, the compilation of references becomes more or less complete at a certain point. One is then usually in a position to make a reasonable estimate of the number of man-hours it will take to cover these references.

This time estimate may be thrown off somewhat, however, by the discovery of a new cache of references resulting, for instance, from bibliographies in articles abstracted, and the location of pertinent journals that were overlooked before. Nevertheless, unless the original spade work was really careless, large numbers of extra references do not usually materialize. Mention of bibliographies is now common in abstracts, and a preliminary search for bibliographies is often good practice.

It is much harder to estimate time for searches connected with legal matters, as they may end abruptly. It is possible, however, to set a maximum time limit beyond which the search is not likely to stretch. We can, for instance, judge about how long it will take to cover 300 accumulated references. If, after completing 100 of them, we have found all the information we need, we can conclude the search, having taken a third of the maximum time estimated.

Looking first at the most promising references increases the chance of cutting short a search.

Some references take longer to abstract than others; allowance must be made for foreign language problems and the complexity of some articles. Occasional references in less widely known languages must be translated in full. As the search progresses, some revision of the time estimate is usually necessary.

The Conference. Generally a conference is held before a search is started. It may be merely a talk between two people, but it is generally more than that. Attorneys and laboratory chemists may be present. Occasionally the conference is replaced by a memorandum of instruction, but this can cause misunderstanding. After some search work has been done, additional conferences may be held for reorientation.

Training Outside Searchers. Conferences are even more important for outside searchers than for company employees, who can take up problems as they arise. A training period for an outside searcher implies no lack of searching know-how. Its purpose is to orient him on the company's viewpoint, methods, and desires; to bring him into contact with company personnel and the people he must satisfy; to let him know what will be expected, and how to report results;

and, of course, to give him the details of the subject and time scope of the search.

Terms for Types of Searches. The uninitiated are often baffled needlessly by the "patent search," which they imagine is a search confined to the investigation of printed patents. A so-called "patent search" is something of a misnomer. It is actually a search made to solve some patent problems, and involves searching journals, books, and other documents as well as patents themselves.

Toulmin (*58*) classifies types of patent searches as: preliminary, prior art, infringement, validity, combined infringement and validity, index, and assignment searches. Some other authors use a slightly different terminology, but the meaning adds up to the same thing.

Some books refer to a patentability search as a novelty search. A background search may be called a general information search or, if it is made for legal purposes, a state-of-the-art search. A preliminary search is made to determine whether a patent should be applied for when an invention is complete. In contrast to a state-of-the-art search, it is short, made by checking only the most obvious sources.

Sometimes infringement and validity searches, being closely related, are combined. In such cases the searcher simply rolls back the 17-year time period of the validity search, recording all references, including expired patents, that he can find on the subject, regardless of dates.

An index search establishes what patents a company holds, but does not reveal license agreements or unrecorded assignments. However, an assignment search can be made at the Patent Office.

When looking for the uses of a product, searchers sometimes speak of a "use search." This is related to a market survey but differs in emphasis. The use search deals mainly with applications of products, while the market survey revolves around statistics.

There is no hard-and-fast list of type of searches. One set of terms, if precise and applicable, is as authentic as another, as usage among experts shows.

Lack of ambiguity, however, is essential. For instance, talk of a "priority search" is not acceptable. However, "comprehensive prior art search" is a satisfactory synonym for "state-of-the-art search."

Presentation of Results. Standard journal abbreviations, the form for recording references, the physical setup for search records, etc., must be fixed to give the search a uniform appearance and make it easy to deal with. Searchers must adhere to these standards to prevent extra work for others. It is a nuisance, for instance, to have a searcher turn in material on loose-leaf sheets when the rest of the search material is on paper of another size or on cards.

Sometimes the search is written up in two parts. Part I is usually a series of numbered abstracts, consisting in each instance of answers to the list of questions set up in bounding the search. It is convenient to assign class numbers or symbols to each item, to indicate the presence in it of certain kinds of information.

The second part contains lists of items falling into each class. For example, if we have a search on the oxidation of some material with special catalysts, Class I might be for an antimony catalyst with added promoters, Class II, oxidation at a certain pressure, etc. Then we would list all abstracts (by item numbers) falling into Class I, Class II, etc. For instance:

Class I. Oxidation with Antimony and Added Promoters
1. Item 3, F. J. Jones, *J. Am. Chem. Soc.* (1945)
2. Item 9, P. M. Avery, U. S. Patent . . . . (1950), etc.

Thus lists of items dealing with special aspects of the search are ready for study. We must, of course, turn back to Part I to read the abstracts.

Occasionally tabular form may be suitable for reporting a search on the uses of a product. One column can be used for the author, a second for the reference, a third for uses, etc. In employing tables it is necessary to make certain in advance that there is a place for all needed information and that the sheets are wide enough to hold all columns.

Sometimes searches lend themselves to recording on punched cards. Of course, details must be worked out well in advance. However, large-scale use of machines for searching involves considerable expense for preparatory work; material to be searched later must first be analyzed and encoded. Some of the guiding principles are discussed by Casey and Perry (*3, 40*).

Searchers are not only finders and recorders of information; they are also systematizers and interpreters.

Interpretation and the Searcher. The superficial disagreement as to whether search abstracts should be interpretive or not stems from different conceptions of the meaning of "interpretive."

Everyone will agree that a searcher, like any other investigator, should be competent in his own specialty—searching. A good searcher decides on the relative value of the references he finds for the search objectives, and states his evaluation in the search report.

Those who object to the idea of interpretive search abstracts usually mean they object to searchers' passing on the scientific validity of experiments or theories. Such evaluation falls in the province of the specialist in the field.

To illustrate, let us assume that a searcher reads that a chemical compound has a certain effect on a chromium catalyst. He cannot vouch for the scientific validity of this. However, he can say, assuming the statement to be true, that it has considerable, some, or little bearing on the search objectives. If his task is to locate information pertinent to patent validity, he may say, "This information may anticipate claim 5, U.S. patent . . . ." Lawyers later may agree or disagree with his statement, but it has called their attention to the possible usefulness of the reference. Such highlighting is what is meant by saying the search abstract should be interpretive relative to the search objectives.

Interpretive search abstracts also facilitate the work of writing the search summary, a wholly interpretive document. Some people make an outline before writing the search summary; others evaluate the entries for the search aims, systematize them, and then summarize their conclusions, listing the most important search items. The search summary is a timesaving device prepared for the benefit of administrators, attorneys, chemists, and engineers who use the search.

Timesaving Is Largely Foresight. There are also timesavers for searchers. They depend on foresight. Cognizance of company needs and technical trends makes it possible for a search department to anticipate possible future searches. Keeping a card file on likely search subjects as pertinent material turns up in the daily routine is especially helpful in a small company that does not print abstract bulletins.

In larger companies, the subject classification or indexing of technical articles, patents, and books greatly facilitates searching. A company with such a program is actually accumulating continuous searches in the subject classes of the classification system.

Such classification programs also enable searchers and others to orient themselves quickly if a new search or other project is started.

In designing and selecting classification systems, the needs of both the laboratory scientists and the searchers should be studied, rather than merely the theoretical merits of the system. Even the failure of a system can be instructive.

Current-literature abstract bulletins also indirectly save searching time by keeping investigators informed. These investigators, in turn, will not have to make requests for information already supplied to them in the bulletin. It may be argued that such information sometimes stimulates further requests as the investigator has been inspired with a new idea. If so, the request is on a higher level, the creative level, and thus again the abstract bulletin has scored.

Information groups may also serve by collecting patentable ideas on laboratory or plant operations and supplying them to the patent attorneys. Such a group, in view of its extensive reading, will have much information on tap with regard to these ideas. Besides indirectly saving time for the chemists served, such efforts can add to the patent wealth of the company.

Routine Timesaving Methods. Organization of routine search tasks is essential for fast, efficient operation. After a search is well along the way, a searcher should be able to take a pack of references from a drawer and start working without undue attention to clerical details.

The intelligent use of clerical and stenographic help saves much searching time. Nontechnical personnel can make author indexes, keep search records, copy marked lists of references from journals for future abstracting, and check bibliographic references against files to prevent duplication.

The paths of no two searches are quite alike, but usually in any search at times a welter of detail turns up that can be handled by a careful clerk, either alone or with technical supervision.

The use of nontechnical help in searching requires great care, however. The practice can be abused to the detriment of the search. At no time should stenographers be asked to search technical journals or to perform any other task that requires technical knowledge or judgment.

Cooperative Searching for Timesaving. Many companies have made identical or almost identical searches, especially in broad fields, such as alkylation, oxidation, aviation fuels, and tranquilizers. This constitutes an unfortunate duplication of work.

One partial solution is publication of searches after they have served their purpose. However, the company at whose expense the search was made may object to footing the bill, while permitting other companies to acquire the search for the price of a book.

At present, the only practical way of implementing cooperative searching seems to be through the use of outside consultants. Usually the consultant must take all or at least a large part of the initiative. He must discover a more or less general subject of interest to a number of companies. He then announces his intention of making a search on it and solicits subscriptions.

While the bounds of the search do not exactly fit the detailed requirements of any one company, the sharing of expenses with others often makes the search worth buying. Indeed, companies usually do not want others to know their precise needs. Consequently, the more general cooperative search is the only feasible one.

The company's own searchers can then use this general search as a basis from which one or several precise searches can be wholly or largely made.

The development of machine searching may favor the cooperative search. As both suitable machines and their storage with useful information are beyond many companies' ability to pay, the companies may be more ready to collaborate.

Machine searching and machine translation have received considerable attention in recent years. Adequate codes must be developed and tested in machines of various types. It is essential to discover experimentally exactly what performance a machine can give, as the danger lies in relying on machines for performance beyond their range of reliability. Full awareness of the true situation can then be coupled with concrete efforts to improve it.

Thorough Use of Searching Principles Saves Time. Searching principles were evolved for two reasons: to produce better searches, and to produce them more quickly. Consequently, the more the searcher applies these principles, the less will he waste his energies.

For example, if he uses existing bibliographies, stops the search when further efforts yield diminishing returns, limits the subject area, and arms himself with adequate legal knowledge and any other needed information, he will not only make a better search but will also finish it in less time.

Growth in Stature Is a Prime Timesaver. The searcher who makes an effort to keep up with both his technical field and the literature about chemical literature will become a better and a faster searcher.

Professional society participation is especially helpful—lobby conferences as well as hearing and delivering papers. Keeping informed on what others are doing brings rich dividends. Personal contacts provide an insight into the viewpoints and the methods of other companies.

Bibliography

(1) Am. Chem. Soc., ADVANCES IN CHEM. SER., No. **10** (1954). 582 pp. Literature resources for chemical process industries.
(2) Berle, A. B., Sprague de Camp, L., "Inventions, Patents and Their Management," Van Nostrand, New York, 1959.
(3) Casey, R. S., Perry, J. W., "Punched Cards. Their Applications to Science and Industry," Reinhold, New York, 1951.
(4) Cole, B. J., *J. Chem. Educ.* **21**, 319–21 (1944). Library *vs.* laboratory as a basis for research.
(5) Connolly, A. G., *Ibid.*, **20**, 531–3 (1943). Library *vs.* laboratory research.
(6) Crane, E. J., *Chem. Eng. News* **22**, 1478 (1944). Growth of chemical literature, contributions of certain nations, and effects of the war.
(7) Crane, E. J., Patterson, A. M., Marr, E. B., "A Guide to the Literature of Chemistry," Wiley, New York, 1957. 397 pp.
(8) Culhane, P. J., *J. Chem. Educ.*, **20**, 601–2 (1943). Importance of scientific literature in patent applications.
(9) Dean, R. B., *Ibid.*, **28**, 642 (1951). A literature search assignment.
(10) Dyson, G. M., "Chemical Literature," Longmans, Green & Co., London, 1951. 144 pp.
(11) Dyson, G. M., "Short Guide to Chemical Literature," Longmans, Green & Co., New York, 1951.
(12) Egloff, G., Alexander, M., Van Arsdell, P. M., *J. Chem. Educ.* **20**, 393–8 (1943). Problems of scientific literature research.
(13) *Ibid.*, pp. 587–92. Problems of the scientific literature survey.
(14) Egloff, G., Davis, R. F., *Chem. Eng. News* **25**, 1046–8 (1947). Patent investigations.
(15) Egloff, G., Hulla, G., "Alkylation of Alkanes. Vol. I. Patents on Alkylation of Alkanes," Reinhold, New York, 1948.
(16) Ellis, G. P., *Research (London)* **11**, 276–8 (1958). Literature problems in organic chemistry.
(17) Ericksen, E., *Tid. F. Dok.* **14**, No. 5, 57–63 (1958). Literature search methods.
(18) Hardie, B. G., Voigt, M. J., *Oil & Gas J.* **49**, No. 2, 121, 159–71 (1950). Use of periodicals in petroleum research.
(19) Hennion, G. F., *J. Chem. Educ.* **21**, 33–5 (1944). Searching the literature of organic compounds.

(20) Heyel, C., "Handbook of Industrial Research Management," Reinhold, New York, 1959.
(21) Hill, N. C., "Some Problems in Literature Survey," Division of Chemical Literature, 111th Meeting, ACS, Atlantic City, N. J., April 1947.
(22) Hoseh, M., ADVANCES IN CHEM. SER., No. **10**, 541–7 (1954). Pitfalls of transliteration in indexing and searching.
(23) Hoseh, M. A., *J. Chem. Educ.* **33**, 397–402 (1956). Scientific and technical literature of the U. S. S. R.
(24) Howerton, P. W., "Russian Chemical Literature Since 1917," Division of History of Chemistry, 118th Meeting, ACS, Chicago, Ill., September 1950.
(25) Huntress, E. H., "Methods of Rapid Location of Data on Organic Compounds," Division of Chemical Education, 113th Meeting, ACS, Chicago, Ill., April 1948.
(26) Janicki, W., *Schweiz, Arch. angew. Wiss. u. Tech.* **9**, 185–92 (1943). Methods of scientific literature searching.
(27) Kohnke, E. L., Lewenz, G. F., "Detecting Corresponding Patents from Different Countries," Division of Chemical Literature, 137th Meeting, ACS, Cleveland, Ohio, April 1960.
(28) Lane, J. C., Georgia Inst. Technol., State Eng. Expt. Sta., Circ. **20**, 15–21 (1948). Patent searching.
(29) Lanham, B. E., *Ind. Eng. Chem.* **43**, 2494 (1951). Chemical patent searches.
(30) Lanham, B. E., Leibowitz, J., *J. Patent Office Soc.* **40**, 86–109 (1958). Classification, searching and mechanization in the U. S. Patent Office.
(31) Lewton, L. O., *Chem. Eng. News* **29**, 5125–7 (1951). Contributions of the Special Libraries Association to searching.
(32) Lewton, L. O., *J. Chem. Educ.* **28**, 487–91, 539–43 (1951). The art of searching the literature.
(33) Little, G. D., *Special Libraries* **35**, 373–9 (1944). Locating difficult periodical references.
(34) McCrum, B. P., Jones, H. B., "Bibliographical Procedures and Style; a Manual for Bibliographers in the Library of Congress," Library of Congress, Washington, D. C., 1957. 13 pp.
(35) Mellon, M. G., "Chemical Publications, Their Nature and Use," 3rd ed., McGraw-Hill, New York, 1958. 327 pp.
(36) Murphy, W. J., *Chem. Eng. News* **30**, 505 (1952). Lost literature legend.
(37) Nickerson, M. H., Barker, K. T., ADVANCES IN CHEM. SER., No. **10**, 129–33 (1954). Literature searching for plastics engineering.
(38) Oatfield, H., Emilio, B. R., *Am. Document* **9**, 238–76 (1958). Some aspects of searching in the pharmaceutical literature. Reference fringe benefits.
(39) Padwe, M. M., "Searching the Literature of an Industrial Chemical Organization," Division of Chemical Literature, 117th Meeting, ACS, Detroit, Mich., April 1950.
(40) Perry, J. W., Casey, R. S., "Encyclopedia of Chemical Technology," R. E. Kirk and D. F. Othmer, eds., Vol. **8**, pp. 449–67, Interscience Encyclopedia, New York, 1952.
(41) Phelps, R. H., *Science* **129**, 25–7 (1959). Engineering information–all is not lost.
(42) Potter, D. J. C., Bassett, F. J., *Chem. in Can.* **9**, 39–44 (1957). Use of indexes for searching chemical literature.
(43) Premo, J. G., *J. Chem. Educ.* **35**, 353 (July 1958). Simplified procedure for searching U. S. chemical patents.
(44) Price, M. O., *Special Libraries* **31**, 118–28 (1940). Patent searching, with special reference to chemical patents.
(45) Rabinow, J., *Elec. Eng.* **77**, 494–8 (June 1958). Available tools for information retrieval.
(46) Randall, L. E., Sharpnach, D. M., "Market Research Sources," U. S. Bur. Foreign and Domestic Commerce, Domestic Commerce Series, No. **20**, 9th ed., U. S. Government Printing Office, Washington, D. C., 1950.
(47) Schaler, C. M., Smith, J. F., ADVANCES IN CHEM. SER., No. **10**, 441–8 (1954). Sound and unsound short cuts in searching the literature.
(48) Shipman, J. C., *Inst. Spokesman* **14**, No. 6, 17–20 (1950). Technical libraries and the literature search.
(49) Short, M. A., *Research (London)* **10**, 313–8 (1957). Searching the literature of physical and inorganic chemistry.
(50) Singer, T. E. R., *Record of Chem. Progr.* **18**, No. 1, 11–29 (1957).
(51) Smith, J. F., "Chemical Literature in America, 1876–1950," Division of History of Chemistry, 118th Meeting, ACS, Chicago, Ill., September 1950.
(52) Smith, J. F., "Information and Communication Practice in Industry," T. E. R. Singer, ed., pp. 157–65, Reinhold, New York, 1958.
(53) Smith, J. F., Schaler, C. M., ADVANCES IN CHEM. SER. No. **10**, 438–40 (1954). Basic principles of literature searching.
(54) Smith, J. F., Scott, J. D., "Encyclopedia of Chemical Technology," R. E. Kirk and D. F. Othmer, eds., Vol. **8**, pp. 418–49, Interscience Encyclopedia, New York, 1952.

(55) Soule, B. A., *J. Chem. Educ.* **21,** 333–5 (1944). Finding the literature.
(56) Spitzer, E. F., ADVANCES IN CHEM. SER., No. **10,** 487–93 (1954). French chemical literature and its use.
(57) Taylor, F. L., *Ind. Eng. Chem.* **40,** 470 (1948). Numerical index key for the Beilstein system.
(58) Toulmin, H. S., "Handbook of Patents," 2nd ed., W. H. Anderson Co., Cincinnati, Ohio, 1954. 928 pp.
(59) Union List of Serials in Libraries of United States and Canada, 2nd ed., 1943, 1st suppl., 1945; 2nd suppl., 1954, Wilson Co., New York.
(60) Van Luik, J., associates, "Searching the Chemical and Chemical Engineering Literature with an Analysis of 229 Journals and Handbooks," 2nd ed., Purdue University, Lafayette, Ind., 1957. 119 pp.
(61) Wade, W., "Patents for Technical Personnel," Chemonomics, New York, 1951.
(62) Wehr, H. W., Jr., Thayer, G. B., ADVANCES IN CHEM. SER., No. **10,** 134–8 (1954). Literature searching for plastics fabricating methods and machinery.
(63) Weil, B. H., *J. Chem. Educ.* **28,** 572–5 (1951). Literature summary.
(64) Weil, B. H., *Petrol. Processing* **5,** 452 (1950). Increasing attention paid to literature research.
(65) Wimmersperg, H. V., *J. Patent Office Soc.*, March 1960, Reprint, "Subclasses of Patents: The Most Important Tool of the Development Engineer."
(66) Wylie, G. J., *Australian J. Instr. Technol.* **4,** 130–44 (1948). Literature research, its possibilities and technique.

BASED on papers presented before the Division of Chemical Literature, Symposium on Searching the Chemical Literature, at the 130th Meeting, ACS, Atlantic City, N. J., September 1956. Revised 1960.

Indexes, Happy and Unhappy Hunting Grounds

JULIAN F. SMITH
Lenoir Rhyne College, Hickory, N. C.

Indexers devote thought and toil to the effort to place subject matter where searchers are most likely to look for it. They must avoid the pitfalls of omitting significant information, burying information under obscure listings, and making poor choice of nomenclature. The searcher must bear in mind connections between English and Latin derivations, reason out probable preferred locations for entries not as precise as chemical names, check specific as well as general terms, and take into consideration peculiarities that creep into the English language from foreign language sources. Successful searching demands a balanced blend of training, experience, and common sense.

Indexers devote much thought and toil to the task of placing subject matter where searchers are most likely to seek it. In a sense, each indexer projects his mind into the future, hoping that searchers will project their minds back to meet his. Often, but not always, they do.

The whole operation is essentially a guessing game of indexers and searchers, playing on the same team against the invisible gremlins of error, mischance, mishap, and false trails. The minds win when the searcher arrives at the wanted information.

Suppose the indexer is directing the searcher to a new, precise determination of "Stannous chloride solutions, density." He makes that entry and moves on to the next item. The gremlins win if the searcher gives up when he finds nothing under "Tin chloride solutions, density."

There are many ways in which indexers and searchers can make success easier and surer than it would be without their skill and care. Assuming that the indexer has avoided the pitfalls of omitting significant information, of burying it under his own obscure fantasies, and of errors or poor choices in nomenclature, what must the searcher do to make sure that his mind meets the indexer's?

First, he can bear in mind such little matters as the connection between "tin" and "stann-," "iron" and "ferr-," "lead" and "plumb-."

Secondly, he can reason out probable preferred locations for entries not as precise as chemical names. He can remember that "Glazes" and "Enamels, vitreous" are sufficiently similar to justify searching both when interested in either, whereas organic baking finishes such as "Enamels, tung oil" may hide under some such congener as "Paints, tung oil," but not under "Glazes."

Thirdly, he can cultivate mental agility when his first thought misses the indexer's in such matters as designating properties or products. He can search "Bactericides" as well as "Germicides," and he can switch from specific to general terms, or vice versa. If "Luminescence" does not serve, he can proceed to its special cases such as "Chemiluminescence," "Fluorescence," "Iridescence," or "Phosphorescence."

Finally, he can allow for peculiarities which creep into English language indexes from foreign language sources. Biochemists should know that the German way of calling enzymes "ferments" sometimes is carried over into our literature and indexes. Still worse is *Verseifung*, applied in German to all hydrolysis, so that "Saponification" for "Hydrolysis" seems impossible to eradicate from our literature and indexes.

These are merely examples to illustrate how the searcher can do his share toward the meeting of the minds. Engineers tunneling from opposite sides of a mountain or stream are expected to meet without deviating so much as an inch; but their success does not come by haphazard drilling. So the searcher, starting from his end, cannot expect to meet the indexer's mind without skilled attention to orientation.

Chemical Indexing as It Was

Early chemical indexes were sorry specimens as compared with today's best. The preface to the cumulative index of Volumes 1 to 100 (1832–56) of Liebig's *Annalen der Chemie* complained that the first two collective indexes (for Volumes 1 to 40, 1842, and Volumes 41 to 70, 1851) were appallingly bad. A few simple rules for better chemical indexing were prescribed and followed.

The *Annalen*'s first indexers should not be blamed too much; they were amateurs, without experience or precedent, and the small bulk of literature to be covered did not need an elaborate index. Chemists of 1832 could probably read that year's whole output of chemical literature in less time than we would need now to read one annual index of *Chemical Abstracts*. The *Annalen* for 1832 (Volumes 1 to 4) was indexed by the use of less than 800 subject headings.

The leisurely pioneers used long phrases instead of one or a few words as main entries. Early searchers accepted "Nitro-bromo-phenesic and ampelic acids, on chlorophenyle, and chloralbine and on the relations which exist between the composition of some organic substances and their crystalline forms" [*Chemist* (*London*), Vol. 1 (1841)] whereas modern searchers would resent anything longer than "Nitrobromophenesic acid, crystalline form," and would demand separate entries for the other compounds. Even after more and shorter entries won favor, subject indexes remained scanty as judged by modern standards. Cross references were rare and sometimes loosely used, as in *Chemist* (*London*), Vol. 1 (1841), "Metallic salts," *see* "Remarks."

Indexers seemed to assume that searchers had minds grooved exactly like their own.

Early chemical indexing did not approach the 67 words of index per 100 words of text which is approximately the present level for *Chemical Abstracts*. But gradually indexers sensed more of the searcher's needs; as chemical literature grew in bulk and complexity, subject indexes made halting but persistent efforts to keep pace. One of the early concessions, dating back at least to 1801 (*3*), was the publication of collective indexes (*9*), covering 5 to 100 volumes or years of a periodical. This time-saving practice spread widely later in the 19th century.

The growth of chemical literature also drove indexers beyond the word base to formula and number bases for indexing. When empirical formulas were recognized as inherent characteristics of chemical compounds, inevitably some restless spirit would think of indexing compounds by formulas.

The restless spirit was that of Max Moritz Richter; he brought out his first formula index of all known organic compounds in 1884. Isomers complicate the situation, but Richter devised a way of coping with them which still serves in today's formula indexes: He numbered isomers, grouped by similarities; *Chemical Abstracts* names them.

Patent grants were burgeoning late in the 19th century, with an added impetus from the German chemical industry's complex marvels of coal tar chemistry. Pressure on patent indexing finally led abstract periodicals to publish numerical indexes of patents. *Wagners Jahresbericht der chemischen Technologie* started the custom in 1889, followed by *Zeitschrift für angewandte Chemie* in 1890 and *Journal of the Society of Chemical Industry* in 1901.

Thus, at the turn of the century, chemical indexing was established on its four main bases:

Names (of authors, firms, agencies, laboratories, patentees, assignees, etc.)
Subjects
Formulas (empirical and ring formulas of compounds, organic and inorganic)
Numbers (chiefly of patents)

Chemical Indexing as It Is

As the number of known chemical compounds neared the million mark, literature about them and less definite substances or products became increasingly difficult to index. *Chemical Abstracts* and *Chemisches Zentralblatt* responded with improvements in entry selection and arrangement, and explained their improvements to searchers (*5, 7*). The German science press of the early 1930's warmly praised the *Zentralblatt*'s new "encyclopedic" system, which departs further from the strict alphabetic base than does the *Chemical Abstracts* system.

Book indexing is still in a very spotty state, but has improved somewhat under pressure. Beilstein (*4*) and like compendia can be well indexed in relatively small space because their arrangement has self-indexing features. Unfortunately, the arrangement in Beilstein is covered by such elaborate rules that an official guide (*14*) is needed. There are also shorter guides (*10, 15*). Friedländer (*8*) was for many years a monumental example of inadequate indexing, falling far short of the needed detail. The numerous handbooks for chemists and engineers illustrate the spotty character of modern book indexing. In general, the chemical handbooks fare better than those in engineering. In some respects chemical subject matter is more amenable to precise indexing than are engineering topics; but there is a hard core of fact in the fable that engineers cannot read, and it influences indexing.

Searchers who are sensitive to the idiosyncrasies of indexers can quickly sense goodness or badness in an index. The needed sensitivity can be acquired if not inherited. Either way, the searcher can train himself to step up his ingenuity voltage when confronted with a bad index.

To illustrate, a certain index (anonymous here) has many entries under "Acoustics" and "Physics, sound" along with a few under "Supersonics," but not even a cross reference under "Sound" or "Sonic(s)." Searchers detoured at "Sound" pass to "Acoustics" without much resistance, but the jump from "Sound" to "Physics, sound" is more difficult.

Skilled searchers start with a list of the significant words relating to any topic complex enough to have a vocabulary. Probably on the old Indian's theory, "No settum trap, no catchum mink," they are called catch words. Because usage varies with place and time, catch words differ in different indexes and in different periods of any serial index. This adds a challenging risk of oversight. Suppose the topic is soils, and the obvious words such as "alluvium," "clay," "humus," "mulch," "peat," "silt," "turf," etc., are all listed. But in recent literature the word "perma-frost" demands attention. So a new catch word must be entered. Success in searching depends much on a sensitive alertness to the words used by indexers.

Numerous published current indexes serve the dual purpose of informing subscribers concerning current developments, and aiding searchers in tracking down past records. Generally these indexes are put in collective form at suitable intervals. They use ingenious tricks of typography and arrangement to aid searchers. Some of the notable examples serve the interests of medicine (*2*), industry (*10*), and agriculture (*1*). But no conjuring trick is yet known which will make the same publication serve current awareness and permanent reference utility equally well. So Chemical Abstracts Service has started *Chemical Titles*, a permuted index of key words from all significant titles in over 550 selected periodicals in about 20 languages. It is a machine-made index on the Keyword-in-Context (KWIC) system (*6, 12*). By concentrating on current awareness, this service takes up much of the lag incurred by *Chemical Abstracts* in concentrating on permanent reference utility. Its reliance on words *as they occur* illustrates a major difference between *words* and *subjects* as index bases.

Formula indexes remain basically the same, except that the increasing number of known compounds gives them greater utility. Their drawbacks, notably difficulty in distinguishing between isomers, have caused discontent and drastic action. Codes which can be written on one line, without any structural ambiguity, are now serving recorders and searchers of chemical information, with promise of broadening utility in the future. Such codes have received attention in programs of the Division of Chemical Literature. Their prospects of wider application are closely tied in with their adaptability to storage in and retrieval from mechanized searching systems. Competing codes which neglect this aspect may expect short shrift.

Subject Heading Lists

Chemical formula codes, like empirical formula indexes, depart from the alphabetic base. Another type of special indexing aid which remains on the alphabetic base is found in subject heading lists. A few enthusiasts see a master subject heading list as the panacea for every ill our documentation flesh is heir to. Their opposites, also few in number, see all woe and no weal.

Proponents see the advantages of accepted standard designations, and of agreeing on one correct term for a given item to the exclusion of other terms even if equally correct. Claiming ample flexibility through skilled use of cross references, they are prone to overlook the irresistible force by which subject heading lists attract the formalists and ritualists. In fact, many of the proponents are the formalists and ritualists of documentation.

The deadening chill of formalism is as fatal to good indexing of facts as it is to worship. The letter kills; the spirit gives life. Dynamic subject heading lists are compiled, maintained, and administered with informed skill and care as potent instruments for better indexing and potent aids to skilled searchers. Static subject heading lists, compiled and administered under slavish adherence to a frozen set of rules, are road blocks.

An apple of discord among the formalists is the inverted heading. One camp will fight for "Acids, fatty," "Esters, keto-," and "Gas, natural." The opposite camp will do battle to the last man for "Fatty acids," "Keto esters," and "Natural gas." Ridicule is a favorite weapon, for it is not hard to trap either form in a *reductio ad absurdum* such as "Halogenated unsaturated fatty acid amides," or "Unsaturated fatty acid amides halogenated," or "Fatty acid amides halogenated unsaturated," or "Acid amides halogenated unsaturated fatty," or "Amides halogenated unsaturated fatty acid." While battle rages, the emancipated makers and users of dynamic subject heading lists concentrate on grappling with problems instead of with each other. When inversion is indicated, they invert; then, if it becomes contraindicated, they restore the pristine order.

Searchers tend to prefer accepting (and perhaps criticizing) the indexing tools prepared for them, not joining the battle. But frequently they preserve neutrality at the expense of insight into the mental processes of indexers. This insight is important to a high percentage of successes in the meeting of the minds.

Subject Classifications

Coded classifications of chemical subjects are indexes on a number or number-and-letter or punch-position base, designed for detailed subject searching. Within their limits of scope and coverage they can be used for that purpose, unlike book-shelving classifications such as those of Melvil Dewey and the Library of Congress.

The Universal Decimal Classification (UDC) is an effort to ride both horses at once. It succeeds within a fixed path directed from Brussels, but not in the struggle to serve academic, industrial, and military needs for bibliographic control. Though the decimal classification has shifted from positioning books to positioning index cards, it is still a position-designating system with only limited applicability to the infinitely variable demands of subject searching. It has, however, made a concession to flexibility in its auxiliary tables, applicable wherever appropriate in the main tables. This is a major departure from the rigid Dewey system and is a forerunner of the multiple-base classifications now finding a broadening range of applications.

The final step in multiple-base classifications is coordinate indexing, which amounts to making each indexing term a base of its own. The idea is old; one of its modern forms is Uniterm indexing (*13*).

Advice to Searchers

Searchers need not become expert indexers of chemical literature, but the better they understand indexers' problems and answers, the shorter the path to information needed from an index.

Through all the maze of word, formula, number, and punch-position lanes for placing and retrieving information, the searcher must choose his starting point and his path. If he chooses wisely in a well-indexed area, his search turns up all pertinent information entered in the system. If he knows how well the system covers the field, he has a fair estimate of how near his search comes to totality.

The searcher must have a mind of his own, and use it. Every system has some advocates who can see merit in other systems, and shortcomings in their own. But others, if he lets down his guard, will persuade him that:

Alphabetic sequence is his sole need.
The alphabet is a worse-than-useless mess.
A decimal (or other) classification answers all his prayers.
Punched cards will exorcise every problem.
Selectors needing no cards are his elixir of life.

Successful searching demands a balanced blend of training, experience, and the faculty known as horse sense.

Training drills the candidate in theory and practice. Knowing that coverage is never perfect, he learns to estimate its thoroughness for each source. He is taught tricks of the trade for tracing the indexer's line of thought, and acquires extensive knowledge of index bases and source materials. He learns how to adapt them to requirements, and to interpret findings according to the interests prompting the search.

Experience teaches him more tricks of the trade, broadens his knowledge of sources, sharpens his detective faculties, and increases his skill in applying the theories and principles learned in training.

Finally, any searcher tempted by easy searching paths, against the promptings of common sense, should ponder the consequences. Wasted effort, delays, missing of existing information, and high costs for small results are among the penalties for violating these rules:

Start with exact definitions of coverage in time, subject matter, and sources.

Find out where prior searchers stopped (on all three counts), and start there.

Slant the whole job to the basic purpose (background, critical review, reading list, anticipation, interference, infringement, state of the art, etc.).

Reserve bulldog tenacity for "must" assignments; on all ordinary jobs abandon any line of inquiry when yield value drops below operating cost, and close the project when the results are reasonably adequate.

Searchers who team training and experience with applied sense will produce effective results efficiently; no reasonable employer will ask more.

Literature Cited

(1) Agricultural Index, H. W. Wilson Co., New York, 1916–.
(2) Am. Med. Assoc., Chicago, Ill., "Quarterly Cumulative Index Medicus" (various titles and sponsors), 1879–.
(3) *Ann. Chimie,* general index to Vols. **1–30** (1801).
(4) "Beilsteins Handbuch der organischen Chemie," 4th ed. and supplements, Julius Springer, Berlin, 1918–.
(5) *Chem. Abstracts,* "Naming and Indexing of Chemical Compounds by *Chemical Abstracts,*" *Chem. Abstracts* **39**, 5867–975 (1945); also issued as a separate.
(6) *Chemical Titles,* No. **1**, Introduction (1960).
(7) *Chem. Zentr.* **96**, II, 2581–91 (1925); *Generalregister* **VII**, Part 4A, iii–iv (1932).
(8) Friedländer, P., "Fortschritte der Teerfarbenfabrikation," Vols. 1–, 1877–.
(9) Haskell, D. C., "Check List of Cumulative Indexes of Individual Periodicals in the New York Public Library," N. Y. Public Library, 1942.
(10) Huntress, E. H., "Brief Introduction to the Use of Beilsteins Handbuch der organischen Chemie," 2nd ed., Wiley, New York, 1938.
(11) "Industrial Arts Index," J. W. Wilson Co., New York, 1913–.
(12) Luhn, H. P., "Keyword-in-Context (KWIC) Index for Technical Literature," Advanced Systems Development Division, IBM Corp., Yorktown Heights, N. Y., 1959.
(13) Mines, Patricia, "Uniterm System of Coordinate Indexing," in "Advances in Documentation and Library Science," Vol. II, pp. 193–208, Interscience Publishers, New York, 1957.

(14) Prager, Bernhard, Stern, Dora, Ilberg, Konrad, "System der organischen Verbindungen, Leitfaden für die Benutzung von Beilsteins Handbuch der organischen Chemie," Julius Springer, Berlin, 1929.
(15) Richter, Friedrich, Ilberg, Konrad, "Kurze Anleitung zur Orientierung in Beilsteins Handbuch der organischen Chemie," Julius Springer, Berlin, 1936.

Based on paper presented before the Division of Chemical Literature, Symposium on Searching the Chemical Literature, 117th Meeting, ACS, Detroit, Mich., April 1950. Revised 1960.

The Use of Indexes

G. J. C. POTTER

Pulp and Paper Research Institute of Canada, Montreal, Canada

FRED J. BASSETT

The Upjohn Co., Kalamazoo, Mich.

As the index is the key to the information contained in a publication, its proper use is of paramount importance. This is particularly striking with regard to abstracting and indexing periodicals which have elaborate indexes based on their own systems. Effective use of the subject, author, and patent indexes of *Chemical Abstracts, British Abstracts, Chemisches Zentralblatt, Bulletin de la Société Chimique de France, Biological Abstracts, Applied Science & Technology Index,* and *Engineering Index* is demonstrated with their distinctive features and systems. The Richter and Hill systems of formula indexing are explained and discussed as used in *Chemical Abstracts, Chemisches Zentralblatt,* Beilstein, and Richter-Stelzner. Examples of arrangement of formulas, inclusive coverage dates, and hints in using formula indexes are given.

The Oxford Dictionary and Webster's have practically the same definition for the word "index" used as a guide to information—viz., "an alphabetical list, usually at the end of a book, of the names, subjects etc., occurring in it, with indication of the places where they occur." This definition is elementary, and though it may be applicable to books in general literature, it is only partially applicable to technical textbooks, which index to a greater extent than that. Still less applicable is it to such an abstracting periodical as *Chemical Abstracts* or an annual index like the *Engineering Index*. The index appearing in each of these is verily a key to the literature each covers rather than just "an alphabetical list of names, subjects, etc." It is more than a key, as, with each subject heading, there are cross references not only to synonymous terms but also to cognate subjects, instructing the searcher as well as aiding him to obtain the information desired. In consulting these indexes to obtain references on some specific subject, the searcher is also able to observe the scope of information available on the subject—an observation which will serve him in good stead in the future.

It is necessary to understand the use of indexes in order to make a thorough literature search in the least possible time. The necessity of this understanding is acknowledged by Beveridge (*3*), who states, "Students need some guidance in ways of tracing references through indexing journals and catalogues and in using libraries." This remark is equally applicable to the neophyte in literature searching as an occupation, since in few university curricula is a course in literature searching included.

In addition to understanding how to use an index, a knowledge of different indexes is important, as, included in the time and thoroughness factors, is the consideration of consulting the index most appropriate to the purpose of the search. For example, in looking for information on chemical equipment it may be time-saving to consult the *Engineering Index* rather than *Chemical Abstracts*, particularly as the index entries in the former are classified and abstracted descriptively. Again, if one is seeking the title of a paper on a certain substance, it is best to consult the *Applied Science & Technology Index* (prior to 1958 the *Industrial Arts Index*) first, as references are given by titles of papers, whereas the references in *Chemical Abstracts* are for the most part to information contained in a paper. These isolated examples in no way detract from the fact that *Chemical Abstracts* is best consulted first for the most part because of the excellence of its index.

In consulting an index, the searcher of course has his part to play. He must not be disappointed if he does not find the subject heading he uses on his first approach. Accordingly, the searcher should select words or wording synonymous with the first subject heading he has in mind or, if possible, the proper chemical name of the subject heading. He will then be sure to find one of these headings in the index. Smith (*19*) draws the searcher's attention to this, and the introduction to the annual index of *Chemical Abstracts* states, "For the best results in the use of an index the user must meet the index maker part of the way in an understanding of the indexing problem and, in particular, of nomenclature." *Chemical Abstracts* is most helpful in supplying synonymous headings, which are listed with a "see" reference to the heading under which the references are entered. For example, synonymous terms given for "furfural" are "furfuraldehyde, furfurole, fural, 2-furaldehyde, furole" and the references are listed under "2-furaldehyde." *British Abstracts* on the other hand lists all references to this compound under "furfuraldehyde" with no cross references, and does not list synonymous terms. *Chemisches Zentralblatt* lists "furfural, furfuraldehyde and furfurol" with references under "furfurol."

It is also important for the searcher to understand the wording of the reference entries, for these vary from one index to another, as pointed out by Singer (*18*), who shows differences in spelling and in the common meanings of words in British and American usage. *Chemical Abstracts* has some distinctive wordings—for example, "detection of" is the equivalent of "qualitative determination of," including "tests for" and "reaction for." Hence some discretion must be observed in interpreting reference entries.

Subject Index

The subject index is the most important part of the index and the searcher should make himself familiar with the system of subject indexing used by indexing periodicals.

Let us first consider the subject index of *Chemical Abstracts,* the most revealing of the chemical indexes. Some idea of the indexing system is given in the introduction to each annual index, but the system is fully explained in the 1945 issue (*6*). The first consideration is that subject indexing is used rather than word indexing. For instance, a book entitled "Chemists' Handbook" would be word-indexed under "Chemist" but subject-indexed under "Chemistry," if the subject matter were chemistry rather than chemists. Another book on "Who's Who in Chemistry" would be word-indexed under "Chemistry" but subject-indexed under "Chemists."

Another guiding principle to the *CA* index is that of inversion, whereby the subject is usually the chemical substance of which the compound is a derivative. For instance, "trinitrobenzene" is indexed as "Benzene, 1,3,5-trinitro-" and not as "Trinitrobenzene," though there may be a reference such as "Nitrobenzene, see Benzene, nitro-."

Compounds that have common names are listed under their common as well as their chemical names, but the reference entries may be made under either. For example, styphnic acid has the chemical name 2,4,6-trinitroresorcinol, but the index entries are under styphnic acid with a cross reference to Resorcinol, 2,4,6-trinitro-, see Styphnic acid. On the other hand, the well-known insecticide DDT is listed with a "see" reference to its chemical name and the reference entries are under the latter, "Ethane, 1,1,1-trichloro-2,2-bis (*p*-chlorophenyl)." In general, it may be said to be the exception, not the rule, for the common name of a compound not to be listed. All names, common and chemical, are listed alphabetically.

The entries under headings in *Chemical Abstracts* describe the information contained in the abstracts with the page on which the abstract occurs; the entries are not the titles of papers. These entries are again arranged alphabetically, but prepositions and articles are not considered in this arrangement. Careful consideration must be given to the wording of these entries, to be certain no pertinent reference is missed. Wording is used that will give as much guidance as possible with the minimum of words. Successive entries are made in line under each other, but when entries are indented they include the word under which the indentation is made.

The system of subject indexing in *British Abstracts* [which ceased publication with the December 1953 issue] is described in the 1948 index (*4*). Subject indexing is used rather than word indexing, but the range of subject headings listed is very much narrower than that of *Chemical Abstracts.* These subject headings or key words do not always include the chemical name but are "the words under which the information is most likely to be sought."

Sometimes cross references to synonymous terms and cognate subjects are given and sometimes not; the example of furfural has been mentioned. Far more use is made of adjectives in the alphabetical arrangement than in *Chemical Abstracts,* which prefers nouns. "Catalytic hydrogenation," for instance, is listed with "catalytic" as the key word in the alphabetical arrangement, whereas in *Chemical Abstracts* it is listed with subject heading "catalysts" and subheading "for hydrogenation."

The reference entries under the subject headings follow the pattern of *Chemical Abstracts,* except that prepositions like "for" and "in" follow the alphabetical arrangement, though their use is restricted as much as possible. Prefixes like *cyclo-, iso-, di-,* etc., are written in italics and are not included in the alphabetical arrangement, unlike *Chemical Abstracts,* which includes them. Again, these entries must be carefully read.

The index of *Chemisches Zentralblatt* has been described by Spitzer (*20*), but a few of its essential features may be mentioned here. The index is classified with main subject headings in heavy black type, subheadings in smaller black type, and other headings under these in yet smaller black type. For instance, "chlor" (chlorine) is in large heavy black type, "chlorverbindungen" (chlorine compounds) is a subheading in smaller black type, and "chlorwasserstoff" (hydrochloric acid) is a subheading to "chlorverbindungen" in yet smaller black type. As in the case of furfural, several synonymous names may be listed but, when not listed, they must be found under the larger type headings, so that one must know in which of these headings or subheadings the desired information is to be found. A unique feature of this index is that sometimes a substance is listed with a "see also" reference to its formula in the formula index, where the reference entries to the pages of the abstracts are to be found. Unlike *Chemical Abstracts* and *British Abstracts,* the reference entries are of the "running" type, one following another on the same line, not a separate line for each entry. In all entries, of course, the arrangement is for the most part alphabetical but, as in *British Abstracts,* prefixes like iso-, tri-, etc., are disregarded.

The *Engineering Index* is on a par with *Chemical Abstracts* for including with subject headings a list of synonymous terms and cognate subjects. The headings are classified with subheadings, and under each heading or subheading descriptive abstracts of the reference papers are given. Under the subheadings there are also "see also" references to synonymous terms and cognate subjects. The headings are, like those of *British Abstracts,* those words under which the information is most likely to be sought. A valuable feature of the index is that short descriptive abstracts of books are included. This index is most useful for giving information pertaining to applied chemistry, particularly any chemical operation in which engineering plays a big part—for example, the "see also" references to the heading "Chemical Processes" are comprehensive. The headings, subheadings, and titles of papers abstracted are arranged alphabetically. In the titles, prepositions and articles are not included and titles of foreign papers are given in the original language.

The *Applied Science & Technology Index* has its particular uses and is much favored by, and most useful to, those who have no chemical training. It gives literature references to substances and processes, and it is useful for collecting references to papers on a certain subject, especially if authors' names are not known. Headings may be also said to be those under which the information is most likely to be sought and, for the most part, words or wording in common use. From the chemical point of view, however, the literature it covers is restricted. Its great value lies in giving references to new items, and business and marketing information. It also describes several magazines which are not well known.

The index of *Biological Abstracts* contains headings for which the majority of searchers would look. Chemical compounds are not indexed in accordance with chemical nomenclature but by their common names. The same applies to drugs. Substances of interest to biologists, such as individual insecticides, plant hormones, etc., are listed under headings corresponding to their usage. The indexing system is described in a few pages immediately before the subject index.

Author Index

In most indexes the names of authors are arranged alphabetically. "Mc," however, is usually treated as "Mac" and interfiled. Names beginning with "de" and "von" are indexed under "d" and "v," or cross-referenced to the index entry used.

Chemisches Zentralblatt, however, does not consider "von" in the alphabetical arrangement. Spellings of authors' names generally are those given in the papers. In some instances, however, there is confusion in names, especially in transliterating from Cyrillic and other script.

The author index is particularly of value in tracing the papers an author has published, as the titles of the papers are given after his name, with the page reference to the abstract. In general, when there are two or more authors to a paper, the title of the paper is given under the name of the first author.

Patent Index

Chemical Abstracts, British Abstracts, and *Chemisches Zentralblatt* have patent indexes in which the numbers of the patents, issued in different countries and abstracted by them, are listed with the page of the abstracts on which they appear. When the number of a patent is known, finding an abstract of that patent presents no difficulties.

In searching for patents on a certain subject, the index is used as in searching for information on any subject. In *British Abstracts* and *Chemical Abstracts* the reference entries under subject heading concerning patents are prefixed by the letter "P," and in *Chemisches Zentralblatt* they are marked with an asterisk. The same prefixes are placed before the titles of patents in the author index, which also lists the names of the assignee. In *Chemisches Zentralblatt* the name of the country in which the patent was first issued is included after the title of the patent in the author index.

Formula Index

There are two systems of formula indexing in common use today, the Hill and the Richter systems.

In the original Hill system (*11*) formulas are written in strict alphabetic order, omitting water of crystallization, except that with carbon compounds carbon is written first, followed immediately by hydrogen if present—i.e., trichloropropanol, $C_3H_5Cl_3O$. Each compound is arranged in the index by its own formula; the sodium salt of propionic acid, $C_3H_5NaO_2$, is entered as such.

The Hill system is used in modified form today by *Chemical Abstracts* and *Referativny Zhurnal, Khimiya* (*17*) and indexes both inorganic and organic compounds. Beilsteins Handbuch (*2*) formula index to the second supplement uses the Hill system. This index covers the original work and two supplements.

In the modified Hill system as used by *Chemical Abstracts* today the arrangement of symbols in formulas is alphabetic, except that in carbon compounds C always comes first, followed immediately by H if hydrogen is also present. For deuterium and tritium compounds, D and T, respectively, are used. These are placed alphabetically in formulas; the exception in arrangement made for H is not extended to include these isotopes. Glutamic-*d* acid is therefore written $C_5H_8DNO_4$. The names of certain elements and their respective symbols are given preference over former names. The preferred names are astatine, beryllium, niobium, hafnium, and promethium (but not wolfram) (*7*).

The arrangement of formulas is also alphabetic, except that the number of atoms of a specific kind influences the order of listing. All formulas with one carbon atom only come before formulas with C_2—thus, CF_2, $CHFI_2$, CHNO, CO, CZr, C_2HF_3, $C_2H_2F_2$.

Compounds are not always formula-indexed under their own formulas. This is a departure from the ideal, but is reasonable. The interest in a salt of a complex organic acid is likely to be mainly in the acid. It is more valuable to have the record of the salt under the formula of the acid for the use of searchers looking up the acid. In *Chemical Abstracts* entries under their own formulas are made for all strictly inorganic and strictly organic compounds, both addition compounds and true reaction derivatives (esters, acetals, hydrazones, oximes, picrates, semicarbazones, etc.); the diethyl ester of malonic acid is found under $C_7H_{12}O_4$.

Inorganic salts of organic acids and inorganic addition compounds of organic compounds (hydrohalides, perchlorates, sulfates, etc.) are not given separate entries but are indicated in modifying phrases under the formula of the compounds from which they are derived (under the acid in the case of a salt). Salts of formic, acetic, and oxalic acids are exceptions; these are entered under their own formulas, and lithium acetate is found under $C_2H_3LiO_2$.

The arrangement of entries under any formula heading is alphabetic according to the preferred names of the isomers. Isomerism is not indicated in the formula index in cases in which the names differ only in position numbers or letter; 2- and 3-pentanone are both indexed under $C_5H_{10}O$, pentanone.

Polymers having different names and recognized as different substances are all entered under their accepted formulas. But a definite compound for which different polymeric formulas are in use is entered under the simplest formula, as Cl_3Fe for iron chloride.

In the case of labeled compounds, entry is normally without special designation in the formula, but name entries under such formulas show the labeled nature of the compound; $C_4H_8O_2$, isobutyric-1-C^{14} acid, indicates that the number one carbon atom is labeled. Deuterium and tritium compounds show labeling in the formula index, as CH_3DO, methanol-*d*, or $C_2H_2D_2O$, acet-d_2-aldehyde.

The formula index only of *Chemical Abstracts* lists new compounds for which no names or structures have been given in the original literature.

Entries under a formula heading consist of the formula, in bold-faced type; the name as it has been used in the subject index, in lightface roman type—that part of the entry in this type is the exact equivalent of the formula given; occasionally a modifying phrase or word in italics which represents that part of the compound indexed not represented in the formula, as "Na salt" or "di-HCl"; and the column-fraction reference to the abstract proper.

Cross references to the subject (primary) index are used for many simple inorganic compounds: $AlCl_3$, see Aluminum chloride; all minerals of definite composition, $F_2Mg_6Na_2O_{22}Si_8$, see Richterite; and the more common organic compounds, C_4H_4O, see Furan.

Water of hydration, omitted in the formula when indexed, is often given in lightface type following the formula, as $AsHO_4Zn.H_2O$, Zinc arsenate.

The Richter system, devised for organic compounds only, was formerly used in modified form by Beilstein (*1*) and *Chemisches Zentralblatt*. In this system carbon always comes first, followed by the other elements in an arbitrary arrangement termed the chemical alphabet—e.g., H, O, N, Cl, Br, I, F, S, P—and the remaining elements in alphabetic order: A—Z, of their symbols. Beginning with the 1956 formula index, *Chemisches Zentralblatt* adopted the Hill system of indexing (*15*). The formula index to the second supplement of Beilstein changed to the Hill system at the same time (*2*). This index covers the original and first supplement material in addition to the second supplement.

The arrangement of formulas within the index by the Richter system may be termed a semiclassified order, depending on:

1. The number of carbon atoms
2. The number of other elements which, in addition to C, are contained in the compound
3. The kind of elements (which in addition to C are contained in the molecule) in accordance with the chemical alphabet stated previously
4. The number of atoms of each element which, in addition to C, is contained in the compound

Water of crystallization is not made a part of the formulas indexed.

According to this arrangement all compounds containing one carbon and one other element in any proportion are listed before compounds containing one carbon and two other elements in any proportion.

1I	1II	1III	1IV
CH_2	$CHCl_3$	CHO_2Cl	CHONMg
CH_4	CH_2	CHNS	CH_2ONBr
CCl_4	CH_2O_2	CH_2O_2S	CH_8ON_2Cl
CS_2	CH_3Cl	CH_3ON	CH_5O_4NS
	CCl_3Br	CH_4OMg	

At the top of each page of all publications using the Richter system will be found Arabic and Roman figures serving as searching aids. The Arabic figure denotes the number of carbon atoms in the formulas listed on the page; the Roman figure denotes the number of other elements combined with carbon.

In the third edition of Richter's formula index (*16*) each compound has only one place in the compilation, with the exception of the salts, which are placed with the compounds from which they are derived. The chlorides, bromides, iodides, and cyanides of quaternary ammonium bases, however, are entered under the parent compound.

Polymeric compounds with fixed molecular weights are entered under their own formulas—e.g., $(CHON)_3$, cyanuric acid, is found under 3III, $C_3H_3O_3N_3$.

Certain modifications of the Richter system have been made in Stelzner (*21*), Beilstein, and *Chemisches Zentralblatt* (Table I). Unless otherwise stated, the following rules apply to all three formula indexes. Corresponding entries are given for *Chemical Abstracts*.

Methyl and ethyl esters of organic acids are placed under the acid, except in Beilstein, where these esters and all other esters are found under their own formulas. In Stelzner and *Chemisches Zentralblatt* polycarboxylic polyesters with methyl or ethyl ester groups are placed under the acid group after removal of these ester groups; the propyl methyl diester of malonic acid is found under $C_6H_{10}O_4$. Any higher esters above ethyl are found under the formulas of the esters. Esters of orthoacids are considered as ethers of polyalcohols and are found under their own formulas: $CH(OC_2H_5)_3$ under $C_7H_{16}O_3$.

Esters of inorganic acids are found under the formula of the ester. For mixed esters the same rule applies as for organic acid esters.

Salts of organic acids with basic inorganic parts (metals, ammonia, hydrazine, etc.) are found under the acid.

Salts of primary, secondary, and tertiary amines with inorganic acids are found under the amines.

Salts of organic bases and organic acids are found under both the base and

Table I. Modifications of Hill and Richter Systems

Type	Compound Indexed Under				
	Beilstein	*Chemical Abstracts*	*Chem. Zentr.*	*Richter*	*Stelzner*
Organic esters	Ester	Ester	Methyl and ethyl under parent, all other under ester	Ester	Methyl and ethyl under parent, all other under ester
Mixed organic polyesters	Ester	Ester	Convert Me and Et groups to acid, leave higher ester groups and use resulting formula	Ester	Convert Me and Et groups to acid, leave higher ester groups and use resulting formula
Inorganic esters	Ester	Ester	Ester	Ester	Ester
Salts of organic acids, amines	Parent	Parent with exception of formic, acetic, and oxalic	Parent	Parent	Parent
Salts of organic bases and organic acids	Both parents	New formula	Both parents	Both parents	Both parents
Metal derivatives of organic compounds	Parents unless attached directly and only to C	New formula except for salts of organic acids	Parent unless attached directly and only to C	Parent	Parent unless attached directly and only to C
Salts of Grignard type compounds	Hydroxide	Salt	Hydroxide	Hydroxide	Hydroxide
Salt of ammonium oxonium, etc., compounds	Hydroxide	Salt	Hydroxide	Hydroxide	Hydroxide

the acid. Rare or unusual compounds of this type (picrates, oxalates, and aniline salts) are found under the formula of the salt, because the free base and free acid usually do not exist as such.

Metal derivatives of organic compounds are indexed under their own formulas when the metal is immediately attached only to carbon. In all other cases they are indexed under the formula of the parent compound.

Metal derivatives of acetoacetic acid, malonic esters, acetylacetones, etc. (reactive methyl group in common), are found under the formula of the parent compound.

Salts of Grignard and analogous compounds are placed under the formula of the hydroxide. Organic silicon compounds are treated in the same manner when only one acid group is present. If more than one acid group is present, the salt is indexed under its own formula.

Salts of ammonium, oxonium, sulfonium, etc., are placed under the formula of the corresponding hydroxide. $(C_6H_5)_2ICl$ is found under $C_{12}H_{11}OI$. Diazonium compounds are handled in the same manner, under the corresponding amine.

Definite double and molecular compounds of simple composition are indexed under their own formulas. Complicated compounds of this type are found under the formulas of both their components.

Various criticisms (*5, 8, 13, 14*) of existing formula indexing systems have appeared in the literature. It is beyond the scope of this paper to discuss these at this time.

From the dawn of organic chemistry as such to the present time there exists a continuous record in formula index form (Table II) of the compounds of this large branch of chemistry. Inorganic chemistry is not so fortunate. [Hoffman (*12*) indexed organic compounds by formula to 1909.] From this date to 1920, when *Chemical Abstracts* began indexing by formula, there is no compilation of inorganic compounds by formula.

Table II. Year Coverage on Formula Indexes

ORGANIC	1828	1910	1920	1930	1940	1950
RICHTER						
STELZNER						
BEILSTEIN						
CHEM. ABSTR.						
CHEM. ZENTR.						
BRIT. ABSTR.						
REF. ZHUR. KHIM.						
INORGANIC						
HOFFMANN						
CHEM. ABSTR.						
REF. ZHUR. KHIM.						

Conclusion

The above is just an indication of the use of indexes. More detailed information on this important subject is given in the chapter on indexes in the "A Guide to the Literature of Chemistry" by Crane, Patterson, and Marr (*10*). The more one uses an index the more one learns about it, particularly if the index is approached receptively. The importance of indexing and the part it plays in giving information can be judged by the finding of Crane (*9*) that 700 words of indexing are necessary for each 1000 words of abstract.

Literature Cited

(1) Beilsteins Handbuch der organischen Chemie, 4th ed., Vol. 29, Julius Springer, Berlin, 1939.
(2) *Ibid.*, 2nd suppl., 1956.
(3) Beveridge, W. I. B., "The Art of Scientific Investigation," 2nd ed., Wm. Heinemann, London, 1953.
(4) *British Abstracts*, Abstracts A, B, and C, Index, **1948**, 3–4.
(5) Britton, E. C., Coleman, G. H., Perkins, R. P., *Chem. Eng. News* **27**, 1236, 1251 (1949).
(6) *Chem. Abstracts* **39**, 5867–975 (1945).
(7) *Ibid.*, **52**, 1F (1958).
(8) Cockburn, J. G., *Chem. & Ind.* (London) **1949,** 837.
(9) Crane, E. J., *Ibid.*, **1956, 41.**

(10) Crane, E. J., Patterson, A. M., Marr, E. B., "Guide to the Literature of Chemistry," p. 227, Wiley, New York, 1957.
(11) Hill, E. A., *J. Am. Chem. Soc.* **22,** 478–94 (1900).
(12) Hoffman, M. K., "Lexikon der anorganischen Verbindungen," 3 vols., J. A. Barth, Leipzig, 1910–19.
(13) Huntress, E. H., *Chem. Eng. News* **27,** 79 (1949).
(14) Laakso, P. V., *Chem. & Ind. (London),* **1948,** 387–8.
(15) Pflücke, M., *Chem. Zentr.,* Formelregister, FI (1956).
(16) Richter, M. M., "Lexikon der Kohlenstoff-Verbindungen," 3rd ed., Leopold Voss, Hamburg and Leipzig, 1910–12.
(17) Serpinsky, V. V., *J. Document.* **12,** 105 (1956).
(18) Singer, T. E. R., ADVANCES IN CHEM. SER., No. **4,** 24 (1951); No. **30,** 75 (1961).
(19) Smith, J. F., *Ibid.,* No. **4,** 19 (1951); No. **30,** 16 (1961).
(20) Spitzer, E. F., Slamecka, Vladimir, *Ibid.,* No. **4,** 30 (1951); No. **30,** 136 (1961).
(21) Stelzner, R., "Literatur-Register der organischen Chemie," Friedrich Vieweg & Sohn, Braunschweig, 1913–26.

BASED on paper presented before Division of Chemical Literature, Symposium on Searching the Chemical Literature, 130th Meeting, ACS, Atlantic City, N. J., September 1956. Revised 1961.

Relation of an Abstract to Its Original

G. MALCOLM DYSON
Chemical Abstracts Service, Columbus, Ohio

A chain of inquiry, made up of the links of original communication, abstract, index, and search, must exist between the searcher and the original source of information, and all links must be in order. Abstracting may be subdivided into the considerations of title, numerical data, critical consideration, authors and references, creation of the abstract, and indexing.

The nature of inquiry is in itself a subject for study, more especially the division of the inquirer's work into the two departments of discovery and verification. In this paper, however, the most important factor is the chain of inquiry which must exist intact between the searcher and the original source of information. The links in this chain are the original communication (journal, thesis, patent, or other source), the abstract, the index to the abstract, and the searcher.

To arrive at one end of this chain from the other, all the links must be in order. The probability that this will be so depends on the efficiency with which each link operator works; if searcher, indexer, and abstractor are all 95% efficient, the overall efficiency is 85.7% and the chance that a given piece of original information will reach the searcher is approximately 5 in 6. While it is the main object of this contribution to say a little about the link between abstract and original, it is not always possible to avoid encroaching on the subjects of indexing and searching; the main object is, nevertheless, to examine the relation between the original communication and those abbreviated forms which are indispensable to the chemist.

Very few editors of scientific journals today allow any verbosity on the part of their contributors, and it is unlikely that any contribution to a scientific journal as published can be cut down appreciably without losing something of the author's meaning. The days are gone when W. H. Perkin (Senior) could say of a compound "it crystallizes from alcohol in magnificent pale yellow columnar prisms, which, on slow cooling of the solution, often attain a length of several inches"; today this would be "yellow prisms (EtOH)." This being so, it is clear that the abstractor has to make the difficult decision of what to retain and what to reject. This decision must be consistent—and in this respect consistency is one of the highest of virtues, since it will not benefit users of an abstract system if abstracts prepared by different abstractors, or by the same abstractor on different occasions, are based on varying conventions. Much could be added on the subject of the selection of data from originals for abstracting. It is fundamentally important to realize that the pattern of selection will necessarily alter from discipline to discipline. A selection pattern for chemistry would be of no use in astronomy or medicine. In chemistry we try to "print the facts" but nevertheless something is inevitably lost in the course of compression. There is a growing tendency to print long tables of very similar compounds with small modifications, from which it is hoped that large physiological differences will arise; such tables are not reproduced in abstracting and all the compounds may not be named in the abstract; in the index (subject and formula) *all* the names will be recorded, however, if relative to positive physiological results, so that occasionally the indexes may compensate for material unavoidably rejected in abstracting.

The subdivision of the considerations of abstracting into the following sections is purely arbitrary, and is for convenience of the author.

Title

The statement that the title should be descriptive of the matter of a communication seems to be a truism, but insufficient attention appears to be paid to the titles of papers submitted to learned journals. This is particularly true when papers are part of a series—for example, one of a series of papers may be entitled "Studies in the Chemistry of X and Y, Part 47. Attempted Synthesis of Y." Suppose X and Y are complex alkaloids; often such a paper deals only with the preparation of some complex ring structures—oxaäzulenes, perhaps—from which the investigators hope ultimately to synthesize the subject of their main interest. Hence the paper is really about oxaäzulenes and not alkaloids X and Y. The repercussions of this on indexing are serious. However, the new "keyword in context" indexes (*Chemical Titles*) which are compiled by computer from titles of papers and used for awareness in the period between original publications and effective use of chemical and physical abstracts, may alter this. As special keyword indexes are compiled from titles, authors may give more thought to the relation of a title to its paper.

Numerical Data

In abstracting it is desirable to transfer many of the numerical data of the original communication, if they are relative to properties and not to arbitrary readings taken during experiments. Thus, the determined melting point, boiling point, refractive index, density, and even such lesser known properties as specific inductive capacity and dipole moment are always to be placed in an abstract. Their presence will often obviate a search through the original, which is one of the objects of abstracting. It is not possible, however, to index many of these data; this results in having to make searches under various entries for a desired physical property. This is the complement to the situation where more information is available in the index than in the abstract; here the reverse is true. That "consultation of abstracts cannot replace the reading of original literature," like all such sweeping statements, is true only up to a point; it would be better to say that while much useful information can be gathered from abstracts without consulting originals, we cannot do all our reading in the abstract journals. This academic scientist who could keep abreast of his microslice of science by reading half a dozen papers in half a dozen journals is a being of the past; modern chemists have to be more versatile. Some academic colleagues who have researched in a limited field for a lifetime can, no doubt, keep abreast by reading only original papers; for most chemists, however, abstracts are "of the essence."

It is important, where the lesser known constants have been determined, to index them not only under the compound but under the property—e.g., the dielectric constant of camphor should be indexed as "Dielectric constant, of camphor" as well as "Camphor, dielectric constant." Such a feature (used in *Chemical Abstracts* consistently) adds vastly to the value of the abstract service.

Critical Consideration

When an abstract is being made, selecting and rejecting may be considered a process of criticism, and in the last analysis may become so; the dismissal of a paper by an abstract consisting of the single word "polemical" is a case in point. In general, however, technical criticism in abstracting is rightly to be avoided, although it is perhaps a pity not to indicate physical constants that have been determined with more than the usual precautions. This is sometimes taken care of in the title, but often there is no means of telling whether a particular constant has been determined with great accuracy or just casually, as the melting point of an organic compound is determined.

Authors and References

The names of authors are best preserved in abstracts exactly as printed in the original communications. The Chemical Society of London has (1933) dropped its old custom of printing each author's name in full, and uses Christian names only where confusion is likely to arise—as between Sibelius Smith and Samuel Smith. The innovation practiced by *Chemical Abstracts* of including the addresses of authors has much to commend it.

The Nature of an Abstract

Fortunately for chemists, it is scarcely possible to write a paper without establishing, so to speak, a reference framework of matter. The chemical paper will always be "about" a substance, or group of substances, so that its framework in this respect can always be expressed in terms of material structure—inorganic or organic. Thus, an abstract, in mentioning the old and new compounds with which its original dealt, is becoming studded with reference or indexing points which are (assuming a satisfactory nomenclature) noncontroversial—either a paper deals with phenanthrene or it does not. On the other hand, concepts arise which do not always admit of such sharp characterization; when, for example, "tuberculosis" is mentioned in relation to a chemical structure, several different concepts can be implied and additional terms are necessary to make communication possible. Thus the concept "phenanthrene" is of first-order precision and that of "tuberculosis" is of second-order. With "tuberculosis" we need to know whether the disease is exacerbated or ameliorated by the compound; which particular organism and which host is being considered; the route and frequency of administration of the drug, and so on. Thus, a concept of second-order precision needs a modification, as in "tuberculosis, dermal, treatment by intradermal application of phenanthrene."

The concept of each unit in such a modification—"skin," "intradermal application," and "phenanthrene"—is important. Fortunately, phenanthrene is easily coded ($B6_313$), but the other centers of conceptual significance need arbitrary codes. Physical properties are fairly easily defined and are intrinsic— that is, they are permanent—while the chemical nature and physical environment of the compound remain unchanged. The biological activities are not in all cases measurable or capable of being objectively described, and must therefore be dealt with by a series of arbitrary symbols. Analytical procedures, technical and industrial applications, and patent data are all different, but correlated, data centers that may arise in connection with any compound or group of compounds; these features must all be constantly in mind as an abstract is built up, for each symbol and each center must in some way appear in the abstract; if physiological investigations have been made on a new organic compound, not only must the preparation and physical properties appear in the abstract, but reference to the nature of the physiological data is essential. It may, perhaps, be well to reiterate the value of including negative results in the abstract. If a new compound was examined and found to be entirely devoid of local anesthetic activity, this should be stated, in the hope that the statement will avert a useless repetition of the work.

Indexing

Consider the abstract:

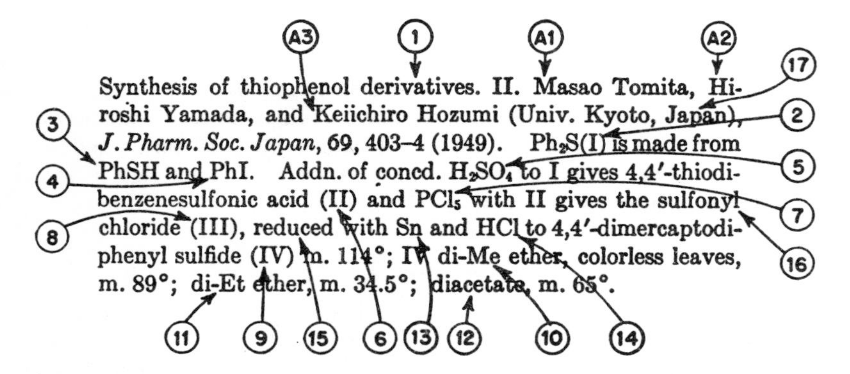
Synthesis of thiophenol derivatives. II. Masao Tomita, Hiroshi Yamada, and Keiichiro Hozumi (Univ. Kyoto, Japan), *J. Pharm. Soc. Japan*, 69, 403–4 (1949). Ph_2S(I) is made from PhSH and PhI. Addn. of concd. H_2SO_4 to I gives 4,4′-thiodibenzenesulfonic acid (II) and PCl_5 with II gives the sulfonyl chloride (III), reduced with Sn and HCl to 4,4′-dimercaptodiphenyl sulfide (IV) m. 114°; IV di-Me ether, colorless leaves, m. 89°; di-Et ether, m. 34.5°; diacetate, m. 65°.

All the possible indexing points are marked and summarized in Table I. All these points may not be used in practical indexing, items 5, 7, and 13 to 17 being

TABLE I. Indexing Points

A1	Tomita, Masao	Author entries
A2	Yamada, Hiroshi	
A3	Hozumi, Keiichiro	
1	Thiophenol, derivatives of (synthesis)	
2	Biphenyl sulfide	$B6/_2S$
3	Thiophenol	B6S
4	Iodobenzene	B6I
5	Sulfuric acid, condensing agent	
6	Thiodibenzenesulfonic acid	$B6SO_2Q:4/_2S$
7	Phosphorus pentachloride	
8	Thiodibenzene sulfonyl chloride	$B6SO_2Ch:4/_2S$
9	4,4′-Dimercaptodiphenyl sulfide	$B6S:4/_2S$
10	4,4′-Dimercaptodiphenyl sulfide diMe ether	$B6SC:4/_2S$
11	4,4′-Dimercaptodiphenyl sulfide diEt ether	$B6SC_2:4/_2S$
12	4,4′-Dimercaptodiphenyl sulfide acetate	$B6S(EQC_2):4/_2S$
13	Tin	
14	Hydrochloric acid	
15	Reduction ($SO_2Cl \rightarrow SH$)	
16	Chlorination ($SO_3H \rightarrow SO_2Cl$)	
17	Japan	

considered too trivial to index. This line must be drawn with some care; for, in the case of, say, phosgene ($COCl_2$), its use even in a reagent capacity may be an indexing point of importance. On the other hand, punched card techniques permit the use of all these associations simultaneously.

In searching, the searcher must weigh whether or not the path available to him is capable of leading him to the bulk of the information on a topic. He cannot do the abstractor's work for him; he can only assess, on the basis of experience, the probability of the work's having been well done.

BASED on paper presented before the Division of Chemical Literature, Symposium on Searching the Chemical Literature, 117th Meeting, ACS, Detroit, Mich., April 1950. Revised 1960.

The Use of Chemical Abstracts

E. J. CRANE[1]
The Ohio State University, Columbus 10, Ohio

The editorial policies of *Chemical Abstracts*, adopted to meet the wishes of its users, have given this journal certain emphasized properties. These properties are described and discussed, because a knowledge of what to expect in a publication is essential to its most effective use. The scope of *Chemical Abstracts* is outlined, the three essentials for complete coverage within this scope are described, the efforts for quality in abstracts and for promptness in their appearance are discussed, form and arrangement are mentioned, and the five kinds of indexes published are considered, with the emphasis on subject and formula indexing. In the interest of growth in the service rendered by *Chemical Abstracts*, the editor offers an attentive ear to users of this journal.

An editor needs ears more than he needs a pen when the use of his journal is discussed. It is better for him to listen to users than to try to tell them how to proceed. It is only because this former editor did a lot of listening, as does the present editor, and tried to build his journal accordingly that he consented to discuss the use of *Chemical Abstracts*.

Chemical Abstracts (*CA*) has a large staff of abstractors, well over 2000. These chemists constitute a representative group because all kinds of chemists are needed in approximate proportion to the research activities in the various branches or fields of chemistry. One or more section editors, each well informed in the field of his section, are in charge of the 33 sections and 19 subsections of *CA*. The abstractors and section editors, active specialists in many kinds of chemical work, are often consulted as to matters of policy, so that right in the *CA* family the editor has users of *CA* regularly available for consultation and advice. In addition, many others are consulted and many write to tell of their needs. Carefully worded and distributed questionnaires have been sent out from time to time from the *CA* office. In 1958 a professional information service (Herner & Co.) made an extensive interview study of the use of *CA*. Listening is a source of growth.

[1] Editor of *Chemical Abstracts* 1915–1958.

CA's editorial policies, adopted to meet the wishes of its users, have given this journal certain emphasized properties. These properties are discussed briefly here because a knowledge of what to expect in a publication is essential to its most effective use.

Coverage

Complete coverage of chemistry and chemical engineering has long been attempted as a significantly worthy goal. The approach to completeness has been so close that a searcher can use *CA* with reasonable confidence that he will not miss important contributions if his search is careful and thorough. The publication of adequate abstracts and of full, well constructed indexes is a factor in completeness, as well as is the reporting of all suitable, published papers and patents.

The words defining limitations in the coverage by *CA* are "chemical," "new," and "published." A paper to be covered must contain *new* information (the results of experiment or experience) which is of *chemical* interest, except that good reviews, accompanied by references, and papers of biographical or historical interest are briefly reported. Users of *CA* sometimes expect to find nonchemical information therein. The scope of *CA* is determined by a broad and generous interpretation of what is of chemical and chemical engineering interest and considerable nonchemical information gets into the journal in the brief abstracting of papers only partially of chemical interest, but no user of *CA* should count on this journal for complete coverage of any nonchemical subject.

It is not easy to define the borderline between chemistry and other sciences. This borderline is often indefinite and indistinct. In general, the policy is to abstract a paper in case of doubt as to its chemical nature. In particular, it is difficult to draw a line between the various branches of biology and chemistry. In this effort the abstractors and editors are guided by a six-page statement entitled "Biochemical Borderline and the Classification of Biochemical Abstracts in *Chemical Abstracts*." Copies of this will be sent to interested *CA* users on request. Clinical papers involving the use of chemical compounds in the treatment of disease, but with no chemical results reported, are counted as being outside of our chemical field.

Another useful publication issued by the Chemical Abstracts Service is "Directions for Abstractors and Section Editors of *Chemical Abstracts*." This 52-page, indexed booklet contains much information about the nature, style, and form of abstracts and about nomenclature, spelling, forms, and abbreviations. While these directions are intended primarily for the producers and editors of abstracts, they have proved their helpfulness to users of abstracts and to chemical writing in general. They contain special sections devoted to abstracting (1) organic papers and (2) patents. Copies can be obtained from the Chemical Abstracts Service for 25 cents each.

CA now systematically covers more than 9000 journals. We are sometimes asked what determines whether or not a journal is covered. The answer is that a journal is regularly examined as soon as it is discovered that at least occasionally it contains new information of chemical interest. Coverage, of course, does not mean abstracting all papers in a journal. As a matter of fact, *CA* abstracts all papers of only a comparatively small percentage of the journals in the "List of Periodicals Abstracted by *Chemical Abstracts*" (those devoted strictly to original papers in the field of chemistry). The above criteria for inclusion are applied to individual papers, not to journals. Many trade journals are covered, as well as scientific and technical publications. House organs are occasionally the source of abstracts suitably published in *CA*, but articles in these are not abstracted when they have an advertising flavor. *CA* rarely abstracts anonymous articles; they seldom contain information not already published elsewhere in signed articles. Published miscellaneous bulletins, circulars, and the like, such as those issued by government agencies, are abstracted if they are readily available and are identifiable, but mimeographed or otherwise unpublished governmental reports, documents, etc., are not covered. Interim progress reports that do not give results are avoided. Books are not usually a source of new information, but when they do report for the first time the results of experimental investigation they are abstracted. Otherwise new books are merely announced by title.

Sometimes we are asked whether or not the possessor of a file of *CA* needs also to turn to *British Abstracts* (discontinued at the end of 1953), to *Chemisches Zentralblatt,* and to *Referativnyi Zhurnal, Khimiya* to make chemical searches complete. This is difficult to answer categorically. The abstracts in these European abstract journals have been systematically checked (*Referativnyi Zhurnal, Khimiya* for Russian papers only) against our record of abstracts after a period of time, and when they have covered a paper of chemical interest which *CA* has missed, we have proceeded in one way or another to get an abstract. *British Abstracts,* as contrasted to the former *British Chemical Abstracts*, was not strictly a chemical abstract journal, and *Chemisches Zentralblatt* covers some papers which we regard as clinical or otherwise not chemical. It is our belief that *CA* covers every chemical paper which these other three abstract journals have abstracted. This does not mean that in general *CA*'s abstracting is less prompt. However, there is a human element in abstracting and indexing and no two abstractors will report a paper exactly alike nor will two indexers always select exactly the same information to record. Owing to the human element there is some advantage in having access to more than one chemical abstract journal in making the most thorough kind of search. *CA*'s coverage of Russian chemical papers is as complete as that of *Referativnyi Zhurnal, Khimiya* and often more prompt.

Quality of Abstracts

The user of an abstract journal naturally wants to know what kind of abstracts to expect and something about their quality. For strictly chemical papers, particularly those from the less accessible publications, *CA* endeavors to publish informational abstracts, not merely descriptive or indicative abstracts. Completeness enters into the picture again in the kind of abstracts published. *CA* places special emphasis on having abstracts complete from the indexing point of view. Abstractors are instructed to report every measurement, observation, method, apparatus, suggestion, and theory that is presented in papers as new and of value in itself, and to include all new compounds and all elements, compounds, and other substances for which new data are given.

The quality of abstracts is determined in part by the kind of abstractors used. *CA* endeavors to have each abstract made by an individual who is well informed as far as the subject matter and language of the assigned paper or patent are concerned. With a small group of full-time professional abstractors this would not be possible.

CA does not publish critical abstracts. This policy is based on the assumption that *CA* users, both present and future, will want to judge what is of interest and value to them and will prefer not to have the editor select their diet. Most papers abstracted have been accepted for publication after having passed critical scrutiny by referee and editor. *CA* attempts merely to report the chemical content of each faithfully.

Accuracy in an abstract journal is naturally of interest to users. Mistakes occur, too often it seems to us, but it is fair and perhaps helpful to point out that a good deal of care is exercised and much checking is done to keep abstracts and indexes accurate. The more serious mistakes and omissions discovered are corrected by supplementary abstracts or suitably worded index entries. Minor errors are not corrected, since an abstract journal is filled with secondary information; it is not source material. There is no periodic erratum section. The editor invites word from readers who discover significant errors.

Nomenclature

The users of an abstract journal have a right to expect good nomenclature in the make-up of abstracts and indexes. It is the policy of *CA* to accept and use the nomenclature recommended by the Nomenclature, Spelling, and Pronunciation Committee of the American Chemical Society and that approved by the International Union of Pure and Applied Chemistry (IUPAC). There is rarely any conflict, but, in the interest of international agreement, the IUPAC nomenclature rules are regarded as the last word. As long as names used by authors are not misleading, ambiguous, or contrary to basic rules, these are used in abstracts (there are advantages in this), but a special effort is made to use good, consistent, systematic nomenclature in the subject indexing of *CA*, with an adequate supply of cross references. This avoids scattering of entries. These subject indexes are sometimes used as a source for nomenclature information in addition to their use as a key.

Promptness of Publication

Promptness in the publication of abstracts is of much interest to users of an abstract journal. As abstract journals go, *CA* has a reputation for reasonable promptness. For example, a study by Dwight E. Gray has shown that, during the 6-month period of 1948 from January to June, 1731 abstracts were published in *Physics Abstracts* (a part of *Science Abstracts*) and that of the papers covered by these 1731 abstracts 811, or 47%, were abstracted by *CA* (because the papers are of chemical interest). Of these 811 papers 55% were reported sooner in *CA* than in *Physical Abstracts*, while 15% were reported simultaneously by the two abstract journals. Our showing is better in covering chemical than in covering primarily physical journals. However, prompter abstracts are desirable and much effort is made in that direction. It takes a little over a month for abstracts to go through the printing mill. On an average it takes perhaps a little more than a month to get papers assigned and abstracted, with a week or two of additional time needed for recording, checking, and editing. There is always a scattering of abstracts of relatively old papers in *CA* because a journal has been missed, an abstractor has been ill or on a trip or has had other reason to delay, a question has come up concerning a paper or an abstract which has required correspondence, etc. Some overseas journals appear long after the dates carried on their covers, or at least reach this country late. With world-wide coverage, the effort for completeness means the continuous picking up of papers from remote places or obscure publications. Discovery of these is possible only after a period of time. Wars play havoc with promptness and regularity in the obtaining of papers and abstracts. The users of *CA* can count on this journal continuously striving to make amends for things missed. Most of the periodicals published during World War II were covered currently (*1*) and all but a few of the papers missed were later obtained and abstracted in one way or another.

Chemical Titles

In the interest of the quickest possible notification of the appearance of chemical papers the Chemical Abstracts Service has developed a publication called *Chemical Titles.* This very prompt, computer-produced bibliography and key-word index to chemical papers in 575 scientific journals will begin its regular appearance as a semimonthly journal in January 1961. This service, independent of *CA,* will bring new chemical information to the attention of subscribers on an average of two weeks after the appearance in Columbus of the more significant journals of the world as far as chemistry is concerned. The extensive key-word index to the bibliography will be prepared by computer to provide a display of significant words in titles through which the user can readily learn of articles in his field of interest. The regular issues of *CA* with their broader coverage, fuller information, and more thorough indexing will not be altered because of the publication of *Chemical Titles.*

Arrangement and Forms

Discovery of the form and arrangement of *CA* must largely be a matter of ready observation by users.

While the development of chemistry has required some changes in the classification of abstracts in *CA* through the 54 years of its existence, these changes have purposely been kept to a minimum. *CA* users get accustomed to looking in certain places for certain kinds of information. Changes in classification which might disrupt such habits are made only when there is urgent need.

With exception of the sections on Biological Chemistry (this section annually contains about three times as many abstracts as its nearest competitor) and that on Organic Chemistry, the sections of *CA* are not subdivided. However, in many of the sections and subsections there is an implicit classification of abstracts that can be discovered by inspection.

When an abstract bears a more or less direct relation to the subject matter of more than one section of *CA,* it is placed in the section considered most suitable, with a cross reference entered in the one or more related sections. Users of *CA* will understand that several limitations affect this use of cross references. Aside from the human factor, which results in suitable cross references being overlooked at times, there is the necessity, for the sake of economy, of avoiding cross references among certain more or less closely related sections. For example, a large percentage of the abstracts in the section on Nutrition are of interest to the food chemist as well as to the nutrition chemist, so that many cross references might properly be placed in the section on Foods or *vice versa.* Instead of using wholesale cross references, it is expected that those who use *CA* will remember to look in sections other than the one in which they are principally interested when there are distinctly related sections. Most chemists who use *CA* regularly examine groups of sections rather than single sections. Of course, after the annual indexes appear, these usually take the place of classification and cross references as a means of locating information.

CA pioneered in numbering columns instead of pages and in designating fractions of a column. A large amount of time can be saved by the use of these devices.

Authors' addresses as a part of abstracts have not always been supplied, for lack of space, but since 1950 it has been the regular policy to furnish them. These addresses are regarded as helpful in seeking reprints or for communicating with authors for other purposes, and are often of value in evaluating work reported. Omissions are usually due (1) to absence of an address in the paper being abstracted, or (2) to inadequacy in the address as given. Not infrequently overseas publications merely give the name of an institution without saying where it is.

Indexing

CA is thoroughly, carefully, and, we believe, properly indexed. This is an important factor in its usefulness. The journal is regarded as of great value as a permanent record of the progress of chemistry as well as a source of current information obtained by scanning. The Herner interview study (1958) disclosed that during the year preceding the canvass 82% of the 398 carefully sampled interviewees had used *CA* as a retrospective searching tool and that 60% had used it for keeping abreast of current developments. About half of the effort expended in the production of *CA* is devoted to building the indexes. Five kinds of indexes are produced, devoted to: (1) authors, (2) subjects, (3) formulas, (4) patent numbers, and (5) organic rings. The indexing program and methods of *CA* have been discussed (3).

No discussion of the use of author and numerical patent indexes seems necessary.

The Subject Index is the most frequently used index published by *CA*. Statistics show that this is true by a wide margin.

Here is a table showing in percentages the order in which 500 representative chemists have reported finding our indexes useful to them.

	Subject	*Author*	*Formula*	*Numerical Patent*	*Organic Ring*
First	76.0	20.1	2.9	0.8	0.2
Second	18.7	62.0	12.7	5.5	1.1
Third	2.1	17.2	45.5	26.9	8.3
Fourth	0.7	4.5	28.6	32.5	33.7
Fifth	0.0	2.4	3.2	33.4	61.0

This same inquiry brought forth the information that 71.9% of our abstractors use the *CA* Formula Indexes, though they find the Subject Indexes primarily more useful by the wide margin shown in the table. Another more extensive inquiry has shown that 48.6% of our readers use the Subject Index regularly, while 33% use it occasionally. The corresponding figures for the Author Indexes are 19.9 and 40.0%, respectively.

Roughly and in general the Herner report agrees with the information of the preceding paragraph. The Herner figures indicate some growth in the use of the Formula Indexes.

Incidentally, 81.7% of the subscribers to *CA* use the Author Indexes to the individual numbers of this journal and 73.4% favor 5-year instead of 10-year collective indexes in the future, with 17.3% on record as in favor of continuing the 10-year span for such collective indexes; the remaining 9.6% expressed no preference. After completion of the Fifth Decennial Index to *CA* it will be the policy to issue 5-year collective indexes.

Information in an extensive abstract journal becomes buried, so that part of the purpose of such a journal is defeated, if the indexing, particularly the subject indexing, is not thorough and thoroughly well done. The indexes to *CA* are built with this conviction constantly in mind and with the hope, encouraged by readership surveys, that they serve as a workable key to all of the recorded chemical information. In subject indexing, titles of papers are usually inadequate for complete indexing. As a matter of fact the subject and formula entries in *CA* indexes are based not only on whole abstracts, but often on the original papers. Much of this indexing is done with original papers before the indexers. This means that, while the abstracts are normally built to be adequate from the indexing point of view, experienced indexers sometimes discover omissions and remedy them. In the use of these indexes this fact should be borne in mind. The words used in indexing information omitted from abstracts, or referred to there only in general terms, are chosen in such a way as to help identify such a situation.

Subjects, not words, are indexed by *CA*. There is a wide difference. Word indexing leads to omissions, scattering, and unnecessary entries. True subject indexing avoids these defects. Subject indexing means, of course, that the words used in the index may differ from those used in the abstract. For the best results index users must be subject-minded rather than word-minded, so to speak.

Cross references, abundantly used in the subject indexes to *CA*, not only guide the index user from place to place as a help in making his search a thorough one, but also overcome some of the limitations of words as an exact and definitive medium of expression. It pays good dividends to use cross references in *CA* indexes more than inexperienced index users sometimes do. The *CA* master cross-reference file contains more than 60,000 entries.

It is the custom of *CA* to publish an Introduction to its Subject Indexes. The indexes are built to stand on their own feet. The introduction is not essential to the ready and effective use of the *CA* Subject Index. Nevertheless, for the best results in the use of any index the user must meet the index maker part way in understanding the indexing problems and nomenclature in particular. Use of the information in our Subject Index Introductions is recommended to the searcher who is doing more than incidental searching.

Nomenclature has just been mentioned, as has also the fact that words have limitations. In spite of these limitations, particularly as they apply to the naming of chemical compounds, words play a tremendously important part in the work of scientists as well as of all others. The cooperation necessary for scientific progress depends principally on the use of words. For some purposes chemical formulas, mathematical expressions, and the like take the place of words usefully in scientific communication, but by a wide margin words come first in general usefulness, and this is true for indexing as well as for the everyday types of communication. A good knowledge and appreciation of word values and significances, with thought thereon in operation, are helpful in the use of abstracts and indexes, an obvious statement which is nonetheless worthy of emphasis.

Because chemical names are subject to a certain amount of developmental change and because complex compounds are difficult to name and lend themselves to correct naming in more than one way, *CA* as long ago as 1920 adopted the practice of indexing compounds by systematically arranged molecular formulas (these do not vary), but it did not abandon the use of words also in the indexing of compounds. Readers are given their choice, with both the index by names and the index by formulas made complete. Entry in the Formula Index of the simpler and commoner compounds in the form of cross references to the Subject Index is regarded as wholly adequate formula indexing. Reference to the Subject Index from the Formula Index is possible for all entries because the names following formulas in the Formula Index are given just as they are to be found in the Subject Indexes. We feel convinced that this indexing of compounds in two ways effectively serves the purposes of the many kinds of users of *CA;* some prefer indexing by names, others prefer indexing by formulas, and many others use both kinds of indexes, with one kind of index more helpful in some circumstances and the other kind more helpful in others. The Formula Index is primarily useful in locating information concerning individual compounds.

Simplicity of form and structure and suitability to serve the needs of all kinds of chemists have been important considerations in the indexing of chemical compounds. The use of both name and formula indexes helps in this connection. It is not considered wise to limit the indexing of compounds to the Formula Index or to adopt a formula-indexing plan which is not applicable to all kinds of known compounds. Many kinds of chemists would not find the indexing of compounds exclusively by formulas convenient or satisfactory. How many analytical chemists would like to be required to look up specific indicators by formulas; how many biochemists would want to look up folic acid, riboflavine, cholesterol, etc., by formulas; how many agricultural chemists would be happy if they always had to look up specific insecticides by chemical formulas when definite compounds are involved; how many industrial chemists and how many physical chemists would want to figure molecular formulas before hunting up the more or less common compounds in which they are often interested? As a matter of fact, how many organic chemists would want to go to that trouble for the commoner, well known compounds?

The calculation of formulas is not a simple and easy matter in many instances.

CA uses the Hill instead of the Richter or Beilstein system of arranging formulas and of placing the symbols of the elements within these formulas. This practice has the advantage of simplicity and of suitability for inorganic as well as organic compounds. Beilstein has changed to this practice.

The inclusion of inorganic compounds in a Formula Index of chemistry is considered highly desirable. Although many of the simpler inorganic compounds can be readily named and are given only cross references to the Subject Index in the Formula Index, many complex inorganic compounds, intermetallic compounds, etc., are best indexed by formulas. Inorganic nomenclature is not so well developed as is the nomenclature of organic chemistry.

Certain other interrelations of indexes are helpful in searching. The Ring Index aids in the use of the Subject Index, for example. Another example is the use of the Author Index to learn of possible other related work of an author when his work on some subject of interest has been discovered by use of the Subject or Formula Index.

In using *CA* there is no need to refer to the annual indexes if one of the collective indexes is available. The annual indexes contain nothing of value which is not also in the collective indexes. There are a few more entries in the collective subject indexes than in the annual indexes for the periods covered and these collective indexes are improved to reflect the growth of chemistry and of the language of chemistry which has taken place during these periods. Mistakes of both commission and omission discovered in the annual indexes are corrected in the collective indexes.

A factor in the usefulness of any publication is confidence that it will serve its purposes. This confidence can best be gained by use rather than by basing it on an editor's claims and reassurances. Attitudes influence confidence. *CA's* editors have always been willing to admit mistakes, eager to improve their service, and ready to listen to criticism and suggestions from users of *CA*. It is hoped that our record of "firsts" in abstract-journal development (*2*) proves the validity of this claim as to attitude. The abstract-journal staff has long believed in reasonable conservatism for the sake of stability in its service, but has never been afraid of change when real progress could be made within the journal's economic limitations. The Chemical Abstracts Service now has a strong, separate Research Department. This service is conscious of the many problems presented by the current well-nigh explosive growth of scientific research and literature and it is not flinching, retrenching in service rendered, or failing to grow as to methods and accomplishment. *CA's* level of service in making scientific information available has not been attained as yet by others using other methods; abstracts and indexes are expected to be helped and supplemented rather than supplanted by machine methods.

Literature Cited

(1) *Chem. Eng. News* **23**, 1757–8 (1945).
(2) *Ibid.*, **33**, No. 26, 2752–4 (1955).
(3) *Ind. Eng. Chem.* **40**, 725–30 (1948); *Chem. Eng. News* **28**, 540 (1950).

BASED on paper presented before Division of Chemical Literature, Symposium on Searching the Chemical Literature, 117th Meeting, ACS, Detroit, Mich., April 1950. Revised 1960.

Influence of Nomenclatural Evolution upon Comprehensive Literature Searches

ERNEST H. HUNTRESS

Massachusetts Institute of Technology, Cambridge, Mass.

Orismology, the science of definitions and defining, especially with reference to scientific and technical terms, is of special concern to all branches of chemistry. A concise survey of the more outstanding attempts of the past two centuries to reduce nomenclatural principles to law and embody them in systems reveals that in this area progress lags far behind experimental discoveries and developments. Truly sound and permanent nomenclature in the rapidly growing and expanding field of chemistry can no longer be achieved merely through its part-time nurture by devoted individuals or the occasional hurried attention of committees composed of geographically scattered and professionally preoccupied persons. Modern conditions demand from the professional chemical society its generous, sympathetic, and protracted support of a small but full-time staff specifically and solely charged with this responsibility.

Among the intriguing tidbits which make up so much of the daily press, a brief item once appeared which purported to have determined the dozen words most pleasing to the layman's ear. The specific content of this list has no concern for us, but one word which was not included does have interest and bearing. This word is "orismology," the science of definitions and defining, esecially with respect to scientific and technical terms.

Once we have recognized orismology as the science of definitions, let us next be sure to extract the real juice of both of these words. Science comprises exact knowledge of facts, together with their correlation by means of recognized principles, methodically formulated into some rational and systematic arrangement. Factual knowledge by itself is mere information; its correlation through perception of regular principles advances the art, but not until this correlated factual knowledge is expressed in a regular systematic formulation do we arrive at a science. Science is knowledge reduced to law and embodied in system.

If we accept orismology as the generalized, systematic formulation of definitions, let us be sure of the significance of the latter. A definition implies a formal and exact expression of a concept. A definition defines, limits, and specifies; it must include all that properly belongs while excluding all which does not. Definition differs from exposition and from interpretation, though these processes may felicitously amplify and enrich its significance. A definition is specific and compact; it may be described or illustrated, but neither description nor example in itself defines.

The field of nomenclature is one whose orismological characteristics both deserve and require the best efforts of all persons concerned with chemistry. Here indeed we must truly develop a science of definition, or soon we shall become the victims of a confusion of tongues beside which the Tower of Babel will seem a room of silence.

Although the current difficulties of chemical nomenclature are both formidable and pressing, it may be encouraging to recognize that the existence of difficulties in this field is not new. The problems faced by contemporary chemists, perplexing and refractory though they may be, are merely variants and extrapolations of those that have faced the science from its beginning.

In this brief contemplation of the evolution of chemical nomenclature, no attempt can be made to probe into the multiplicity of small changes in usage of prefixes, suffixes, etc., which have occurred during the past two centuries. The number of such variations is legion, and to attempt to recapitulate even selective examples would quickly become tedious and soporific. This paper, therefore, proposes first to re-examine our nomenclatural foundations, next to review their extension to the organic field, and finally to direct attention to a few contemporary problems which are beginning to assume substantial magnitude.

The Foundation of Nomenclature

At the time of the Declaration of Independence (1776) there were known a total of 23 elements: carbon, sulfur, phosphorus, sixteen metals (gold, silver, platinum; copper, iron, lead, mercury, tin, zinc; arsenic, antimony; bismuth; cobalt, nickel, tungsten, manganese), and four gases (hydrogen, oxygen, nitrogen, and chlorine). Although numerous substances containing these materials were recognized, the composition of not a single compound of the group which we now call organic had been established. No one had ever heard of either atoms of molecules, much less of radicals, ions, electrons, protons, neutrons, magnetons, photons, mesons, and the rest. Nevertheless even then men of science were disturbed over the chaotic state of their scientific language and soon there appeared a quartet who were truly the pioneers of chemical nomenclature.

In fact, it was 174 years ago on April 18, 1787, that Antoine Laurent Lavoisier, then aged 44, personally appeared before a public assembly of the Royal Academy of Sciences in Paris and presented a paper entitled "The Necessity of Reforming and Bringing to Perfection the Nomenclature of Chemistry." Lavoisier was acting in this respect as the spokesman for three compatriots, de Morveau, Berthollet, and Fourcroy. In the following year this group published a volume entitled "Méthodes de Nomenclature Chimique," subsequently translated into English and still appropriately venerated (*14*) as the foundation stone of modern chemical nomenclature.

Even before the delivery of his speech there had been numerous other expressions of consonant ideas requiring only the prestige of Lavoisier to make them generally acceptable. Of these perhaps the most significant is a paper by de Morveau (*13*), who laid down even in those early days certain desiderata and principles well worth our review at this time. These were concentrated into a platform, each of whose six principal planks we may profitably note and discuss.

A chemical name should not be a phrase. In the early days of chemistry prior to the general acceptance of atomic and subsequent theories, many substances were characterized by clumsy and inconvenient expressions derived from various associations. Examples of these would include "oil of vitriol," "butter of antimony," "cream of tartar," "flowers of zinc," "liver of sulfur," "milk of lime," "sugar of lead," "spirits of nitre," etc. Very possibly de Morveau anticipated the probability that the substances designated by such names would occasionally, by careless classification, become indexed under "oil" "butter," "cream," "flowers," "liver," "milk," and "sugar," and thus be withdrawn from the chemist to the kitchen. Despite his warning, however, chemical names were frequently rendered as phrases for the next one hundred years and such forms as "acetate of sodium," "peroxide of hydrogen," and "permanganate of potash" have only recently disappeared from texts and books of reference.

The name should be neither arbitrary nor trivial nor involve the name of the discoverer. Presumably de Morveau sensed that in time there would be found a limited number of components whose combination in various ways and proportions would yield the numerous substances with which he was familiar. Perhaps he sensed the confusion which would arise if a substance designated by a name derived from one chemist should subsequently be found to have, still earlier, been recognized by another or numerous others. Perhaps he recognized that such terminology would eventually place upon the minds of chemists an entirely unnecessary and laborious task. Names such as Glauber's salt ($Na_2SO_4.10H_2O$), Fremy's salt (KHF_2), Mohr's salt [$FeSO_4(NH_4)_2SO_4.6H_2O$], Rochelle's salt ($KHC_4H_4O_6$), etc., give no inkling of the nature of their composition.

It is, of course, in the field of organic chemistry that this second postulate is most extensively and frequently violated or disregarded. The number of trivial names—i.e., special or nicknames—which are in common use is colossal, and so many of these are so firmly embedded in the literature that their perpetuation by successive generations of chemists is possibly unavoidable. One type is represented by such common examples as aniline, glycerol, oxalic acid, succinic acid, and the numerous homologs and analogs which these individuals suggest. Another type is recalled by such designations as Michler's ketone, Laurent's acid, Martin's yellow, methyl orange, and thousands of others.

The name should recall or suggest the constituents of a compound. In this prescription de Morveau placed in a positive and constructive admonition the principle which its predecessor had expressed negatively. The name sodium sulfate decahydrate is precise, concise, complete, and unambiguous and requires no mental effort to interpret, whereas the term Glauber's salt gives no suggestion that a sodium salt, a sulfate, or a hydrate is involved. Potassium hydrogen difluoride cannot be misunderstood, whereas the designation Fremy's salt carries no suggestion of its nature. Many would with difficulty recall the structure of Michler's ketone but would instantly appreciate the nature and reactions of 4,4′-bis-(dimethylamino)benzophenone.

As we contemplate the application of this postulate to the vast field of organic chemistry which has developed since de Morveau's time, we might even be permitted to recognize in its spirit somewhat more than the literal wording states. If a name should suggest the components of a compound, this may be interpreted to cover not merely the qualitative but also the quantitative aspects. After all, precise nomenclature consists of stating in an orderly and unambiguous manner what is present and where it is. If reference is made to the neutral ester of phthalic acid with ethyl alcohol, why not express it as diethyl phthalate; if the half ester is meant, why not call it ethyl hydrogen phthalate?

Perhaps this plea for precision seems to scientists pedantic, affected, and obvious. Chemists engaged in the execution and/or consideration of research are well aware of the necessity for precision. This viewpoint, however, is obviously not yet shared by chemical industry, as perusal of its advertising matter and price lists will soon disclose. By their loose practices the advertising divisions of even some highly reputable chemical companies weaken the position of teachers of organic chemistry and confuse their students. How are instructors to persuade their pupils to refer to diethyl phthalate when they see it advertised by well-known companies as "ethyl phthalate"? How can they be persuaded that phthalic anhydride and phthalic acid differ in composition when they see the words used interchangeably in advertisements? How are they to be induced to write 3,5,5-trimethylhexanoic acid when it is offered for sale as nonanoic, or 3,5,5-trimethylhexylamine when advertised merely as nonylamine? How are they to be taught that ethylamine is one word when the great chemical companies advertise it as "ethyl amine" in two words?

In the absence of knowledge concerning the constitution of a substance the name assigned to it should be noncommittal. With this cautious admonition it would appear that little fault could be found. It amounts to an encouragement of trivial naming, yet does so only as recognizing this procedure as the lesser evil. With modern rate of advance in research, adherence to this prudent principle is even more desirable than in de Morveau's era. Especially in the biochemical field new physiological materials are being isolated in great numbers and in most cases their structures are established with commendable dispatch.

An example of laudable discrimination and caution is afforded by the case of folic acid. In 1941 (*12*) there was isolated from spinach a nutrilite found to possess extraordinary activity in stimulating the growth of certain strains of bacteria. Because their product appeared to be a definite chemical entity, especially abundant in numerous leaves, they suggested for it the name "folic acid" from the Latin *folium* = leaf and defined it "as the material responsible for growth stimulation of *Streptococcus lactis* R on a given medium." Soon afterward a material with similar properties was isolated (*15*) from liver and designated as liver *L. casei* factor. Presently the synthesis of this material was announced (*1*). Meantime the name folic acid had become popular as a term to represent any material with such activity without regard for differences in chemical nature, and this usage made it subsequently unsuitable to represent a particular chemical entity. The complexity of the compound precludes general usage of their dull precise chemical names and renders desirable a short designation for the fundamental parent from which the names of relatives may be derived. For the case of the liver *L. casei* factor, this has since been established (*16*) as pteroylglutamic acid—i.e., *N*-[*p*-{[(2-amino-4-hydroxy-6-pteridyl)methyl]amino} benzoyl]glutamic acid.

Thus the noncommittal name, "folic acid," served its purpose in permitting simple designation of the material during the period between its discovery and the definite establishment of its structure, in this instance a matter of only 7 years. It must be admitted that in what is presumably the ultimate name there remain two roots of admittedly trivial character—viz., pteroyl and glutamic. The latter may be presumed to be so important and of such frequent occurrence that chemists should regard it as making no more excessive demands on the memory than scores of other radicals. The same cannot currently be said for "pteroyl," but presumably it will ultimately become valid. In any case "pteroylglutamic acid" is evidently far to be preferred for indexing purposes to its polysyllabic synonym.

New names are to be coined preferably from Latin or Greek to make their significance more easily and widely understood. This exhortation is no doubt now the least valid of the principles set forth by de Morveau. In his day and for 150 years thereafter, the widespread study of the classical languages gave point and substance to his purpose. Subsequently the extent and intensity of the study of ancient languages have narrowed and diminished, until it is now the exception rather than the rule to find a chemist who has been exposed to systematic instruction in these tongues. There is, however, a substantial body of nomenclature which has become established in the period when this precept was faithfully followed and its very existence tends to protract an analogous practice.

The form of the names should be adapted to the genius of the languages in which they are to be used. Here again we find expressed an idea which was probably more important in de Morveau's day than it is now. At that time the scientific world was entirely European and the dominant languages were French, German, and English. These were at the time of approximately equal importance and the entire foundation of chemical discovery of fact, principle, and theory remains recorded primarily in these three forms. While this scientific reservoir was being built up, however, vast political, social, and economic changes took place, whose net result has been to make English the currently dominant scientific language. The rapid and prolific development of chemistry in America, taken together with serious economic declines in Europe, has completely changed the balance of nomenclatural power. Just as today the nations of the world look to America for economic assistance, so their science is profoundly responsive to American opinion and leadership.

Another new factor has an important bearing on the great part now played by American science in influencing world opinion: the great speed of modern communication. In its utilization for the dissemination of scientific information we are not ordinarily so much concerned with advances in radio, telephony, or even facsimile reproduction, as with air mail and microfilm reproduction. These facilities become instruments for the dissemination of scientific and technical information throughout the world in less time than formerly was required for communication between many European countries. Inevitably what scientists and professional societies do and say in America has, in 1961, a far greater and more immediate effect around the world than the corresponding European activities could have had in 1750. "Some men are born great, some achieve greatness, and some have greatness thrust upon them." It is even so with nations and with professional societies.

These several principles of nomenclature were promptly applied by de Morveau, Lavoisier, Berthollet, and Fourcroy to the naming of 474 substances belonging to the earths, alkalies, acids, and metals. Their procedure was based on a dualistic hypothesis and forms the basis of our present system. The elements retained their accustomed roots, and the terms "oxygen," "hydrogen," and "azote" were introduced. The term "oxide" was employed for the first time and the class was regarded as intermediate between the element and its acid. The suffixes "ic" and "ous" for acids, together with the corresponding "ate" and "ite" for their salts, were first employed. These views found acceptance throughout Europe. They were, of course, gradually amplified, notably by Berzelius, to whom we owe the establishment of many other present practices such as the expression of simple compounds in the forms exemplified by ferrous sulfide, ferric oxide, etc.

The second milestone in the evolution of chemical nomenclature came almost exactly a century later, and this time from a British source. Although the foundation had been securely laid by the French group, chemical progress during the next century was relatively rapid and the nomenclatural superstructure finally again began to develop some insecurity. Eventually, the British Association for the Advancement of Science appointed a committee "for the purpose of drawing up a statement of the varieties of chemical names which have come into use, for indicating the causes which have led to their adoption, and for considering what can be done to bring about some convergence of the views on chemical nomenclature obtaining among English and foreign chemists."

This committee of thirteen distinguished British chemists comprised H. E. Armstrong (1848–1937), A. Crum Brown (1838–1922), James Dewar (1842–1923), H. B. Dixon (1852–1930), E. F. Frankland (1825–1899), F. R. Japp (1848–1925), A. G. Vernon Harcourt (1834–1919), W. Odling (1829–1921), H. F. Morley (1855–1943), H. E. Roscoe (1833–1915), J. Millar Thomson (1849–1933), V. H. Veley (1856–1933), and A. W. Williamson (1824–1904). This committee made two extensive reports (*2*). The committee adhered strictly to inorganic chemistry, effected a certain clarification and systemization of current usage in this area, and achieved a codification of uniform practice, but brought forth no particularly startling or revolutionary changes in nomenclature.

Development of Nomenclature of Organic Chemistry

Although obviously progress was constantly being made from earliest times in the area subsequently designated as organic chemistry, virtually all systematic development of its nomenclature necessarily awaited the rise of a comprehensive and coordinating theory. The early part of the nineteenth century saw the evolution of the concept of radicals, and the notion of types, together with numerous subordinate and transitional modifications. Indeed, the situation had by 1860 reached a point where such confusion prevailed that chemists were hardly able to make themselves intelligible to each other.

At this critical moment there was organized at the suggestion of Kekulé the first international congress of chemistry (*3, 4, 8, 11*), which was held September 3 to 5, 1860, at Karlsruhe, capital of the Grand Duchy of Baden, Germany, and has therefore become designated as the Karlsruhe Conference. It was attended by 140 chemists who recognized the importance of "(1) a more exact definition of the concepts expressed by the words atom, molecule, equivalent, valency, and basicity, (2) the investigation of the actual equivalents of substances and their formulas, and (3) the beginning of a more rational nomenclature." Although this great group of distinguished scientists effected much clarification of the first two items of their agenda, its consideration of the third was diverted into a discussion of symbolism and it made small contribution to nomenclature as the term is now used.

Very shortly after the Karlsruhe Conference the epochal structural theory of Kekulé began to be widely recognized. This promptly led to a rapid increase in the synthesis and study of organic compounds and thus to increased pressure for a systematic nomenclature. Nevertheless, three decades passed before this need found specific response. In connection with the Paris Exhibition of 1889 (which left as a relic the Eiffel Tower) there was held an international congress of chemistry on whose agenda was placed the reform of organic nomenclature. The topic proved so refractory, however, that it was remanded to an international standing committee. A Parisian subcommittee, after considering during 45 meetings various suggestions from abroad, made a report which served as the basis for an international meeting held at Geneva, Switzerland, April 19 to 22, 1892–i.e., 69 years ago and 105 years after Lavoisier's speech to the French assembly.

Membership in the Geneva Conference was by invitation only and not by delegation from national societies. Its eight sessions were attended by 35 chemists drawn from nine different countries, were presided over by Friedel, and resulted in the formulation of what is still known as the Geneva nomenclature. Although the principles thus formulated applied only to aliphatic compounds, this conference represented almost the only real progress on systematic organic nomenclature achieved during the entire century and as such comprises an important milestone. The 35 participants were: Amand, Armstrong, Baeyer, Barbier, Behal, Bouveault, Cannizzaro, Cazeneuve, Combes, Cossa, Filati, Emil Fischer, Franchimont, Friedel, Gladstone, Graebe, Guye, Haller, Hanriot, Hantzsch, Istrati, Le Bel, Lieben, Maquenne, Victor Meyer, Monnier, Nietzki, Noelting, Olivier, Paterno, Pictet, Ramsay, Reverdin, Skraup, and Tiemann. A group photograph of the conference with facsimile signatures was published in the *Journal of the Chemical Society* in 1938, facing page 1117. The only American invited to the congress was Ira Remsen, and he was unable to attend.

Subsequent to the Karlsruhe and Geneva conferences, the supreme court of nomenclatural problems in chemistry has been vested in what is currently known as the International Union of Pure and Applied Chemistry. Histories of the evolution of this organization have been published (*4, 7*).

Although the activities of the International Union were seriously impaired by World War II, it resumed its meetings in 1947 (London) and has met every two years since then (*7*). Nomenclature has been an important concern of the union. The first statement on nomenclature was the "Definitive Report of the Commission on the Reform of the Nomenclature of Organic Chemistry," unanimously adopted at Liege in September 1930 (*9*). For inorganic chemistry a corresponding report was adopted in 1940 (*10*). Recent IUPAC meetings have made great progress in advancing systematic nomenclature for both organic and inorganic chemistry (*5*).

Current Aspects of Nomenclatural Difficulties

One of the current problems is the increasing extent to which letters, numbers, and combinations of these symbols are being employed to designate chemical compounds. Fundamentally, these cryptogramic conglomerations derive from the natural desire for utmost brevity and convenience. They stem from the same motives which led our scientific predecessors to represent the names of the elements first by pictures, and later by a letter or at most two letters. With the development of chemical knowledge and the consequent necessity for compact expression of their composition, these elemental symbols were combined and provided with numerical subscripts denoting the number of particular atoms involved. The organic chemist faced with the additional problem of representing the structure of numerous compounds having the same composition and molecular weight responded first by drawing pictures (structural formulas). In time he came to realize that composition and structure were not enough; he must further represent configuration. As soon as the technical hieroglyphics which thus resulted were sufficiently numerous to require some form of orderly classification for indexing purposes, the necessity arose for precise, definite, and unambiguous literal names. With increasing magnitude and complexity of organic compounds, the resultant designations have become really impressive. In many instances, the mere magnitude of the chemical framework common to a large group of related compounds has necessitated its designation by a concise form and thus we have the evolution of the trivial name. Despite certain obvious advantages of trivial names, there is currently considerable effort to restrict their employment.

There is, however, a relatively recent type of chemical cryptogram whose rapid development and wide popular usage lead to new problems. The genesis of this type appears to have occurred about the time of the second world war. It may be reasonably supposed that the practice developed as a result of the exposure of chemists to the use of initial letters to designate the infinite number of govern-

Table I. Examples of Literal Cryptograms Selected from Current Literature

AATP	Diethyl *p*-nitrophenyl thiophosphate (parathion)
ACh	Acetylcholine
ACTH	Adrenocorticotropic hormone
ANTU	1-Naphthylthiourea
ATP	Adenosine triphosphate
BGG	Bovine γ-globulin
BHA	Butylated hydroxyanisole
BHC	Benzene hexachloride
BMU	β-Methylumbelliferone
BON	β-Oxynaphthoic acid
CEPC	2-Chloroethyl *N*-(3-chlorophenyl)carbamate
CMU	3-(*p*-Chlorophenyl)-1,1-dimethylurea
COT	Cyclo-octatetraene
CTAB	Cetyltrimethylammonium bromide
DBS	3′5′-Dibromosulfanilanilide
DDD	1,1-Dichloro-2,2-bis-(*p*-chlorophenyl)ethane
DDT	1,1,1-Trichloro-2,2-bis-(*p*-chlorophenyl)ethane
DEG	Diethylene glycol
DMBC	Dimethylbenzyl chloride
DNA	Deoxyribonucleic acid
EBC	Ethylbenzyl chloride
EDB	Ethylene dibromide
EDNA	*N,N′*-Dinitroethylenediamine
EDTA	(Ethylenedinitrilo)tetraacetic acid
HET	Hexaethyl tetraphosphate
MBA	Methylbenzyl alcohol
MBDSA	*m*-Benzenedisulfonic acid
MBC	Methylbenzyl chloride
MEHQ	Monomethyl ester of hydroquinone
NA	Nicotinic acid
NBS	*N*-Bromosuccinimide
NGDA	Nordihydroguaiaretic acid
OMPA	Octamethyl pyrophosphoramide
PAS	*p*-Aminosalicylic acid
PETN	Pentaerythritol tetranitrate
POPOP	1,4-Bis-[2-(5-phenyloxyazoyl)benzene]
TBA	Tris-(β-chloroethyl)amine
TCP	Tricresyl phosphate
TDE	1,1-Dichloro-2,2-bis(*p*-chlorophenyl)ethane
TEAB	Tetraethylammonium bromide
TEP	Tetraethyl pyrophosphate
TMC	2,2,6,6-Tetramethylolcyclohexanol
TNB	1,3,5-Trinitrobenzene
TNT	2,4,6-Trinitrotoluene

ment agencies. Citizens became familiar with the sound of TVA, WPA, ERA, FEPC, and UNESCO quite naturally as chemists began to adopt analogous procedures for unwieldly chemical names. As a result we have now accumulated an impressive number of cryptogramic expressions.

Examples culled from the recent scientific and technical literature include, first, the purely literal species, most frequently found in combinations of three letters, but occasionally running to four or even five as illustrated in Table I. Then there is the mixed species comprising combinations of numbers and letters, samples of which are shown in Table II. The examples cited are not imaginary, but have been collected from the scientific and technical literature.

Table II. Examples of Mixed Cryptograms Selected from Current Literature

G^4	2,2′-Methylene-bis-(4-chlorophenol)
T_4	Hexahydro-1,3,5-trinitro-*S*-triazine (hexogen)
2,4-D	2,4-Dichlorophenoxyacetic acid
2,4,5-T	2,4,5-Trichlorophenoxyacetic acid
C-3259	2-Benzylimidazoline
G-11	2,2′-Methylene bis-(3,4,6-trichlorophenol)
G-410	Pentachlorophenol
P-4000	1-*n*-Propoxy-2-amino-4-nitrobenzene
V-147	*p*-Guanylbenzenesulfonamide
IB-946	2,4-Dinitrophenol
KP-504	Bis-(dimethylbenzyl)carbonate
SR-406	*N*-(Trichloromethylthio)tetrahydrophthalimide

There is another troublesome factor in the extensive modern use of trade names and the like. Every practical organic chemist will readily think of numerous examples of trade-marked names which, because they represented true chemical individuals and were thoroughly publicized, have become so firmly established in the literature that many contemporary students do not even realize that they are trade names. This type may be exemplified by the following:

Cellosolve	2-Ethoxyethanol
Methyl Cellosolve	2-Methoxyethanol
Carbitol	2-(2-Ethoxyethoxy)ethanol
Decalin	Decahydronaphthalene
Drierite	Anhydrous calcium sulfate
Novocaine	Procaine hydrochloride or 2-diethylaminoethyl *p*-aminobenzoate

Other examples of the same nature will occur to every chemist.

Regular readers of the technical literature will be well aware, however, of the modern flood of trade names which now attempt to force themselves upon the consciousness of their readers. No longer need the product comprise a chemical individual; it may be a mixture, the components of which are not known even by the producer in the true chemical sense. The name devised and flung before the hapless reader may not convey the slightest suggestion of the nature of the components, nor the character of the use for which the product is intended. Such names are nothing more than fantasies dreamed up by advertising departments and deserve no recognition by professional societies or reputable scientific journals. They represent, however, a professional hazard to elementary students as yet unprepared to distinguish their lack of merit from other superficially similar but better justified cognomens.

Between these two extremes there is a type of arbitrary designation which strongly resembles a trade name but is actually a coined name more or less officially recognized as representing a particular chemical individual. A group of examples of this type is found in the action (*6*) of the American Phytopathological Society with respect to five fungicidal salts:

Ferbam. Ferric *N,N*-dimethyldithiocarbamate
Ziram. Zinc *N,N*-dimethyldithiocarbamate
Nabam. Disodium ethylene-bis(dithiocarbamate)
Zineb. Zinc ethylene-bis(dithiocarbamate)
Thiram. Tetramethylthiuram disulfide or bis-(dimethylthiocarbamyl)disulfide

Information concerning these names and the approval and acceptability of their use as coined common names for these specific chemicals has been filed by the society with the Trade-Mark Division of the U. S. Patent Office to pre-empt the use of the names as trade-marks.

Outlook for Future

We find ourselves in the middle of the twentieth century with a nomenclatural heritage of 174 years. Our meager progress appears in retrospect to have been due largely to lack of anticipation of predictable difficulties. Except for the initial occasion when de Morveau and his compatriots exhibited their genius with an organized plan adequate for their times, the subsequent history of the evolution of chemical nomenclature is largely a story of attempts to reform defective and inadequate practices already thoroughly established by unguided usage.

Despite some definite though sporadic efforts to effect systemization and simplification, by and large our nomenclatural definitions are often vague and we are not yet entitled to regard them as knowledge reduced to law and embodied in system. The science of definitions will achieve neither the degree nor rate of progress required by this modern age until we recognize that orismological research and development cannot be left to part-time nurture by devoted individuals or the occasional attention of committees composed of geographically scattered and professionally preoccupied persons. As an aspect of chemistry profoundly affecting the daily activities of every member, the generous, sympathetic, and protracted support of a full-time official effort to keep pace with and to anticipate our nomenclatural evolution seems not only a properly appropriate but an indispensable function of a professional chemical society.

Literature Cited

(1) Angier, R. B., *et al., Science* **102,** 227–8 (1945); **103,** 667–9 (1946).
(2) Armstrong, H. E., *et al., Brit. Assoc. Ann. Rept.* **1884,** 39–74; **1885,** 262–75.
(3) Blokh, M. A., *Uspekhi Khim.* **9,** 1178–91 (1940).
(4) Bogert, M. T., *Chem. Eng. News* **27,** 1992–5 (1949).
(5) Capell, L. T., ADVANCES IN CHEM. SER. No. **30,** 59–60 (1961).
(6) *Chem. Eng. News* **27,** 3196–7 (1949).
(7) *Ibid.,* **36,** 83–8 (Sept. 15, 1958).
(8) *Chem. News* **2,** 226–7 (1860).
(9) Commission on Reform of Nomenclature of Organic Chemistry, *J. Am. Chem. Soc.* **55,** 3905–25 (1933).
(10) *Ibid.,* **63,** 889–97 (1941).
(11) de Milt, C. M., *Chymia* **1,** 153–69 (1948).
(12) Mitchell, H. K., Snell, E. E., Williams, R. J., *J. Am. Chem. Soc.* **63,** 2284 (1941).
(13) Morveau, Guyton de, *J. phys.* **19,** 310, 382 (1782); *Ann. chim. phys.* (1) **25,** 205–14 (1798).
(14) Oesper, R. E., *J. Chem. Educ.* **22,** 290–2 (1945).

(15) Stokstad, E. L. R., *J. Biol. Chem.* **149**, 573 (1943).
(16) Waller, C. W., *et al.*, *J. Am. Chem. Soc.* **70**, 19–22 (1948).

BASED on paper presented before Division of Chemical Literature, Symposium on Searching the Chemical Literature, 117th Meeting, ACS, Detroit, Mich., April 1950. Revised 1961.

The Effect of Changes in Nomenclature on the Use of Indexes

LEONARD T. CAPELL

Chemical Abstracts Service, Ohio State University, Columbus, Ohio

The struggle for a consistent, systematic nomenclature has grown gradually stronger as the science of chemistry has developed. This struggle has penetrated all fields of chemistry and has engaged the interest of both academic and industrial chemists. All must use the records of chemistry. Nomenclature development and standardization have increased with special rapidity during the last twenty years. It is important to publicize the results of this activity widely, so that exact chemical communication can be facilitated and, in particular, the effects on the building and use of indexes be understood.

Everyone concerned with chemistry should exert his best efforts to use good chemical nomenclature. He should learn good usage for his own sake and for the good of his science. Exactness in communication is essential to effective scientific progress. In particular, good nomenclature must be used in scientific record keeping and a knowledge of naming rules and principles helps a chemist to become an efficient user of chemical records. Without systematic nomenclature it is impossible to build useful indexes. Without good indexes effectively used the research worker would find himself repeating, at great expense of time and money, work already done by others. Learning nomenclature rules and keeping up with its developmental changes are essential to the good use of indexes, regardless of how excellent the indexes may be. The user of the index must meet the indexer half way.

A chemist (*21*) who is much interested in nomenclature recently has listed ten factors which chemists would like to have included in the names of compounds. These might be considered a modern version of the principles laid down by de Morveau (*19*) in 1872. Briefly stated, these ten factors are: A name should (1) be simple (easy to recognize, spell, and pronounce), (2) be unique, (3) tell the kinds of atoms, (4) tell the number of each kind, (5) show the relationship of atoms, (6) be easily derivable from the structural formula, (7) be easily translatable into the structural formula, (8) give clues to relationships with other compounds, (9) contain clues as to reactivity, and (10) lead to grouping in an index.

Obviously a name cannot always fit all of these standards, but if some such standards had been followed many indefinite, misleading, and troublesome names would never have been formed. A name cannot always be simple and yet give information as to structural characteristics. Often compromise is necessary in naming compounds.

The number of known chemical compounds is very large. A few years ago an estimate of 600,000 was announced. Probably 50,000 to 60,000 new compounds are prepared annually now and the total of known compounds undoubtedly has passed the million mark. Many of these new compounds are already listed in the files of industrial research laboratories, where some kind of names are being used for them. It is much better if the right kind of name is given to each compound as soon as structural and other needed information has been obtained, because names once coined and used tend to continue in use.

In the nomenclature of inorganic chemistry there have been few fundamental changes through the past century and a half. The original proposals of Guyton de Morveau were so fundamentally sound that the same general plan has been followed for years. However, the development in inorganic nomenclature has not kept pace with the development of the science. Many inconsistencies and confusions in inorganic nomenclature plague chemists of today. Some of these were pointed out by Scott (*28*) in 1942.

A Commission on the Nomenclature of Inorganic Chemistry was established by the International Union of Chemistry (referred to hereafter as IUPAC, since the union is now again officially called the International Union of Pure and Applied Chemistry) in 1921. As a result of many meetings a report (*15*) was published in 1940. It was later decided to undertake a thorough revision of these "1940 Rules." A revision (*10*) was published in the minutes of the Stockholm IUPAC Meeting of 1953. A more thorough revision and rearrangement was published in 1959 (*9*) in definitive form. These rules will undoubtedly lead to many changes in inorganic names, but this will bring more system into inorganic nomenclature.

Organic chemists are probably all familiar with the results of the Geneva Congress of 1892 (*27*). This congress placed the main emphasis on the need for names which would be suitable for the systematic indexing of organic compounds. Suffixes such as -ol, -one, -al, and -oic were prescribed for the naming of alcohols, ketones, aldehydes, and acids, respectively. The Geneva names are used systematically in the fourth edition of Beilstein. Their influence on nomenclature can be seen in any index or record of organic compounds.

IUPAC appointed a Commission on Nomenclature of Organic Chemistry in 1922. This commission formulated the report which was adopted unanimously at Liége in 1930 and is commonly referred to as "The Definitive Report of the Commission on the Reform of the Nomenclature of Organic Chemistry" or just "The Definitive Report" (*16*).

This report has been the guiding light for all nomenclaturists in organic chemistry. The chief criticism has been its lack of specificity in many of its rules. This IUPAC commission is continuing its work by meeting annually for at least a week. Correspondence is more or less continuous among its members. It is working on a complete revision of the Definitive Report, thus codifying existing practice in organic nomenclature. The first two sections of this revision covering (A) aliphatic and cyclic hydrocarbons and (B) fundamental heterocyclic systems were published in 1959 (*11*).

Other Commissions on Nomenclature of the IUPAC have not been inactive. In biochemistry reports have been made on steroids (*11*), amino acids (*12*), vitamins (*8*), and carotenoids (*7*). A report on the nomenclature of macromolecular compounds has been approved (*6*).

This activity means some loss of continuity of naming practice in indexes of all kinds. Revisions of indexes and records have been necessary to keep pace. Continuity and consistency in annual and collective indexes and in cumulative index files help the user in any literature search. But sometimes it is necessary to sacrifice continuity in order to keep up with progress in the various sciences. Nomenclature is not static. It must change with increasing knowledge of the science, with the ever-growing complexity of chemical compounds, and with the more precise methods of determining structure.

In order to achieve continuity in indexes one must have a well-considered basic plan. *Chemical Abstracts* (*CA*) developed such a plan in the beginning of its adoption of systematic indexing. In the first nine volumes of *CA* compounds were indexed annually just as the names appeared in the abstracts. Consideration of a collective index emphasized the need of a consistent plan for naming and indexing compounds so that entries referring to the same compound might not be scattered and so that derivatives of the same parent might be grouped together so far as an alphabetic indexing scheme would permit.

In working out such a plan for systematic naming for indexing compounds the designation of functions was a significant consideration. Compounds containing only one kind of function were, with a few exceptions, named with this function expressed in the ending of the name. Compounds of diverse or mixed functions were named by expressing only one function in the ending of the name. The choice of the function to be expressed in the name ending was based on a definite order of precedence of functions which was established for the *CA* system after a study of usage. The order chosen conformed to usage as far as regularity would permit. The following order of precedence now in use is essentially that originally proposed: onium compound, acid (carboxylic, arsonic, sulfonic, stibonic, others), acid halide, amide, imide, amidine, aldehyde, nitrile, isocyanide, ketone, alcohol, phenol, thiol, amine, imine, ether, sulfide (and sulfoxide and sulfone). The fact that this order of precedence of function has been used in indexing *CA* over its 50-year existence is a tribute to the wisdom and foresight of its originators, the late Austin M. Patterson and the late Carleton E. Curran (*20, 23, 26*).

A knowledge of this order of precedence of function is essential to the user of *CA* indexes. It could very well be made the basis of any system of nomenclature for compounds of diverse functions. If this order of precedence of functions were used by authors in naming their compounds, it would simplify the building and use of indexes and make for more consistency in chemical literature in general.

Any change in this order of precedence of functions means a change in the name of a compound and in its location in an index. If alcohols were placed ahead of ketones in this order the name 3-hydroxybutyrophenone, indexed under B (Butyrophenone, 3-hydroxy-) would become 1-benzoyl-2-propanol, indexed under P (2-Propanol, 1-benzoyl-). The importance of maintaining the same order of precedence can be readily seen.

It has been said that most literature searches are now based on the literature of the last ten to twenty years. This is also the period of the greatest activity of nomenclature committees and of the increased interest in nomenclature. It is well to consider the effect of nomenclature work, in the form of both approved reports and suggested changes, on the building and use of indexes during this period.

"The Ring Index" (*24*) was published in 1940. This compilation of ring systems used in organic chemistry gives the approved numberings and names of over 4000 ring systems. The system of numbering is based on "Proposed International Rules for Numbering Organic Ring Systems" by Patterson (*22*). These rules were approved tentatively by the IUPAC Commission on Nomenclature of Organic Chemistry in 1925. "The Ring Index" was compiled under the direction of a joint committee of the National Research Council and the American Chemical Society. A second edition (revised and enlarged) of "The Ring Index" was published in 1960 by the Chemical Abstracts Service (*25*). This edition contains 7727 ring systems. The numbering and naming are based on the more complete rules approved by the IUPAC Commission on Nomenclature of Organic Chemistry (*11*).

CA has been using the numberings of the rules for all ring systems since Volume 31. Several changes in the numbering of ring systems have been made in rings used prior to Volume 31 in order to bring them into accord with the rules. In using other indexes it must be remembered that the British in many cases have not used "The Ring Index" numberings and Beilstein uses them only for the more complex systems. Acridine is an example of the confusion caused by the lack of a generally accepted official numbering.

Rule I of the "Definitive Report" states that "As few changes as possible will be made in terminology universally adopted." This principle was followed in developing the rules for the numbering of organic ring systems. Certain inconsistencies were eliminated and all hetero atoms were numbered, but otherwise commonly accepted numberings were disturbed as little as possible, and exceptions were made in order to retain the well-known numberings for acridine, anthracene, carbazole, cyclopenta[*a*]phenanthrene, phenanthrene, purine, and xanthene. To change the system of numbering without drastically changing the names of the rings would add confusion to the use of all ring names. If numberings are to be changed, names should also be changed, as in the Dyson-Taylor-Patterson system (*1*).

CA and "The Ring Index" names are based on the so-called "skeletal" or "state-of-lowest-possible-hydrogenation" principle. Names very similar to "The Ring Index" names are formed by using plain numbers and primed numbers to indicate the fused sides with retention of the numberings of the original systems. Thus indeno[1,2-*a*]indene is "The Ring Index" name for a $C_{16}H_{10}$ compound, but indeno-2′,3′,2,3-indene is $C_{16}H_{12}$ and is numbered quite differently.

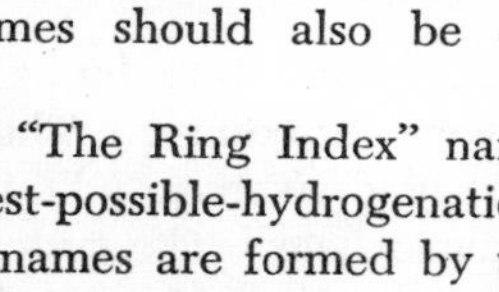

Indeno[1,2-*a*]indene

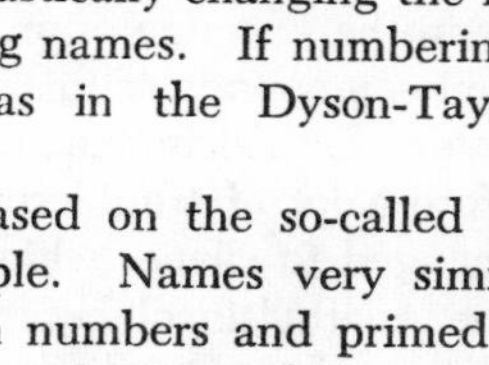

Indeno-2′,3′,2,3-indene

The Definitive Report Rule 16 recognizes the principle of "oxa-aza" ("a") names for heterocyclic ring systems. The chief difficulty at the present time is lack of definitive rules for the formation of these names. It seems to be the opinion of most nomenclature committees that these "a" names should be used only when the older names are less suitable. A general substitution of "a" names for all heterocyclic systems, as advocated by some chemists, would introduce many needless changes in nomenclature.

American practice in forming "a" names is based on the skeletal system, sometimes with the use of indicated hydrogen. This practice differs from the European method. Thus American practice gives 1*H*-2-oxapyrene whereas European chemists name the same compound 2-oxa-1,2-dihydropyrene. The "a" names must follow the numberings of the carbocyclic systems and thus sometimes give numberings different from those obtained by following the "rules for numbering."

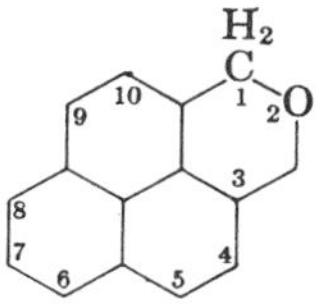

The so-called "a" nomenclature can also be extended to aliphatic compounds. Here again lack of specific rules prevents a useful application of this system of nomenclature. One of the perplexing problems of "a" nomenclature is to define the limits for its application. It is a very useful system for naming unsymmetrical polyethers, polysulfides, and polyamines. Thus 3,5,8,12-tetraoxatetradecane is in many respects a better name than 1-(ethoxymethoxy)-2-(3-ethoxypropoxy)ethane for

$$CH_3CH_2.O.CH_2.O.CH_2CH_2.O.CH_2CH_2CH_2.O.CH_2CH_3$$
1 2 3 4 5 6 7 8 9 10 11 12 13 14

However, the very simplicity of the "a" nomenclature leads some of its proponents to extend it to simple compounds such as 3-thiapentane for ethyl sulfide.

When silicon compounds were becoming more and more important, a group of chemists met to discuss the nomenclature problems involved. The purpose of the meeting is well stated in the preamble to the rules (*13*) which resulted from this and subsequent meetings. "The purpose of the following rules is to provide one systematic and unique name for each of the simple organosilicon compounds and to guide in the selection of an accurate name for each of the more complex or polyfunctional compounds of this nature."

Fortunately for silicon nomenclature, these rules were formulated and put into use before a lot of troublesome names were introduced. Thus, silicane for SiH_4 was changed to silane, which has a host of derivatives. Disilicoethane became disilane, triethylsilicol became triethylsilanol, etc. The system of rules for the nomenclature of organosilicon compounds is an excellent example of what can be accomplished if nomenclature problems in new or rapidly developing fields are studied and solved before bad practices become established.

The nomenclature of boron compounds is now at about the same stage as was that of the silicon compounds when the silicon nomenclature was developed. An advisory committee of the Nomenclature Committee of the ACS Division of Organic Chemistry has been studying this problem (*5*) and expects to present a comprehensive report soon.

A few years ago the workers interested in phosphorus compounds felt the need of uniform nomenclature, at least among English-speaking chemists. They found what seemed an insurmountable obstacle in the different approaches used in naming these compounds. Finally a compromise solution was offered and it was agreed to work on that basis. The rules so far have been limited to monophosphorus compounds (*2*).

The resulting names are quite different from the names previously in use, but they do have the advantage of usually starting with "phosph" (good for indexes and other records). Thus thiophosphoric acids became phosphorothioic, phosphorodithioic, phosphorotrithioic, and phosphorotetrathioic acids. Amidophosphoric acids became phosphoramidic acid and phosphorodiamidic acid. For the halogen-substituted acids such names as phosphorochloridic acid and phosphorodichloridothioic acid are used.

These names are very useful for indexes. The names are in use in British literature and will be used more and more in the ACS journals. European chemists have difficulty in converting the names into their languages, and have made some counter proposals. It will take time to solve all the problems in the nomenclature of phosphorus compounds, especially for polyphosphorus compounds.

As a result of the work of the IUPAC Commission on Nomenclature of Organic Chemistry a report (*14*) was published following the meeting in Amsterdam in 1949. This report gives tentative rules for naming organic radicals and an official list of such radical names. It also makes recommendations for the naming of certain compounds. Thus the commission favors in principle the use of systematic names for the higher saturated monobasic and dibasic aliphatic acids—i.e., those with more than five carbon atoms. This means that the trivial names caproic, enanthic, caprylic, pelargonic, and capric acids should be replaced by the systematic names hexanoic, heptanoic, octanoic, nonanoic, and decanoic acids, respectively. Systematic names should be used for the higher acids and their radicals when substituents are present.

The commission also expressed a definite preference for the name undecyl over hendecyl. As a result of this recommendation all compounds formerly found in indexes under hendec- are now likely to be found indexed under undec-. A further report (*11*) on definitive rules for the naming of acyclic and cyclic hydrocarbons and heterocyclic compounds was published following the 1957 meeting in Paris. The commission is now working on nomenclature involving functional groups.

A very comprehensive report on the nomenclature of terpenes has been approved by the IUPAC and the American Chemical Society (*4*). Some of the significant changes in nomenclature recommended are the replacement of the names camphane and bornylane by bornane. Norbornane replaces norcamphane and norbornylane. Thujane is preferred over sabinane. A definite system of numbering the bicyclo ring systems is recommended. The application of these terpene rules will eliminate many trivial names which are a tax on the memory.

Carbohydrate chemistry presents some special problems in nomenclature. These have been studied by a committee of the American Chemical Society's Division of Carbohydrate Chemistry in close cooperation with a British committee (*3*). The rules are recommended for use whenever systematic names for carbohydrates and their derivatives are required. Further work is being done by these groups.

The IUPAC Commission on Biochemical Nomenclature adopted in Zurich (1955) a tentative report on the nomenclature of steroids, which was made definitive and published in 1959 (*11*). This report has reduced the number of parent names and has eliminated to a large extent the necessity of using such prefixes as etio-, allo-, epi-, iso-, and *i*-. It recommends systematic names, but also recognizes some trivial names. Thus for the saturated polyhydro derivatives of the cyclopenta[*a*]phenanthrene ring the names gonane and estrane are recommended along with the following eight names: 5α-androstane, 5β-androstane, 5α-

pregnane, 5β-pregnane, 5α-cholane, 5β-cholane, 5α-cholestane, and 5β-cholestane to replace, respectively, the names androstane, etiocholane, allopregnane, pregnane, allocholane, cholane, cholestane, and coprostane.

British and American cooperation has reduced to some extent differences in practice in these two English-speaking countries. The British have adopted many of the *CA* practices, including alphabetic order of prefixes. One of the differences has been in the use of italicized prefixes. The British have italicized many more prefixes than have the Americans. This means a different placement of such names in indexes, since italicized prefixes are not considered in alphabetizing. American and British cooperation has been extended and some of these differences have been eliminated. Thus the British no longer italicize bicyclo-, cyclo-, epi-, iso-, seco-, and spiro- (*17*).

One other aspect of this change-in-nomenclature problem affects the user of all indexes and records. This is the changing of the names used by authors in published papers by indexers and record keepers. It undoubtedly is the privilege of every author to name his compounds as he pleases, but it is not always to his advantage to do so. He is writing his paper to make available to others the information which he has experimentally obtained. Yet the names which he uses may be so different from the names the indexer must use that the author himself may have trouble finding his compounds in the index.

An attempt has been made by the ACS Council to remedy this situation by requiring that authors of papers published in ACS journals as far as practical use the nomenclature found in *CA* subject indexes. This is where nomenclature and indexing should have a common meeting place.

Formula indexes are a great help in searching for compounds. If one cannot find a compound in the subject index, he can find it in a formula index, provided he knows its structure. However, even formula indexes depend on rules for arrangement both of the symbols of elements in the formulas and of the completed formulas themselves, and not all indexes are constructed alike.

There are two well-known methods of writing the formulas for formula indexes, the Richter system and the Hill system. Each has its advantages. The Hill system (*18*) has the advantage of simplicity in the use of an alphabetic order of symbols beyond C and H. The Richter system effects a certain degree of classification of compounds by its arrangement of the symbols (C, H, O, N, Cl, Br, I, F, S, P, remainder alphabetic). Further classification is accomplished in the Richter system by grouping according to the number of elements present in addition to C and H.

The primary purpose of a formula index is to enable one to locate a single definite compound of which the formula is known. Both of the above systems classify primarily on the basis of C and H. By rearranging the symbols in the formula, such as relegating the C and H to the end of the formula, classification according to the hetero elements (elements other than C) can be accomplished. Whether such classifications are of sufficient value to justify the introduction of additional types of formula indexes is open to debate. Classification on the basis of functional groups and structural features would have some advantages.

Great interest and activity have been shown in nomenclature problems during the last twenty years. All of this activity means changes in names. The aim is to simplify and systematize. But changes in indexes and records are expensive. It is difficult for the user of indexes to keep track of the changes from one indexing period to the next. Cross references are a help and a necessity.

Changes to ensure consistency are believed to be welcomed by the users. If the changes are well founded, the users accept them despite a period of inconvenience. However, there is a natural resistance to change. Changes which seem to have no real advantage are irritating to users. Changes which result in a name for a compound which is identical to a name previously used for another compound should be avoided.

What is the solution to this problem? At least four things must be done.

1. Codify and extend the nomenclature rules. This can best be done by nomenclature committees. These committees must work together. Developmental work should be done by active committees in the various fields of chemistry.
2. Make nomenclature rules easily available. One of the objectives of the ACS Nomenclature, Spelling and Pronunciation Committee has always been the dissemination of knowledge of nomenclature by distribution of printed rules. A nomenclature guidebook with interpretation of naming rules and with numerous examples would be of great value, but it would require frequent revision (easier with a set of separate pamphlets).
3. Practice what we have. When rules have been formulated and made available, they should be used in keeping records and in writing reports for publication.
4. The user of indexes must become familiar with the rules of nomenclature and the history of their development.

Literature Cited

(1) *Bull. soc. chim. France* **1957,** 45–52.
(2) *Chem. Eng. News* **30,** 4515–22 (1952).
(3) *Ibid.,* **31,** 1776–82 (1952).
(4) *Ibid.,* **32,** 1795–7 (1954).
(5) *Ibid.,* **34,** 560 (1956).
(6) Commission on Macromolecules, IUPAC, *J. Polymer Sci.* **8,** 257–77 (1952).
(7) Commission on Nomenclature of Biochemistry, IUPAC, *Compt. rend., XIV Conference, London,* **1947,** 142–3; *J. Am. Chem. Soc.* **82,** 5583–4 (1960).
(8) Commission on Nomenclature of Biochemistry, IUPAC, *Compt. rend., XVIII Conference, Zurich,* **1955,** 189–90; *J. Am. Chem. Soc.* **82,** 5581–3 (1960).
(9) Commission on Nomenclature of Inorganic Chemistry, IUPAC, Butterworths Scientific Publications, London; *J. Am. Chem. Soc.* **82,** 5523–44 (1960).
(10) Commission on Nomenclature of Inorganic Chemistry, IUPAC, *Compt. rend., XVII Conference, Stockholm,* **1953,** 98–142.
(11) Commission on Nomenclature of Organic Chemistry, IUPAC, Butterworths Scientific Publications, London; *J. Am. Chem. Soc.* **82,** 5545–81 (1960).
(12) Commission on Nomenclature of Organic Chemistry, IUPAC, *Compt. rend., XV Conference, Amsterdam,* **1949,** 187–9; *Chem. Eng. News* **30,** 4522–6 (1952); *J. Am. Chem. Soc.* **82,** 5575–7 (1960).
(13) Commission on Nomenclature of Organic Chemistry, IUPAC, *Compt. rend., XV Conference, Amsterdam,* **1949,** 127–32; *Chem. Eng. News* **30,** 4517–22 (1952).
(14) Commission on Nomenclature of Organic Chemistry, IUPAC, *Compt. rend., XV Conference, Amsterdam,* **1949,** 132–86.
(15) Commission on Reform of Nomenclature of Inorganic Chemistry, International Union of Chemistry, *J. Am. Chem. Soc.* **63,** 889–97 (1941).
(16) Commission on Reform of Nomenclature of Organic Chemistry, International Union of Chemistry, *Ibid.,* **55,** 3905–25 (1933).
(17) "Handbook for Chemical Society Authors," Chemical Society, London, 1960.
(18) Hill, E. A., *J. Am. Chem. Soc.* **22,** 478–94 (1900).
(19) Morveau, Guyton de, *J. Phys.* **19,** 310, 382 (1782); *Ann. chim. phys.* (1) **25,** 205–14 (1798).
(20) "Naming and Indexing of Chemical Compounds by *Chemical Abstracts,*" Introduction to 1945 Subject Index (Vol. 39), Chemical Abstracts Service, Columbus, Ohio.
(21) Nutting, H. S., *Chem. Eng. News* **30,** 2884 (1952).
(22) Patterson, A. M., *J. Am. Chem. Soc.* **47,** 543–61 (1925).
(23) Patterson, A. M., *Rec. trav. chim.* **48,** 1012–17 (1929).
(24) Patterson, A. M., Capell, L. T., "The Ring Index," Reinhold, New York, 1940.
(25) Patterson, A. M., Capell, L. T., Walker, D. F., "The Ring Index," 2nd ed., Special Issues Sales Department, American Chemical Society, Washington, D. C., 1960.
(26) Patterson, A. M., Curran, C. E., *J. Am. Chem. Soc.* **39,** 1623–38 (1917).

(27) Pictet, A., *Arch sci. phys. nat.* [3] **27**, 485–520 (1892).
(28) Scott, J. D., *Chem. Revs.* **32**, 73–97 (1943).

BASED on paper presented before the Division of Chemical Literature, Symposium on Searching the Chemical Literature, 130th Meeting, ACS, Atlantic City, N. J., September 1956. Revised 1960.

Personal Difficulties with the Chemical Literature

M. G. MELLON

Department of Chemistry, Purdue University, Lafayette, Ind.

In the course of many years of experience in using and producing chemical literature in broad areas of analytical chemistry, several kinds of persistent difficulties have been encountered. The troublesome practices relate to titles of papers and other publications, summaries, definitions, abbreviations, symbols, conventions of usage, spelling, nomenclature, classification, and indexing. The people concerned are authors, abstractors, editors, reviewers, indexers, and those responsible for official usage. Present practices will be improved only as we recognize weakness and error, as we give thought to what can be done to improve the practices, and as we do something about it. In the hope of making the criticism constructive, certain improvements and changes are suggested.

So much devoted work is being done by so many earnest workers that the author is hesitant to voice any protest about the product. Yet, there are difficulties with the literature. Furthermore, it should be evident to a scientist that there is likely to be little improvement of the present except as one recognizes weakness and error in the past, gives thought to what can be done to improve or avoid undesirable practices, and does something about it. The Director of Research of General Motors once told a group of senior engineering students that he was interested in employing them only if they would come with the expectation of criticizing the products of General Motors. Better products, he said, will be made only if one is dissatisfied with present products, and then tries to improve them.

It is in this spirit that some problems are mentioned here which have been encountered in the course of using chemical literature and in dealing with a score of editors during the past third of a century. In the hope of making the criticism at least partly constructive, certain recómmendations are suggested for improving the situation.

The topics selected concern both producers and users of chemical literature. More specifically, there are involved authors, editors, reviewers, abstractors, indexers, and those responsible for recommending official usage, such as abbreviations, symbols, and conventions for handling data.

Specific items have been chosen for consideration here. Although they have arisen in connection with teaching and research in the author's own area of analytical chemistry, their general relevancy seems obvious.

Titles

An author introduces himself to a reader through the title of his article or book. Ideally, this title should be attractive, revealing, and adequate for satisfactory indexing. Practically, it may be defective in any or all of these respects.

Assuming that a written production is written to be read, the title should attract the reader. Usually the less technical the work, the more urgent is this requirement. Examples which seemed to catch the eye of the reader are "Analyses by the Million," "Magic Barrel," "The Next Hundred Years," and "The Second Mile." The problem here is primarily that of the indexer. What useful headings could he select for any of these titles?

As a matter of economy, in both time and paper, titles should be short. However, the title "Chemistry" alone might refer merely to a definition of the word; or it could be the title of a multivolume treatise covering all of the known chemical elements and their compounds. As a book title, "Quantitative Analysis" may apply to anything from a very short book, perhaps with simple gravimetric and titrimetric laboratory exercises, to a treatise sufficiently comprehensive to require a score of volumes to cover all kinds of methods applied to all kinds of materials.

An article entitled "Metallurgical Analysis" might be expected to be broad in treatment, but actually it was a description of a method for the simultaneous spectrophotometric determination of chromium and manganese in steel. The reader will be left to guess what was included in two articles, one entitled "Chemical Affinity" and the other "Experimental Results for Some Molecules."

The short and/or appealing title, although generally desirable, may suffer from lack of clarity and accuracy. If something must be sacrificed, one must decide between brevity and interest versus clarity and accuracy.

Summaries

There seems to be increasing editorial recognition of the usefulness of a short digest or summary of an article immediately following the title. Such a resume partly overcomes the deficiencies of a title which is not revealing or needs amplification or limitation.

The title, "The Determination of Phosphorus," for example, would interest the present author, but at once questions arise. In what kind of material is the phosphorus determined? Is a separation of the element necessary? If so, what kind of method is applicable? Is a colorimetric method of measurement used? If so, what is the color-forming reagent? If it is ammonium molybdate, is the system measured molybdophosphoric acid, molybdovanadophosphoric acid, or a heteropoly blue? If the latter, what are the reductant and the conditions of reduction? To the extent that the title does not answer these and other similar questions, the summary should.

In the course of writing reviews on colorimetry, covering many hundreds of articles, the speaker has often been disappointed by the lack of specificity in both summaries and titles. This necessitated reading at least part of the paper to determine whether it pertained to colorimetry at all. Then one finds that Doe's method was used. Unless one is a walking encyclopedia of methods named to honor their originators, he then has to consult the original reference on Doe's method (generally not mentioned). Irritation increases rapidly if it is discovered that the method of measurement was not colorimetric. This experience is most exasperating if the original reference is in a publication which has to be borrowed from another library, or if a translation has to be made from some language such as Russian or Chinese.

Definitions

The misuse of terms having approved definitions causes the literature chemist to lose time. It is not a major difficulty, but it occurs frequently enough to warrant mention. A few examples will illustrate the nature of the trouble.

A title "The Analysis of Potassium," ought to mean a procedure for determining the minor constituents in potassium metal, and not a method for the determination of potassium. A title, "A Micro Method for Copper," may refer to the use of a very small sample containing copper, or to some method for measuring trace amounts of copper. Used in the latter sense, the speaker has learned to assume that any such title may refer to a colorimetric procedure. It is annoying, then, to find that the summary does not clarify the uncertainty, and consequently to have to read the article, or much of it, in order to find out what was done. "A Trace Method for Copper" is just as unsatisfactory for a title, as any one of a half-dozen methods applicable to trace amounts might be described.

Colorimetry is another word used in different senses. To a physicist it means the measurement of color as color, and as such it has no connection with what the colorant is or its amount. To a chemist it may mean identification and/or estimation of the amount of the colorant. To avoid confusion the author, as a chemist, prefers to use visible absorptiometry.

Often the words "light" and "color" are not used according to approved definitions. Light comprises the range of wave lengths of radiant energy which give rise to the sensation of vision in the normal human eye. Then one does not have black, ultraviolet, or infrared light. Color consists of the characteristics of light other than temporal and spatial inhomogeneities. Color has three attributes: hue, lightness, and saturation. Chemists are likely to mean hue when they use the word color. There is, of course, no such thing as colorless color.

Symbols and Abbreviations

Various kinds of symbols and abbreviations are used to save space. With so many different ones employed, authors should conform to recommended practice, if there is one. If not, it is time to agree upon some usable system.

As an example of abbreviations, the usage of *Chemical Abstracts* for names of journals may be mentioned. If these abbreviations, agreed upon by the International Union of Pure and Applied Chemistry, serve for abstracting more than 9000 periodicals, they should serve for other chemical purposes. Examination of editorial practice shows wide variation—for example, instead of simply *J.* for journal, one may find *Jr.*, *Jour.*, or *Journ.*

Spectrophotometry is an example of decades of confusion in usage of terms and abbreviations. At last there is a committee recommendation that $\log_{10} P_0/P = A = abc$, in which P_0 and P are, respectively, radiant flux incident on the detector after passage through the standard and the sample; A is absorbance; a is absorptivity; b is thickness; and c is concentration. Many chemists pay little or no attention to this recommendation. Consequently, one finds *I*, *J*, *E* (energy), or ϕ instead of *P*; *E* (extinction), *D*, or *OD* instead of *A*; *k*, *K*, *e*, or ϵ instead of *a*; and *d* or *l* instead of *b*. Such indulgence in rugged individualism may satisfy the user's inner urges or reflect his early conditioning, but it makes the product difficult to use.

Conventions

Adherence to certain editorial and technical recommendations makes for efficiency and ease in handling various details, in both producing and using publications.

One example is citation of references to periodicals. There seems no very sound reason for editors of chemical publications not to follow the practice of *Chemical Abstracts*. Abbreviation of names has already been mentioned. Here reference is to the characters used and the order of citing series, volume, number, page, and year. If all of these are necessary, one working in a library wants them in the order given. If a volume is continuously paged, the number is superfluous. To put the year first serves for journals having no volume numbers. However, it is not definite for journals, such as *Die Annalen der Chemie*, which may have five or six volumes per year. Two editors might use the following two forms for a citation: Vol. XVIII, No. 6, Art. 2, pages 81–191, Feb. 10, 1948, and **18**, 81–191 (1948). The second has 29 less characters than the first, and yet is just as adequate, if the periodical is continuously paged. Incidentally, from a library viewpoint, there seems little excuse for not using continuous paging for editorial material.

Another example is plotting of experimental data. In general, engineers follow the code of recommended practice of the American Society of Mechanical Engineers. If so, abscissa values are plotted increasing from left to right, and ordinate values increasing from the bottom to the top. Curves constructed from separately determined readings should show the points which determine the position of the curve. Thousands of spectrophotometric curves do not conform to either of these simple recommendations. Also ordinate values should be the dependent variable, and abscissa values the independent variable. Authors, reviewers, and editors all seem involved here.

In another direction, words ending in *-tion*, such as absorption, reflection, radiation, transmission, and diffraction, are process terms. As such, they should not be used for the entity absorbed, radiated, or transmitted, nor for the corresponding measured values, such as absorptance, absorbance, reflectance, and transmittance.

Spelling

Variations in spelling words, although not a major difficulty, do represent inconsistency in usage or failure to follow official recommendations.

A common inconsistency is the coordinate use of acid and basic. It would seem that the first term should be acidic if the second is basic. Another example is the use of reflectometer and absorptiometer. As the process terms are reflection and absorption, it seems that the names of the instruments should be spelled consistently. Reflectometer has long been used. Absorptometer (or absorptimeter) is the obvious, consistent term.

The Committee on Nomenclature, Spelling, and Pronunciation of the American Chemical Society years ago recommended the spellings, "buret" and "pipet."

Nevertheless many writers persist in using burette and pipette, and current advertising has almost completely reverted. This item is covered in Rule 104, "Directions for Abstractors and Section Editors of *Chemical Abstracts*."

Inadequate Data

In reporting something new, such as a method for making a compound, a procedure for an analysis, or a process for making a physical measurement, the author's description should be adequate to enable one interested, if he so desires, to repeat the work. In the case of U.S. patents, one requirement of patentability is to have the description sufficiently explicit and detailed that "one skilled in the art" can make or use the object patented. Famous legal cases have involved this point.

As an example of this kind, we may turn to spectrophotometry again. The numerical value of the absorptivity for a given solution, for instance, may be dependent upon at least the thickness of the absorption cell, the concentration of the solution, the wave length of measurement, the spectral band width passed, the temperature, and the solvent. In addition, the reliability of the value may be related to the type of instrument used—that is, whether it was photographic, visual, or photoelectric. Most current work is done photoelectrically, but older work was not.

Authors seldom omit all such details, but one stated only that the measurements were made in a certain professor's laboratory. Unfortunately, the omission of part of the details is common. Thus, in one issue of one of our best journals 36 articles contained data involving absorption spectra. Thirty-one specified the solvent, but five did not. None stated the nature of the reference medium, although one must have been used. Twenty-five papers gave adequate information concerning the length of the absorption cell, the concentration of the solution, and the readings obtained. The other 11 gave only part of these data, or none at all. Twenty-three papers either stated that the data were obtained with a continuously recording instrument (or implied this by naming the instrument) or marked the points read on a nonrecording instrument. The other 13 were inadequate in this respect. Seven papers did not mention whether visual, photographic, or photoelectric instruments were used. None of the papers specified spectral band width, but in 18 it could be estimated from a knowledge of the instrument used.

All of the information lacking in these papers must have been available to the authors. If they forgot it, reviewers should have noted the deficiency.

Nomenclature

The general objective of systematic nomenclature is to facilitate communication by means of words. A word, as a particle of speech, symbolizes an idea. Ideally, each word stands for a single idea—that is, it has only one meaning.

The advent of modern chemistry, with its expanding products and concepts, has resulted in a corresponding multiplication of the words necessary to designate all that is new. It is a matter of common sense to have clear-cut functional nomenclature to keep at a minimum our problem of vocabulary.

We have two duties in this direction. The first is to use great care in adopting the most generally useful new terms. Oxygen seems to have been well chosen nearly two centuries ago for one of the elements. Very early a compound of oxygen with another element was designated as an oxide. The ending *-ide* came to mean a binary compound—e.g., a carbide, nitride, sulfide, or hydride. After many decades of such usage, suddenly the words lanthanide and actinide appeared, but not meaning a binary compound of lanthanum or actinium with another element. Unless this perversion is stopped, beginning students must now learn two utterly different meanings. Similarly, oxidation once meant a process involving the action of oxygen with another substance. Now it often means the loss of one or more electrons, a process which might much better have been de-electronation. Another word usage much perverted is acid. The early sense still persists in analytical chemistry, but this sense has become so indefinite in other areas that now one must define the environmental conditions to determine whether a compound, such as tin(IV) chloride, is an acid. This seems unfortunate for beginning students, many of whom have at best much difficulty with the language and concepts of chemistry.

The author's most pressing interest in this direction is a usable system for naming methods of quantitative chemical analysis. Several years ago a survey of well known reference works revealed some 20 different ways of designating such methods. In most cases little or nothing of the processes or operations involved was indicated by the names. The situation remains the same in 1960. What is needed is a functional system, in which the name indicates something, at least, of what is done to make a determination by the given method. Thus, the familiar Kjeldahl method for nitrogen might be designated as a volatilization-titrimetric method, as the nitrogen is separated by volatilization and measured by titration. One need for such a nomenclature is suggested in the section on subject indexes.

Abstracting Journals

Abstracting journals, of both general and specialized coverage, are the chief means of keeping abreast of the constantly accumulating mass of new chemical developments. For the present purpose the author is concerned only with what is contained in analytical abstracts and where they are segregated in a periodical covering all of chemistry, such as *Chemical Abstracts*.

If a title is self-explanatory and adequate for indexing purposes, there is no abstract or annotation in *Chemical Abstracts*. Such cases are rare for analytical methods. In general one wants to know what was done, how, and the results obtainable for given substances or conditions. The information desired may be much the same as that suggested for a satisfactory summary. For example, the method may be for small amounts of silica. The reader wants to know if the procedure is colorimetric. If so, was the colored species developed a heteropoly acid? If so, what was the color-forming reagent? Too often these and similar questions are not answered.

Then there arises the question of where the abstract is to be located in a journal. *Chemical Abstracts*, in its over-all abstracting services, is today the outstanding periodical of this kind. Even so, it could be used more efficiently, issue by issue, if all abstracts dealing with analytical chemistry were segregated in Section 7, Analytical Chemistry. This would not mean, of course, the inclusion of the purely inorganic or organic chemistry of each particular reagent of possible use. In general, methods as methods are in this section, along with many which deal with materials. Many of the latter, however, are likely to be in sections dealing with the materials, such as steel (Section 9) or dyes (Section 25). Abstracts on analytical instruments, such as automatic devices or photometers, may be in Section

1 (Apparatus, Plant Equipment, and Unit Operations). References to spectrophotometers, for example, may be in this section, in Section 2 (General and Physical Chemistry), or in Section 3 (Electronic Phenomena and Spectra).

Unless one waits on the annual subject index, or can use the new *Chemical Titles,* during the year all of the sections must be searched which are likely to contain abstracts on the subject of interest.

Those interested in materials want methods dealing with their particular materials in the appropriate section. Such individuals outnumber analytical chemists, of course. If analytical methods, both as such and as applied to materials, cannot be in Section 7, one alternative is full coverage by cross references in Section 7. At present this is not being done adequately. Another alternative, helpful to the analyst, would be segregation of abstracts on analytical methods in each of the sections on applied chemistry.

Subject Indexes

Many subject indexes are defective in being too much indexes of words rather than of subjects. Although this criticism does not apply to present subject indexes of *Chemical Abstracts,* they are deficient for the most effective searching for particular kinds of analytical methods.

It is here that we find one of the greatest needs for a suitable nomenclature or classification for analytical methods. As an illustration, we may consider the fourth decennial index of *Chemical Abstracts*. Under the heading, "Nickel, detn.," there are 70 entries; and under the subheadings, detn., "in iron," "in iron and steel," and "in steel," there are, respectively, 7, 14, and 59 entries. Table I shows the nature of the information found in the index and in the title and annotation for the 150 abstracts.

Table I. Indication, in *Chemical Abstracts,* of Kind of Analytical Methods Used in 150 Papers Dealing with Determination of Nickel

Index Heading		*Method Indicated in*			*Photometric Methods*	
Entry	*Number*	*Index*	*Title*	*Abstract*	*Found*	*Reagent given*
Ni, detn.	70	0	41	55	9	7
In iron	7	0	5	5	0	0
Iron and steel	14	0	8	9	5	5
Steel	59	0	38	53	10	6
Total	150	0	92	122	24	18

Thus, the subject index for these 150 entries shows nothing of the kind of analytical method used. The titles are adequate for 92, and the abstracts for 122, papers. This means that one must examine the 28 papers for which no information is given. It is significant, too, that one fourth of the abstracts for the 24 photometric methods do not give the chromogenic reagent used. Consequently, if concerned with this detail, one must look up at least six more papers.

Conclusions

The difficulties in using the chemical literature that have been mentioned are of general importance to all chemists and technologists who employ the written records of others' work. There are at least two aspects to the importance of improving these present practices.

In the first place, it is economically important. Time lost or wasted means economic loss. More important, it means that so much of our allotted years is unproductive. Industry goes to great effort to achieve efficient mechanical operation. Should we be satisfied with less in our literature? Also industry is spending large sums to equip and maintain libraries. Surely there must be concern for improving our written products in order to decrease the time spent in using them.

In the second place, it is psychologically important for at least two reasons. Better performance in the directions suggested would reduce disappointment, irritation, and even frustration. This would be to the good in the modern world, for one's tolerance of such tensions is limited. Perhaps most important of all, there should be an increased sense of satisfaction in the producer of the products. We take great pride in our machines and in the care given to making measurements out to so many decimal places. It is a curious fact that so few devote equally meticulous care to writing about their work. One of the chief satisfactions in any work is the inner personal feeling that comes when the worker knows that it has been done to the best of his ability.

BASED on paper presented before the Division of Chemical Literature, Symposium on Searching the Chemical Literature, 130th Meeting, ACS, Atlantic City, N. J., September 1956. Revised 1960.

Language Problems in Literature Searching

T. E. R. SINGER
103 Park Ave., New York 17, N. Y.

Differences in spelling names from one language to another can cause problems in searching the literature. Familiarity with sound equivalents in various languages is helpful in overcoming them. Examples are cited from Germanic and Slavic languages. Nomenclature problems are also discussed, with special emphasis on differences between U. S. and British terms, including differences in spelling, different words to designate the same thing or process, and words that have different meanings in the two countries.

Comprehensive literature searches may include a long span of time and lead to a variety of sources. Inevitably, such searches will involve literature in various languages, some of which may have changed over the period being searched. This invites problems in spelling, which we will consider in terms of names of people, publications, and things looked for.

Names of People

Author indexes, where searches often start, list the names of people alphabetically. This seems like an obvious statement, but the question arises, whose alphabet? We know that the name Johnson is sometimes spelled with two *s'es,* or may be Johanssen. Some Smiths, to be different, spell their name with a *y* instead of an *i*—these differences, if they are noticed at all, seldom cause any difficulty. When we come to foreign names, or use indexes published in other countries, the alphabets are by no means the same. Let us consider a very simple German name first of all. Bär will be found under *B-a-r* in dictionaries, for instance, but spelled as *B-a-e-r* in library catalogs. In this instance librarians have logic on their side. We may demonstrate this fact by looking at the title page of Joseph Furstenbachs "Des Aeltern Mannhaffter kunst Spiegel oder Continuatio und Fortsetzung allerhand Mathematisch- und Mechanisch-hochnutzligh So-wol auch erfroͤlichen delectionen. . . . Augsberg 1663."

In the Black Letter of that time, the *o* in "erfrölichen" has a small *e* balanced on top of it. The same small *e* may be seen in the word "Fürsten" on the dedication page of the same book (page 76). In the course of time the small *c* degenerated into the two dots of the umlaut we see used at the present time.

Dedication.

Durchleuchtigister Churfürst/

Durchleuchtigiste Fürsten.

Hochgeborne Graven.
Hochwürdige. ꝛc.
Hochwolgeborne Freyherren.
Hoch vnd wol Adeliche Gestrenge.
Hochgelehrte. Hoch vnd Wolweise.
Großachtbare, Ehrnveste / Wolfürnehme
Auch Kunstreiche / Großgünstig.
Hoch vnd vil geehrte Herren/
vnd Freund/ ꝛc.

When we use indexes published in foreign countries, many complications can arise. Moreover, as with us in English, there are changes in spelling, often made by decree. The German spelling reform of 1908, which took effect rather gradually, applied also to proper names. In general the principal changes were as follows: *C* lost two of its pronunciations, first in the hard form, whereby Carl became Karl. It was also no longer to be used for the sharp *Ts* sound, so that, again, a word we often use, "Zentralblatt," is now spelled with an initial Z instead of *C*. A less important change as a result of the reform was the dropping of the silent *h,* as in T(h)eil (part) or T(h)on (clay). This last-mentioned omission causes but little difficulty, if in fact it is noticed at all. The actual transformation was spread over a period of time, as was only natural.

It is when we use indexes published in languages other than our own that difficulties can arise; indexes published in England do differ from those published in the United States, as will be discussed later on. Van Haagen (7) has pointed out that the Norwegian name "Ålvik" with a small circle over the *A* appears in the *Chemical Abstracts* index under the letter *A*, as one would suppose would be the case. In a Norwegian index, however, this *Å* with the small circle over it is considered a separate letter of the alphabet, and is placed, alphabetically, after the letter Z—quite a change in position. On the other hand, Danish indexes—probably of less interest to chemists—place the *Å* with the circle over it at the beginning of the alphabet. In both countries this kind of *A* is a replacement for the *AA* used at an earlier period.

In Czechoslovakian indexes, to give another example for an altogether different language, the combination of the letters *c* and *h* is considered as a separate letter and is alphabetized after *H,* not after *C*. There is no intention of continuing to list these differences, but these few examples may serve as a warning that imagination and skepticism are both necessary when using indexes. And in our English language usage, we are not guiltless of causing difficulty with author indexes. The prefixes *M-*, *M-c*, and *M-a-c-*, all pronounced as if they were written *M-a-c*, are usually placed in indexes the way they are written and not in the way they are pronounced. Library catalogs usually consider all forms to be variants of *M-a-c* and alphabetize them in this manner.

Thus far we have considered the variations of alphabetization of Roman letters. Since Cyrillic characters differ so greatly from the Roman, and those that do resemble Roman letters often have an entirely different phonetic value, it appears desirable here to limit ourselves to transliterated words. The experts in Russian should have no difficulty with Russian indexes.

Unfortunately there is, even in English, no generally accepted form of transliteration. In the United States we have the *Chemical Abstracts* system, the Library of Congress system, the Government Printing Office system, the New York Public Library system, and perhaps others as well. The system used by *British Abstracts* is similar to, but not absolutely identical to, the one used by *Chemical Abstracts*.

But as stated in defining the scope of this paper, we are not limiting ourselves to indexes in the English language, so we have to consider what happens, for example, if a Russian name is transliterated into German. Suppose we consider the name of the well-known composer Tchaikowsky rather than starting with a chemist. We write it, conventionally, *T-c-h-a-i-k-o-w-s-k-y*. Why? This is a transliteration that is a mixture of the English and German transliteration forms and is neither one nor the other. We might, with equal reason, write the common given name Charles as Tcharles. That seems absurd to us, but it, and more, is necessary in German. The combination *c-h* has an entirely different sound in German—the gutteral *ch* sound not known in English, though used by the Scottish people. Thus the combination *t-c-h* is completely unpronounceable in German—to make it pronounceable the Germans have to insert an *s* into the name—thus, Tschaikowsky. Toward the end of the name there is another Germanism, so to speak, the *w*. In German this is pronounced in the way we pronounce a *v*; in German the *v* has the sound we give to *f*. We should not complain, though, if we consider what we do with the combination *o-w*, as in the pronounciation of the simple words "now" and "slow." And as an example of a different combination of letters, every school child knows the difficulties in spelling *cough, tough, though,* and *through*. A reasonably satisfactory way of transliterating Tchaikowsky into English might be as Cheyekovsky, but who would recognize it? It may be remarked in passing, that it is a pity that we could not use the Russian composer Alexander Borodin to illustrate the difficulty instead of Peter Ilyitch Tchaikowsky, for Borodin happened to be a chemist as well as a musician.

Examples of similar difficulties could be given almost without limit. For those who are interested, the system of transliteration used by the *Chemisches Zentralblatt* may be found in the general index for 1941, volume 9, part 1, page v.

If the foregoing seems to offer complications, what follows will do so even more. The Russians also have to transliterate Slavic non-Russian names into the Cyrillic alphabet as well as English, German, and French names, and so on. Bulgarians use the Cyrillic alphabet; some Serbians do and others do not. But Czech, Slovak, and Polish, for example, do not, and Czech multiplies the letters of the Roman alphabet, so to speak, by the extensive use of diacritical marks. We are not too concerned, presumably, with the difficulties that are caused for Russians:

On the other hand we are very much concerned with what happens when a name is transliterated into the Cyrillic characters, and then is transliterated back again. This is by no means an uncommon occurrence, and if anything, it will become more common. As became known in November of 1955, in London, and was possibly known before then, Russia is now publishing no fewer than thirteen scientific and technical abstracting journals. Apart from the fact that they naturally cover a large number of non-Russian publications, these abstracting journals are also in a position to abstract Russian journals that, for one reason or another, are not available in this country. *Chemical Abstracts* and probably other abstracting journals as well, for the sake of complete coverage, make use of the abstracts in these Russian journals. If we consider the fact that Slavic languages not in the Cyrillic alphabet, from journals also not available in this country, are probably included among those covered in Russia, the complications that can occur become apparent. That these not only can occur but actually do, has been demonstrated by Hoseh (3). He cites the case of a paper published in a Russian journal by Anton Chapek, the *Chapek* being transliterated as *C-h-a-p-e-k-*. It was believed that Chapek was a Czech; if so, the original spelling would be *Căpek*. In the 1951 index of *Chemical Abstracts* the two forms of *Chapek* are separated by 7 pages and in the last decennial index by 42 pages. *Jankowski and Yankowski*, the same name written with *J* and *Y*, is another example of this type of difficulty. Once again, it is obvious that extreme care is needed in searching.

Russian is, of course, only one of the languages used in the Soviet Union. Of the many others, Ukrainian is probably the only one of interest to chemists; the *Ukrainian Biochemical Journal* is well known. Compared to Russian, Ukrainian has four additional letters, and also lacks four letters, thus ending up with the same number as modern Russian. However, three letters common to both Ukrainian and Russian are pronounced differently. As stated before, these are matters that may be left to the Russian experts except where transliteration problems arise.

Publications

Most of the problems with names of publications are discussed in the chapters by Mellon, Labov, and Dyson. The problem of transliteration in names of journals, however, bears special emphasis.

The word for *journal* in Russian, for example, starts with a letter that looks like this: Ж. We sound it as *zhurnal*, and for this purpose start with the letters *z* and *h* to indicate the desired pronunciation. Actually, the sound of *zh* is common in English, as in measure, seizure, leisure, pleasure, and treasure, but we have no means of indicating the desired pronunciation by a combination of the letters *s-u-r-* and *z-u-r-* at the beginning of a word. In transliteration into the Roman alphabet for French use the spelling of our *journal* will do very well, for the French pronunuciation of this word is *zhurnal*. It would almost do for German use as well, for contrary to German rules the word *journal* is pronounced *jourNAL*, with the accent on the second syllable. In practice, however, the German transliteration for the Russian word starts with *S-h*. *Z* would not do, for in German it has a *ts* sound, as in *Zeitschrift*. *Journal* will not do for transliteration into the Scandinavian languages, for there *J* has the pronunciation we give to *y* at the beginning of a word such as *yes*. *Journal* will also not do for Spanish use, for in Spanish *J* has the sound we give to an *H* at the beginning of a word, as in *he*, or *has*.

A great deal of care is needed in interpreting references to Russian periodicals given in journals in foreign languages.

Things

Searching for things, or to put it more formally, nomenclature, should in theory not cause too many difficulties, for we have nomenclature rules, commissions, international commissions, ACS committees, and committees from ACS divisions, all working on the problem of correct nomenclature. We have the so-called Geneva rules dating from 1892, the Liége rules of a later date, and so on. Nevertheless, there is still no agreement as to chemical nomenclature. But the reasons for these friendly disagreements among the nomenclature experts appear, at least in part, to be the following. Our English language, and I naturally include American customs as well, is based, as is well known, on the Anglo-Saxon modified by Norman-French, with the addition of scientific terms largely based on Latin and Greek. But the development has been according to usage, custom, call it what you will. English or American equivalents of the French or Prussian academies, empowered to say that as of such and such a date certain words are to be spelled in the way designated would be unthinkable to us. Curiously enough, nationalism plays a lesser part with us than it does with some other countries. Thus we accept without hesitation a French word such as *detour,* a German one such as *kindergarten,* or even an Arabic one— for example, *sofa,* which by now we have come to regard as an English word.

But to return to chemistry, we call one of the metals sodium; the Germans have Germanized the pronunciation of the Latin natrium into "naatrium"; both of us use the symbol Na to designate it in formulas, and thus there is no difficulty in recognizing it. On the other hand, what is iodine to us is Jod to Germans, and their use of *J* instead of *I* in formulas can cause trouble. If the French prefer to write sulfuric acid as SO_4H_2, as they do, instead of as H_2SO_4 there is no great difficulty in recognizing it even if it does look a little odd. However, once again, if the French call beryllium *glucinium,* and give it the symbol Gl, difficulties can arise. There are, of course, a number of similar variations, but these few examples should show the need for care when using the foreign literature. We ourselves are not unexceptional in such matters; a recent International Union of Chemistry recommendation was that to agree with the usage in most countries, and also to conform with its symbol W, the metallic element should be called wolfram; it is still called tungsten in this country and in England.

The ultranationalistic point of view that prevailed in Germany from 1933 to 1945 created problems in technical terms. The government of the period had such strong views on the subject that it exhorted the populace to speak "German German"—that is, to avoid words of foreign origin—and this endeavor was extended to include technical terms. The Ministry of Labor of the period mentioned issued a pamphlet which formed a kind of preliminary dictionary of the old and of the new terms. Fortunately, this pamphlet, and others like it, did not have the force of law, but its objectives included the elimination of words even of Latin or Greek origin. It went so far as to propose the renaming of some of the elements. Thus *cadmium*—spelled with a *k,* of course—was to become *Kadming,* and *Aluminum* was to be changed to *Alm.* To *aluminize* would have been *veralmen,* and so on. Another extreme contraction was to occur to the word for electricity—that is, Elektrizität—which was to be shortened to Elt. A few more examples, in the order German word, proposed new word, and the English equivalent are: *Ferment, Regstoff, ferment. Maximum, Höchstewert, maximum. Homogenisieren, gleichstoffen, homogenize. Cellophan, Glahaut* (literally meaning glass skin), *cellophane. Email, Schmalt, enamel. Kompressor, Verdichter, compressor. Vitamin,*

Wirkstoff, vitamin. Absorbieren, Aufschlucken, absorb. Automobil, Kraftwagen (literally, a power car), *automobile.*

After the war most of these extreme terms, if they had been adopted, were discarded, but a few remain. Among them are *Kraftwagen* for *automobile, Verdichter* for *compressor,* and in an altogether different field *Wehrmacht* for *army. Armée,* the word originally used, is of French derivation, of course. In reading the German chemical literature, and other technical literature of the years 1933 through 1945 and possibly somewhat later, these ultranationalistic technical terms may be found. It is by no means always easy to determine their meaning, and a great deal of care is needed in interpreting them.

British vs. American Terms

Differences in the English language as it is used in this country and in England are worth noting; they can be illustrated by reference to entries in indexes of American and British scientific and technical publications. They fall into three groups:

1. Differences in spelling of a term or word used in the United States and in England.
2. The use of different words in the two countries to designate the same object or process.
3. The case where a word has a different meaning as used in the United States and in England.

1. As is well known to users of indexes, variations in spelling cause great or little difficulty according to whether the difference in the spelling occurs near the beginning or the end of the word.

Thus while aluminum becomes aluminium in English usage, the additional *i* near the end of the word causes no difficulty when using a British index, if, in fact, it is noticed at all. The word odor, in England has a *u* in it, odour; tumor is tumour; color becomes colour, also with a *u;* but with a lack of consistency, coloration of glass, for instance, and colorimetric analysis do not have the *u.* Polarization is spelled with an *s* instead of a *z* or *zed* as it is called in England. Other words where the difference in spelling is toward the end of the word are found in fibre, where the terminal *"er"* is reversed as *re,* and olefine, Permutite, and adrenaline, each of which in British usage has a terminal *e.* To these examples may be added the whole group of words based on the element sulfur. In England the *ph* spelling is still retained, and we have sulphur, sulphate, sulphide, sulphite, sulphuric acid, sulphurous acid, and so on. This usage extends to verbs, such as sulphonate, for example, and to compound words such as hyposulphite, thiosulphate, and persulphate.

Examples of words where the difference in spelling is nearer the beginning of the word are caesium, where there is an *a* before the *e,* tyres, the kind used on automobiles, and cacao (cocoa).

The nearer the beginning of a word a spelling difference occurs the more trouble it can cause when using an index. In the following examples the first letter in British usage differs from the practice of *Chemical Abstracts:* œdema, œstrin, and œstrous, all of which are to be found in *British Abstracts* or the abstracts in the *Journal of Applied Chemistry* under *o* instead of *e.*

2. For the second classification it will suffice to mention some British terms, and to give their American equivalents. An American who drives an automobile in England very soon learns that he does not obtain "gas" or gasoline at a gas

station, but instead, petrol at a petrol pump. But it is less easy when the terms are: accumulators for storage batteries; Lucerne for alfalfa; or caster sugar, named for the device used in dispensing it, instead of granulated sugar which is descriptive of the appearance or the form of the sugar. The entry Silk, artificial, for Rayon, causes no difficulty, nor do kinematograph films for moving picture films, or the term Kinematography. The terms Oils, mineral, Petroleum, and Petroleum oils, all appear in *British Abstracts* or the abstracts in the *Journal of Applied Chemistry,* and only a careful examination of the abstracts, and possibly of the original articles, would determine how British and American usage compare.

While not precisely a different word in *British Abstracts* or the abstracts in the *Journals of Applied Chemistry* there are the two entries Moulds, biological, and Moulds, foundry, written *m-o-u-l-d* in both cases. In some British indexes of the early nineteen thirties the term used for what is known in the United States as deuterium is diplogen. Later indexes of the same periodicals conform to the American usage.

3. The third type can cause the most difficulty when using an index. In this country no one would think of trying to get a gallon of paraffin. But one would in England, if one desired to obtain kerosine. What is known in the United States as paraffin is called paraffin wax in England. Another typical example is corn. In the United States corn, apart from certain colloquial use, refers to a definite grain. In England, corn is a generic term, descriptive of all kinds of grain. The British equivalent of American corn is maize and it will be so found in British indexes, with subheadings for maize oil, etc.

As a final example in this third category, the word "chemist" may be mentioned. There would seem to be no possible doubt as to the meaning of the word chemist, and it is in fact used in England in the same sense as in the U. S. But it also has a very difficult meaning, and that is its additional use as pharmacist. Thus in England someone desiring aspirin, for instance, does not go to a drugstore, but to a chemist. But in addition to this meaning of the word, which may appear only colloquial, it also appears in technical usage, and in the titles of journals. Thus while the British journal *Industrial Chemist* is a publication very similar to American journals such as *Chemical Engineering* or *Chemical Industries, The Manufacturing Chemist* is devoted to pharmaceutical preparations.

The question naturally arises as to how these differences in American and British usage of words and terms may be readily recognized. There is no simple answer to the problem, for Anglo-American dictionaries, as such, do not appear to exist. Perhaps the constant use of indexes from both countries is the best solution.

Crane and Patterson (*2*), Soule (*6*), and Mellon (*4*) have considered in detail the differences in the construction and use of indexes of many countries and in many languages, and a very recent book by Cahn (*1*) and an earlier one by Mitchell (*5*) are devoted entirely to British chemical nomenclature practice.

Literature Cited

(1) Cahn R. S., "Introduction to Chemical Nomenclature," Butterworths, London, 1959.
(2) Crane, E. J., Patterson, A. M., Marr, E. B., "Guide to the Literature of Chemistry," 2nd ed., Wiley, New York, 1957.
(3) Hoseh, M., Advances in Chem. Ser., No. **10,** 541–7 (1954).
(4) Mellon, M. G., "Chemical Publications," 3rd ed., McGraw-Hill, New York, 1958.
(5) Mitchell, A. D., "British Chemical Nomenclature," Edward Arnold & Co., London. 1948.

(6) Soule, B. A., "Library Guide for the Chemist," McGraw-Hill, New York, 1938.
(7) Van Haagen, E., Advances in Chem. Ser., No. **10**, 505–9 (1954).

Based on paper presented before Division of Chemical Literature, Symposium on Searching the Chemical Literature, 117th Meeting, ACS, Detroit, Mich., April 1950, and on the author's lecture on "The Need for Imagination and Skepticism When Making Literature Searches," *Record of Chemical Progress,* **18,** 11–29 (1957). Revised 1961.

Searching the Older Chemical Literature

G. MALCOLM DYSON

Chemical Abstracts Service,
Columbus, Ohio

The older chemical literature, published between 1750 and 1875, offers the searcher the pitfalls of multiple publication, anonymity, short life of many journals, unfamiliar abbreviations, and frequent changes of journal names. It is essential actually to handle the sources themselves. A list of obsolete journals of the nineteenth century is appended.

The "older literature" for the purposes of this paper is taken to mean that which was published between the years 1750 and 1875. It is, of course, true that something in the nature of chemical literature existed before 1750, but the consultation of such records more properly belongs to antiquarian research than to library work in the field of chemical literature. If the reader is curious to know what types of sources are used for the very earliest researches in the field, he may consult J. R. Partington's erudite monograph on "The Origins and Development of Applied Chemistry" (2), from which he will soon observe that the earliest records of our science involve the inscriptions and papyri of ancient Egypt, and the documents and remains of the early Arabic and Persian civilizations and cultures. Research in this field is the province of the linguistic and archeological specialist.

In the period commencing with 1750, there are several landmarks which the student will come to regard as turning points in the history of the subject.

1. Publication of Lavoisier's "Traité élémentaire de Chimie" 1789
2. Commencement of the *Chemisches Centralblatt* 1830
3. Commencement of the *Chemical Society Abstracts* 1871
4. Commencement of the *Society of Chemical Industry Abstracts* 1882
5. Commencement of the American *Chemical Abstracts* 1907

Thus, the literature from 1875 onward may be said to be fairly well covered by the various abstracting systems, which can give the three major lines of attack in a literature search. Before that date, however, it is not so easy to be sure of having thoroughly covered the ground of a search.

Pitfalls of Searching Early Literature

As the art—perhaps we should say science—of abstracting has become progressively more thorough and skillful, we have come to rely more and more on abstracts and their indexes for surveying the field of chemical endeavor, and today, so complex is the fabric of chemical literature, the abstract systems are the only feasible means of identifying and tracing original communications. The early abstracting systems were much less efficient than those of today; and prior to 1875 it is not sufficient to rely on them for a survey.

It may, perhaps, be of assistance to the beginner to mention some of the pitfalls of searching the early literature, before making suggestions for a plan of attack. One phenomenon encountered by the searcher in the 1750–1840 period is that of "multiple publication." The savants of this age were not content with a single publication of any discovery they chanced to make; often the same paper, with or without minor modifications, appeared in half a dozen journals and in several different languages. Berzelius, for example, often published in Swedish, with subsequent full publication in English, French, and German, and it was something of an indication of the eminence of a scientist of the period to ascertain how many foreign journals had republished his papers. This makes for many wearisome disappointments in searching the older literature; to secure an apparently new reference to an obscure journal, travel to see it or at considerable cost obtain a copy and translation, only to find that it is merely a translation of a paper available in one's own library.

A second difficulty is that of anonymity. Journals of the time frequently published anonymous scientific communications, especially on controversial subjects. An example of such was published in Thomson's *Annals of Philosophy* in 1815, entitled "On the Relations between the Specific Gravity of Bodies in Their Gaseous State and the Weight of Their Atoms." This was later shown to have been written by Prout, and has led, of course, to "Prout's hypothesis" (which does not anywhere occur in his paper, but originates rather in the editorial comments of Thomson). To discover the authors of such contributions is itself a special field of bibliographical endeavor and is outside the scope of the ordinary searcher; it involves an intimate knowledge of historical minutiae and, moreover, an access to letters and documents not usually available in libraries other than those of the Royal Society and one or two similar ancient institutions on the continent of Europe.

Yet another difficulty lies in the short runs of obsolete journals in which important data were frequently published. In the absence of any organized abstracting service it is often impossible to find a path to information thus published. The origin of the many obsolete journals lies in the fact that during the period under consideration publication was a strongly personal matter; a prominent scientist would, on the least provocation, commence a journal of his own to effect prompt publication of his researches and those of his pupils. The old names—*Crell's Annalen, Thomson's Annalen, Scherer's Annalen, Liebig's Annalen*—testify to this aspect of early chemical literature. In many cases the journals died a natural death with that of the first editor and author, but in others the publication was continued under another name and in some instances even maintained continuity until the present time. Such an instance is the *Annalen der Physik*, which commenced life as the *Journal der Physik* in 1790, became the *Neues Journal der Physik* from 1794 to 1798, and then went through the following transformations of title:

1799–1824	*Gilbert's Annalen*
1824–1877	*Poggendorf's Annalen*
1877–1909	*Wiedemann's Annalen*
1909–	*Annalen der Physik*

In such cases the volume numbers follow the series—i.e., each section is numbered *de novo*—but this is not inevitably so, as in the *Archiv de Pharmacie* which commenced Series 1 in 1822, and after 50 volumes commenced a new series *de novo* which continued until Series 2, Volume 151 (1871), after which the series number disappeared and the volume number jumped to 201 in 1872. The reason for this gap is that in 1872 it was decided to renumber the volumes *ab origine*. A similar gap occurs in the volume numbers of the *American Journal of Science* which in 1937 reached Volume 34 of Series 5, but was then numbered *ab origine*, so that the volume number of 1938 is 236.

In working out a plan of search, several factors must be borne in mind.

Purpose of the Search. Research into the older literature of chemistry is an expensive and time-consuming procedure, and must, therefore, be undertaken only when circumstances warrant it. In ordinary industrial laboratory procedure it is seldom necessary to search back beyond 1875, while even the period 1875 to 1900 often yields little of value from the standpoint of modern manufacture. On the other hand, for purposes of fundamental research, or in preparing a detailed historical survey of some field of chemical endeavor, it is often very desirable to prepare properly documented accounts of the earliest work.

Scope of the Search. As in all historical work, research in early documents can be prolonged *ad infinitum* and it is fundamentally important to know where to stop. Thus, for example, in dealing with the history of iodine as an element, it would be proper to commence with the publication by Courtois (*1*) and Clement and Desormes, of what appears to be the true account of the first isolation of this element. Here again, the pitfalls which surround the searcher are apparent, for it was in 1811 (not 1813) that the discovery was first made, but Courtois although a skillful chemist had no time or money to continue the work, but passed it to his friends Clement and Desormes to develop and publish. There is always a lurking suspicion in the mind of anyone who carries out historical research in such a field, that some earlier discovery of the element recorded in an out-of-the-way place may have taken place; unless the worker is very skilled and experienced in chemical-historical searching, such feelings should be ignored, for they can lead to masses of exhausting and abortive work.

On the other hand, if one were interested in the medicinal uses of iodine and its compounds, it would be necessary to carry out quite a different kind of search, for the use of such iodine compounds undoubtedly carries back to a time long preceding the discovery of the element itself; indeed, it appears that the ancient Assyrians used crude iodide preparations for medicinal purposes, and since these early days the ashes of sponges and kelps have been systematically so used.

Thus, a search for the chemistry of the element iodine is a different matter from one for the use of the iodine-containing compounds medicinally, and would have to be differently planned.

In commencing a search for information on inorganic topics an invaluable starting point is the translation (with emendations and additions) of the original Gmelin's Handbuch, made by Watts and published by the Cavendish Society from 1848 onward. At the commencement of each section is a detailed bibliography which covers a very large part of the literature to that date. An excerpt from the bibliography of the section on iodine (page 86) will illustrate many of the points mentioned in the earlier part of this paper.

Students of chemical literature, familiar only with modern abbreviations for journal titles, will find these very unfamiliar, and an additional disconcerting feature is that no date is given. Because the volume numbers of most of these

Some Entries under "Iodine" in Gmelin-Watts Translation

Angelini, *Schw.*, **36**, 319.
Balard, *Ann. Chim. Phys.*, **28**, 178, and *Schw.*, **44**, 350, *Kastn. Arch.*, **5**, 126.
Bernhardy, *N. Br. Arch.*, **26**, 199.
Cantu, *Mem. de Turin*, **29**, 221.
Cementini, *Bibl. univ.*, **25**, 119.
Connell, *N. Ed. Phil. J.*, **10**, 93
Emmet, *Sill, A. J.*, **18**, 260.
Fuchs, *Repert.*, **14**, 276.
Hall, *N. Tr.*, **7**, **2**, 137.
Soubeiran, *Pogg.*, **12**, 604
Straub, *Schweiz. Nat. Anzg. Jahrg.*, **3**, 59, *Brugn. Giorn.*, **19**, 387.

journals are irregular, the year can be ascertained only with difficulty. Readers will be able to identify most of these journals from the list given below, and will find that the editor's name is often the clue to the title abbreviation—e.g., the *Giornale de fisica, chemica, medicina,* etc., is described as *Brugn. Giorn.* because the editor was Brugnatelli.

In checking over this list by consulting each original, further cross references will come to light and may be added to the list. Other additions will result from the careful inspection of the indexes of the various journals, although in some cases no index is provided. The catalogs of the Royal Society library (1839 and 1881–83) are rich in valuable indications of rarer material.

For organic searches the "Traité de Chimie Organique" of Gerhardt makes a good starting point and is well documented, although in common with its contemporaries, no date is included in the reference. It was published in 1853 and may be considered to cover about two thirds of the literature of the period. A most useful desk volume (or volumes) is the first edition of Richter's Lexicon and the first edition of Beilstein, both of which can often be purchased cheaply. They have the merit of being able to give the searcher an ordered account of the literature up to the 1890's.

Finally, there is no royal and simple method by which the older literature may be surveyed; it is essential for searchers in this field to make a careful and detailed study of the literature, and to make a practice of actually handling the primary sources themselves; this is no study for the man who is in a hurry.

Some Obsolete Chemical Journals of the Nineteenth Century

Title	Published from	Date	Vols.	Editors
1. *Afhandlingar i Fysik, Kemi och Mineralogi*	Stockholm	1806–18, irreg.	6	Berzelius and Hisinger
2. *Allgemeine chemische Bibliothek des Neunzehnten Jahrhunderts*	Erfurt	1801–05	5	Trommsdorff
3. *Allgemeines Journal der Chemie*	Leipzig	1798–1803	10	Scherer
Continued as				
Neues allgemeines Journal für Chemie	Leipzig	1803–06	8	Scherer *et al.*
Continued as				
Journal für die Chemie, Physik, etc.	Berlin	1806–10	9	Gehlen
2nd series	Nürnberg	1811–33	69	Schweigger
(This journal was merged with others into the *Journal für praktische Chemie*)				
4. *Almanach de la Chimie*	Rouen and Paris	1854–61	8	. . .
5. *Almanach für Scheidekünstler*[a] *und Apotheker*	Weimar	1780–1802	23	Gottling
Continued as				
Taschenbuch für Scheidekünstler und Apotheker	Weimar	1803–19	17	Bucholz
Continued as				

Some Obsolete Chemical Journals of the Nineteenth Century (Continued)

Title	Published from	Date	Vols.	Editors
Trommsdorff's Taschenbuch für Chemiker und Pharmaceuten (cumulative index for 1780–1803)	Jena	1820–29	10	Trommsdorff
6. *American Chemical Journal* (now merged in *Journal of the American Chemical Society*)	Baltimore	1879–1913	50	Remsen *et al.*
7. *American Chemist*	New York	1870–77	6+	Chandler
8. *American Laboratory*	Boston	1875	1	
9. *Annali di chimica* (Vol. 21 has a collective index)	Pavia	1790–1802	21	Brugnatelli
10. *Annali di fisica, chimica e matematica*	Milano	1841–47	28	Majocchi
Continued as *Annali di fisica, chimica e scienze affini*	Torino	1850	4	Majocchi and Selmi
11. *Annals of Chemical Medicine*	London	1880–	?	Thudicum
12. *Annals of Chemical Philosophy*	London	1828–29	2	Maugham
13. *Annals of Chemistry and Practical Pharmacy*	London	1843	1	
14. *Annals of Philosophy*				
1st series	London	1813–20	16	Thomson
2nd series	London	1821–26	12	Phillips
(absorbed in *Philosophical Magazine* in 1827)				
15. *Annuaire de Chimie*	Paris	1845–51	7	Millon and Reisst
16. *Annuaire des sciences chimique*	Paris	1837	1	Berzelius
17. *Annual Reports of the Progress of Chemistry* (English translation of *Jahresberichte*)	London	1849–55	7	Liebig *et al.*
18. *Annuario delle scienzi chimiche farmaceutiche e medicolegal*				
Series 1	Mantova	1840	1	. . .
Series 2	Mantova	1841–49	9	Sembenini
19. *Archiv für Gesammte Naturlehre*	Nürnberg	1824–30	18	Kastner
Continued as *Archiv für Chemie und Meteorologie*	Nürnberg	1830–35	9	Kastner
20. *Archiv für die theoretische Chemie*	Jena	1800–02	1	Scherer
21. *Archiv für die thierische Chemie*	Halle	1800–01	1	Horkel
22. *Åsberdätteles om Framstegen i Physik och Chemi till Kongl. Vet. Akad., etc.*	Stockholm	1821–40	20	Berzelius
Continued with title altered from *Physik och Chemi* to *Kemi och Mineralogi*	Stockholm	1841–47	7	Berzelius
Continued with omission of *och Mineralogi* in title	Stockholm	1847–49	3	Svanberg
23. *Auswahl aller eigenthümlichen Abhandlungen und Beobachtungen in der Chemie*	Leipzig	1786–87	5	Crell
24. *Beiträge zur Chemie*	Wien	1791	1	Wasserberg
25. *Beiträge zur chemischen Kentniss der Mineralkörper*	Berlin and Stettin	1795–1815	6	Klaproth
26. *Beiträge zur Erweiterung und Berichtigung der Chemie*	Erfurt	1799–1802	3	Bucholz
27. *Beiträge zur physiologischen und pathologischen Chemie*	Berlin	1843	1	Simon
Continued as *Archiv für pharmakologische und pathologische Chemie*[b]	Wien	1844–54, irreg.	8	Heller
28. *Berlinisches Jahrbuch der Pharmacie*	Berlin	1795–1840	43	Gehlen, Rose, *et al.*

Some Obsolete Chemical Journals of the Nineteenth Century (*Continued*)

	Title	*Published from*	*Date*	*Vols.*	*Editors*
29.	*Bibliothek der neuesten physischen chemischen Literatur*	Berlin	1788–95	4	Hermbstadt
	Continued as				
	Annalen der chemischen Literatur		1802	1	von Woolf
30.	*Boston Journal of Chemistry*	Boston	1866–80	14	Nichols
	Continued as				
	Boston Journal of Chemistry and Popular Science	Boston	1881–82	2	...
	Continued as				
	Popular Science News and Boston Journal of Chemistry	Boston	1883+	?	...
31.	*Bulletin des sciences mathematiques, astronomiques, physiques et chimiques*	Paris	1824–31	16	Saigey
32.	*Centralblatt für Agriculturchemie*, etc.	Leipzig	1872–85	24	Biedermann
33.	*Chemical Gazette*	London	1843–59	17	Francis and Croft
	Became				
	Chemical News	London	1860–1932	145	Crookes
34.	*Chemical Review*	London	1871–84	14	...
35.	*Chemical Review*, and *Journal for the Spirit, Vinegar and Sugar Industry*	Chicago	1881	1	Siebel
	Continued as				
	American Chemical Review, etc.	Chicago	1882–84	3	...
36.	*Chemische Ackersmann*	Leipzig	1855–75	21	Stöckhardt
37.	*Chemische Annalen für die Freunde der Naturlehre*	Helmstädt and Leipzig	1784–1803	40	Crell
	Associated with *Beiträge zu den chemischen Annalen von L. Crell*	Helmstädt and Leipzig	1785–99	6	Crell
38.	*Chemische en phijsische oefeningen voor de beminnaars der scheien naturkunde*	Amsterdam and Leyden	1788	3	Kastelyn
39.	*Chemische Archiv*	Leipzig	1783	2	Crell
	Continued as				
	Neues chemisches Archiv and *Neuestes chemisches Archiv*	Leipzig Weimar	1784–91 1798	8 1	Crell Crell
40.	*Chemisches Journal für die Freunde der Naturlehre*	Lemgo	1778–81	6	Crell
	Continued as				
	Entdeckungen (Die neueste) in der Chemie	Leipzig	1781–86	13	Crell
41.	*Chemisch-Technische Mittheilungen der neuesten Zeit*	Berlin	1846–83	33	Elsner
42.	*Chemisch-Technisches Repertorium*	Berlin	1862–82	21	Jacobsen
43.	*Chemist*				
	1st Series	London	1824–25	2	...
	2nd Series	London	1840–45	6	C. and J. Watt
	3rd Series	London	1846–48	1	Newton
	4th Series	London	1849–53	4	C. and J. Watt
	5th Series	London	1854–58	5	C. and J. Watt
44.	*Chemists' Journal*	London	1880–82	6	...
45.	*Chimiste* (agricultural)	Bruxelles	1865–69	5	Berge
46.	*Chimiste* (distillers)	Paris	1859–60	2	Simon
47.	*Crell's Chemical Journal* (translation of No. 37, but with additions)	London	1791–93	3	...
48.	*Edinburgh Journal of Science* (Merged in *Philosophical Magazine* in 1832)	Edinburgh	1824–32	16	Brewster *et al.*
49.	*Gazzetta eclettica di chimica farmaceutica*	Verona	1831–39	7	Sembenini

Some Obsolete Chemical Journals of the Nineteenth Century (*Continued*)

Title	Published from	Date	Vols.	Editors
50. *Gazzetta eclettica di chimica technologia*	Verona	1833–34	2	Sembenini
51. *Giornale di Farmaçia, chimica*	Milano	1824–34	19	Cattanco
Continued as *Bibliothek di Farmacia*	Milano	1834–45	23	Cattanco
Continued as *Annali di chimica applicata* (This journal was carried on well into this century)	Milano	1845+	71+	Polli *et al.*
52. *Giornale di fiscia, chimica e storia naturale*	Pavia	1808–17	10	Brugnatelli
Continued as *Giornale di fisica, chimica e storia naturale e medicina ed arte*	Pavia	1818–27	10	Brugnatelli
53. *Introduction aux observations sur la physique, sur l'histoire naturelle et sur les arts* (second publication of same material in 1777)	Paris	1771–72	18	l'Abbé Rozier
Continued as *Observations et mémoires sur la physique, sur l'histoire naturelle et sur les arts et métiers*	Paris	1773	1	Rozier
Continued as *Observations sur la physique, sur l'histoire naturelle et sur les arts*	Paris	1778–94	42 [numbered] 2–43	Rozier *et al.*
Continued as *Journal de physique, de chimie d'histoire naturelle et des arts*	Paris	1794–1822	53 + two suppts.	la Méthérie *et al.*
54. *Jahrbuch der Erfindungen und Fortschritte auf den Gebieten der Physik und Chemie*	Leipzig	1865–84	20	. . .
55. *Jahresberichte der Agriculturchemie*	Berlin	1875	2	Detmer
56. *Jahresberichte über die Fortschritte der physischen Wissenschaften*	Tübingen	1822–41	20	Berzelius
Continued as *Jahresberichte über die Fortschritte der Chemie und Mineralogie* (translation from Swedish of No. 22)	Tübingen	1842–51	10	Berzelius
57. *Journal de chimie médicale, de pharmacie et de toxicologie*	Paris	1825–34	10	Berzelius
2nd series	Paris	1835–44	10	. . .
3rd series	Paris	1845–54	10	. . .
4th series	Paris	1855–64	10	. . .
5th series	Paris	1865–76	12	. . .
(Minor changes in title take place through series; journal merged with *Repertoire de pharmacie* in 1876)				
58. *Journal für Physik und physikalische Chemie des Auslandes*	Berlin	1851	3	Krönig
59. *Journal für technische und ökonomische Chemie*	Leipzig	1828–33	18	Erdemann
60. *Journal of Applied Chemistry*	New York Philadelphia Boston	1866–75	10	. . .
61. *Journal of natural philosophy, chemistry and the arts*	London	1797–1801	5	Nicholson
2nd series (Merged with *Philosophical Magazine* in 1814)	London	1802–13	36	Nicholson

Some Obsolete Chemical Journals of the Nineteenth Century (*Continued*)

	Title	*Published from*	*Date*	*Vols.*	*Editors*
62.	*Kleine physikalisch-chemische Abhandlungen*	Leipzig	1858	8	Westrumb
63.	*Kritische Zeitschrift für Chemie, Physik und Mathematik*				
	1st series	Erlangen	1858	1	Kekulé *et al.*
	2nd series	Erlangen	1859	1	Erlenmeyer
	Continued as				
	Zeitschrift für Chemie und Pharmacie	Erlangen Heidelberg	1860–64	4	Beilstein and Fittig
	Continued as				
	Zeitschrift für Chemie	Göttingen	1865–71	7	Beil tein and Fittig
64.	*Laboratorium*	Weimar	1825–40	44	. . .
65.	*Laboratory*	Boston	1874–76	2	Babcock
66.	*Laboratory*	London	1867	1	. . .
67.	*Magazin für die höhere Naturwissenschaft und Chemie*	Tübingen	1784–87	2	. . .
68.	*Mechanic and Chemist*	London	1836–42	8	. . .
69.	*Mélanges physiques et chimiques tirés du Bulletin de St. Petersbourg*	St. Petersbourg	1854–84+	12+	. . .
70.	*Memoirs of the Columbian Chemical Society*	Philadelphia	1813–14	2	. . .
71.	*Naturhistorische und chemische technische Notizen*	Berlin	1854–59	11	. . .
	2nd series	Berlin	1860–62	4	. . .
72.	*Nordische Blätter für Chemie*	Halle	1817	1	Sc erer
	Continued as				
	Allgemeine nordische Annalen der Chemie	St. Petersbourg	1819–22	7	Scherer
	Continued as				
	Magazin für die neuesten Erfahrungen, etc.	Carlsruhe	1823–31	36	Hänle and Geiger
	(Merged in 1832 with *Annalen der Pharmacie*)				
73.	*Penny Mechanic and Chemist*	London	1836–42	8	. . .
74.	*Pharmaceutical Times*	London	1847–48	3	. . .
	Continued as				
	Chemical Times	London	1848–49	2	. . .
75.	*Raccolta fisico-chimica italiana*	Venezia	1846–48	3	Zantedeschi
	Continued as				
	Annali di fisica	Padova	1849–50	1	Zantedeschi
76.	*Répertoire de chimie et de physique*, etc.	Paris	1837–39	6	. . .
77.	*Répertoire de chimie pure et appliquée* (Each volume consists of parts A and B). Became *Bulletin de la société chimique* in 1864	Paris	1858–63	A5	. . .
78.	*Repertorium für die Pharmacie*	Nürnberg	1815–34	50	Buchner
	2nd series	Nürnberg	1835–48	50	Buchner
	3rd series	Nürnberg	1849–51	10	Buchner
	Continued as				
	Repertorium (*Neues*) etc.	Nürnberg	1852–76	25	Buchner
79.	*Repertorium für organische Chemie*	Zürich	1841–43	3	Löwig
80.	*Revue hebdomadaire de Chimie*	Paris	1869–75	7	Mène
81.	*Revue scientifique et industrielle*				
	1st series	Paris	1840–44	16	de Quesneville
	2nd series	Paris	1844–47	15	de Quesneville
	3rd series	Paris	1848–51	9	de Quesneville
	4th series	Paris	1852	1	. . .
	Continued as				
	Moniteur Scientifique				
	1st series	Paris	1857–63	5	de Quesneville
	2nd series	Paris	1864–70	7	de Quesneville
	3rd series	Paris	1871–1926	50+	. . .
	(merged in 1927 with *Revue de Chimie Industrielle*)				

Some Obsolete Chemical Journals of the Nineteenth Century (Continued)

	Title	Published from	Date	Vols.	Editors
82.	*Scheikundige onderzoekingen, gedaan in het laboratorium der Utrechtsche Hoogeschool*	Rotterdam	1845–76,	17	Mulder *et al.*
83.	*Technisch-chemisches Jahrbuch*	Berlin	1880–84+	5+	Bidermann
84.	*Tekno-kemisk Journal*	Stockholm	1847–48	1	Alström
85.	*Tidsskrift for anvendt Chemi*	Kjøbenhaven	1869–70	1	Holm
86.	*Tidsskrift for Physik og Chemi samt disse videnskabers Anvendelse*	Kjøbenhaven	1862–70	12	Thomsen
87.	*Tidsskrift voor wetenschappelijke Pharmacie*				
	1st series	Voorburg	1849–53	5	Haaxmann
	2nd series	Gravenhage	1854–58	5	Haaxmann
	3rd series		1859–64	6	Haaxmann
	4th series	Gorinchem	1865–73	9	Haaxmann
88.	*Toegepaste Scheikunde*				
	1st series	Vlaardingen	1865–69	5	Opwyrda
	2nd series	Vlaardingen	1870–75	4	Opwyrda
	Continued as *Maandblad voor toegepaste Scheikunde*	Amsterdam	1876–80+	5+	Opwyrda
89.	*Ueber die neuren Gegenstände in der Chemie*	Breslau	1791–1802	11	Richter
90.	*Untersuchungen aus Liebig's Laboratorium* (mostly published elsewhere)	Wien	1872	1	Liebig
91.	*Vierteljahresschrift für technische Chemie*	Quedlinberg	1859–69	10	Artus
92.	*Zeitschrift für das chemische Grossgewerbe*	Berlin	1876–82	7	Post
93.	*Zpravy spolku Chemiků českých.*[c]	Prague	1872–76	2	Safarik

[a] Scheidekünstler—assayer, old German for chemist.

[b] Not to be confused with *Archiv. fur experimentelle Pathologie und Pharmakologie* started in 1873.

[c] It is thought that *Časopis chemiků českých* (1 vol. 1870) is a logical predecessor of this; and there may have been sporadic numbers published after 1876.

Literature Cited

(1) Courtois, B., *Ann. chim.* 88, 304 (1813).
(2) Partington, J. R., "Origins and Development of Applied Chemistry," Longmans, London, 1935.

DIVISION of Chemical Literature, Symposium on Searching the Chemical Literature, 117th Meeting, ACS, Detroit, Mich., April 1947.

Searching Less Familiar Periodicals

M. G. MELLON, *Purdue University, Lafayette, Ind.,*
RUTH T. POWER, *University of Illinois, Urbana, Ill.*

Most searches of current periodicals of chemical interest can be readily made with the means now available. The problem is much more difficult for publications prior to 1900 because of their smaller circulation, and less effective, or no, organizing agencies for them. Consideration is given herein to what can be done now with the less familiar periodicals, and what might improve the situation.

New information in chemistry and chemical technology appears almost entirely in periodicals, institutional publications, patents, manufacturers' technical pamphlets, and dissertations. The authors' assignment for this symposium is the discussion of the problem of searching the less familiar periodicals. The presentation is concerned, then, with the nature of the problem, with the present facilities and methods available for meeting it, and with the need for other ways and means in order to work more effectively.

In considering the subject it has been assumed that one is trying to locate all available information relevant to a given topic. Searching every periodical to find every item printed may appear as the wasted efforts of a perfectionist. Often something less than complete coverage does suffice. Also, there is no question of the general applícability of the principle of diminishing returns with increase in time spent searching. However, in at least three kinds of searches knowledge of everything recorded on a topic is important: (1) searches to determine merely all that is known; (2) searches to establish priority of publication; and (3) searches to settle the question of novelty or completeness of disclosure for patents. We are very likely to be concerned with the less familiar periodicals in such searches.

Periodicals differ in many ways. In circulation we have those printed in thousands per issue, and those of perhaps only a few hundred. If one is susceptible to the too common Uesanian (a word coined by Armstrong in England some 20 years ago—U.S.A. plus nian, to refer to us and our work) weakness of mistaking quantity for quality, the best material may be thought to appear only in the most widely circulated, and hence the best known, periodicals. The most striking example to serve as a warning against such a conclusion is the great work of J. W. Gibbs on heterogeneous equilibrium. His papers, published in the then obscure *Memoirs of the Connecticut Academy of Arts and Sciences,* were uncovered only many years later by Europeans, with the result that today Gibbs stands as one of the most famous American scientists. It is especially this kind of thing which we hope to avoid in searching.

Under the heading of periodicals which might be considered less familiar to the chemist and chemical engineer there may today be none devoted exclusively to chemical subjects. If there are such, they must be one of very limited circulation and/or printed in an obscure language. *Chemical Abstracts* is currently abstracting more than 9500 periodicals appearing in 51 languages, and the editor makes every effort to cover all periodicals having any new chemical interest. The periodicals discussed in this paper are most likely to be of a more general nature, especially (1) those dealing with science in general, one subdivision of which is chemistry; (2) those dealing primarily with a science other than chemistry, but having incidental articles involving chemistry; and (3) trade journals, or house organs, which an abstractor or editor finds it difficult to justify abstracting.

Recognition of what the problem is ranks high in importance; but equally important is the question of what can be done about it.

Sources for Searching

Attention may be directed to four kinds of publications in order to determine what help they may provide for our problem. These publications include three secondary sources, treatises, bibliographies, and abstracting journals, and one primary source, periodicals. They are considered in the order of the decreasing state of organization of their material.

Treatises. By definition, a treatise is a comprehensive survey of a large general field of knowledge, such as organic chemistry. Ideally the publication should be so comprehensive as to be complete. If so, every relevant reference from every periodical would be cited. One's searching problem would then be simple, at least if the indexing were adequately done. If the treatise itself did not provide the necessary details, one need only turn to the appropriate reference, get the periodical, and read it.

Practically, this ideal has probably never been achieved, and present prospects give one little basis for thinking that it will be in the foreseeable future. Two defects of treatises must be kept in mind: They are never really up to date, the time lag being at times close to a quarter of a century; and they cover only part of the periodicals, those omitted being most likely the ones which concern this paper. The number of periodicals covered by some of the great treatises is shown in Table I.

Table I. Number of Periodicals Covered in Treatises

Publication	*No. of Periodicals Covered*	*No. then Abstracted by Chemical Abstracts*
Beilstein (*1*)	100, Vol. 6 (1931)	1996 (1931)
Berl-Lunge (*2*)	185, Vol. 1 (1931)	1996 (1931)
Friend (*7*)	175, Vol. 6_4 (1938)	2808 (1936)
Gmelin (*8*)	169, Vol. 1 (1907)	475 (1908)
	245, Vol. 1 (1926)	1246 (1926)
Grignard (*9*)	135, Vol. 4 (1936)	2808 (1936)
Hoffmann (*12*)	163, Vol. 1 (1919)	959 (1920)
Houben-Weyl (*13*)	187, Vol. 1 (1925)	1246 (1926)
I.C.T. (*24*)	586, Vol. 5 (1927)	1246 (1926)
Kirk and Othmer (*15*)	52, Vol. 1 (1947)	4318 (1946)
Landolt-Börnstein (*16*)	142, Vol. 1 (1923)	1246 (1926)
Pascal (*19*)	104, Vol. 1 (1931)	1996 (1931)
Tables annuelles (*17*)	569, Vol. 7 (1925)	1246 (1926)
Thorpe (*22*)	120, Vol. 6 (1926)	1246 (1926)
Ullmann (*23*)	213, Vol. 1 (1928)	1246 (1926)

The periodicals listed in the Landolt-Börnstein set (*16*) may serve as an example of warning in two directions. The first possibility concerns balance in an editor's selection of sources. Of the 142 journals listed, 74 are German. One cannot discount the great contributions of German chemists to chemical literature, but it seems improbable that their work warrants any such proportion of the journals chosen. The second possibility concerns coverage. At the time of searching the 142 journals for data for the set, *Chemical Abstracts* was covering 1246 journals. Because physical constants concern much of chemistry, it seems improbable that 1100 journals contained nothing sufficiently significant to warrant listing at least some of them.

What value, then, do such works have for our problem? Primarily, they give a perspective of the field nearly to the date of publication of the treatise. If nothing can be found on our specific problem, then the search by the compilers of the treatise in the periodicals listed yielded nothing. One does not know whether something was missed in one or more of the omitted periodicals—that is, the less familiar publications.

Treatises serve first to show which journals were covered and to give what was found. In case there was anything, the original reference is given. Thus the treatise is likely to serve further, for many such papers will themselves contain references to the less familiar periodicals, many of which may not have been covered directly by the compilers of the treatise.

Bibliographies. A bibliography, being by definition a list of references, may be of occasional help. However, this is a likely additional possibility only in case all such references have not been evaluated and incorporated in a treatise dealing with the kind of chemistry involved. Such bibliographies as may be available serve as a cross check on the work of the treatise compiler.

From the viewpoint of the present problem, bibliographies fall roughly into three groups: (1) those compiled from abstracting journals and/or treatises; (2) those resulting from reading and evaluating all the references found in abstracting journals, to which have been added any others found as this evaluation progressed; and (3) those which are, if possible, still more inclusive as a result of browsing around in all possible sources. The first group is of little value, because the references are already covered by the organizing agencies. The second will aid to the extent that any references are included which did not appear in abstracting journals or treatises. The third, of course, is what we hope to find.

What the authors have particularly in mind here as being desirable is the kind of bibliography exemplified by Howe's "Bibliography of the Metals of the Platinum Group," a work covering some 150 years (*14*), beginning around 1750. Unfortunately, there are few compilations so meticulously done.

Two general collections of bibliographies may be mentioned. West and Berolzheimer's bibliography of bibliographies (*25*) is an alphabetical list of bibliographies found by searching about 100 periodicals and treatises for the years 1900 to 1931. Bolton's "Select Bibliography of Chemistry" (*4*), covering the period 1492 to 1902, is very general in nature but it does list several hundred bibliographies for this early period.

Since 1937 *The Bibliographic Index* has functioned as a means of cumulating a bibliography of bibliographies. The arrangement is by subjects, only part of which concerns chemistry. By 1948 over 1500 periodicals were being covered. Lists of these sources are included.

Abstracting Journals. In most respects abstracting journals are our most important agencies concerned with gathering together and organizing the vast annual accretion of new information. Consequently, they are practically indispensable for any kind of extensive journal search.

Ideally, such a publication should at least provide abstracts which will lead any searcher to the original details he seeks, give complete material coverage at any time for all periodicals then of value in chemistry, and give complete time coverage for all these periodicals.

As with treatises, there is no perfect publication in this class. To the extent that abstracting journals meet these requirements, they are among the most useful means to which the searcher can turn. Any deficiency relating especially to our problem arises from incomplete coverage. Therefore, whatever is involved deserves attention.

These publications roughly fall into selective and general classes. The former group is likely to have limited coverage in terms of time, number of periodicals, or subject matter (*6, 18*). There should be careful checking of all such sources if the authors' proposed list of periodicals were to be made.

For certain purposes or topics one or more of these selective abstracting services, such as *Engineering Index,* may be most practical, but in the great majority of cases three general journals are believed to be most useful: *Chemisches Zentralblatt* (1830–), *British Abstracts* (1875–1953, as *J. Chem. Soc.,* 1871–, as *J. Soc. Chem. Ind.,* 1882–), and *Chemical Abstracts* (1907–). For the past four decades, therefore, one can cross check through all three of these journals. Two of them extend back another four decades, but only the German journal serves for the third period of four decades. The dates given show the time coverage of these three abstracting periodicals.

Prior to 1830, the start of *Chemisches Zentralblatt,* an occasional general journal included some abstracts. Examples are *Annales de chimie et de physique* (1789 to 1870), *Dingler's polytechnisches Journal* (1820 to 1931), *Taschenbuch für die gesammte Mineralogie* (1807–), and *Journal de pharmacie et de chimie* (1809–). However, certain journals were being published prior to part, at least, of such abstracting services. Table II lists examples of such publications. Some titles vary with time.

As far as the authors know, no study has been published on the degree of completeness of the coverage of the big three abstracting journals, let alone all journals which have carried abstracts at some time. Table III lists the number of periodicals covered by each of the big three at various dates. Those not covered at any given time by a particular journal might be determined by checking its list against a list of all known periodicals of that date. The authors have not presumed to attempt this check.

An important aspect of this coverage problem concerns borderline fields, with the periodicals devoted to them. Biochemistry, in all its involvements with physiology, clinical medicine, and other related subjects, may well be the outstanding example of difficulties in this direction. Two less involved cases illustrate the point.

METALLURGY. Some years ago *Metals and Alloys* was abstracting from nearly 400 publications, although *Chemical Abstracts* was listing less than 100 for the metallurgical field. Presumably the other 300 were considered by abstractors of *Chemical Abstracts* as either unimportant or of no chemical interest.

ANALYTICAL CHEMISTRY. For three decades spectrophotometers have found increasing use as a means of making certain kinds of analytical measurements. Thirty years ago chemical abstractors apparently did not consider this instrument of much analytical importance and consequently one could not depend upon finding articles abstracted for equipment of this kind. The obvious answer in this case is that the subject was considered to be physics and the searcher should have turned to that subject. One might reply that all measuring instruments, such as the analytical balance, belong in the strict sense just as much to physics.

These two examples emphasize the importance of maintaining a broad viewpoint in searching in order to avoid missing possibly important borderline periodicals. Many subjects are not exclusively the province of sharply defined fields.

Periodicals. We come finally to the most difficult part of the problem, and, unfortunately, the part for which least advice can be given for searching. Each

Table II. List of

(Number following title refers

No.	Date	Title
1	1665–	*Philosophical Transactions of the Royal Society of London*
2	1665–1792	*Journal des savants* (+ No. 43)
3	1666–1790	*Histoire de l'académie royale des sciences* (+ No. 47)
4	1679–1682	*Philosophical Collections of the Royal Society of London*
5	1710–1743	*Miscellanea Berolinensia ad Incrementum Scientarium ex Scriptis Socictas Regiae Scientarium* (+ No. 10)
6	1720–1760	*Recueil des mémoires les plus interessants de chimie et d'histoire naturelle, contenus dans les actes de l'académie d'Upsala, et dans les mémoires de l'académie royale des sciences de Stockholm*
7	1726–1746	*Commentarii Academie Scientarium Imperialis Petropolitanae* (+ No. 11)
8	1728–1757	*Raccolta d'opuscoli scientifici e fiologici* (+ No. 13)
9	1739–	*Handlingar Kongliga Svenska Vetenskaps-Academiens*
10	1745–1769	*Histoire de l'académie royale des sciences et des belles-lettres de Berlin* (+ No. 17)
11	1747–1775	*Novi Commentarii Academiae Scientarium Imperialis Petropolitanae* (+ No. 20)
12	1752–1755	*Observations sur l'histoire naturelle, sur la physique, et sur la peinture* (+ No. 14)
13	1755–1787	*Nuova raccolta d'opuscoli scientifici e fiologici*
14	1756–1757	*Observations périodiques sur la physique l'histoire naturelle et les arts* (+ No. 18)
15	1769–	*Mémoires de l'académie des sciences, arts, et belles-lettres de Dijon*
16	1769–	*Transactions of the American Philosophical Society*
17	1770–1786	*Nouveaux mémoires de l'académie royale des sciences et belles-lettres* (+ No. 31)
18	1771–1772	*Introduction aux observations sur la physique, sur l'histoire naturelle, et sur les arts* (+ No. 19)
19	1773–1823	*Journal de physique, de chimie, d'histoire naturelle, et des arts*
20	1777–1782	*Acta Academiae Scientarium Imperialis Petropolitanae* (+ No. 26)
21	1778–1781	*Chemisches Journal für die Freunde der Naturlehre* (+ No. 24)
22	1780–1829	*Almanach für Scheidekünstler und Apotheker*
23	1780–	*Memoirs of the American Academy of Arts and Sciences*
24	1781–1786	*Neuesten Endeckungen in der Chemie*
25	1783–1791	*Chemisches Archiv* (+ No. 48)
26	1783–1802	*Nova Acta Academiae Scientarium Imperialis Petropolitanae* (+ No. 54)
27	1783–	*Transactions of the Royal Society of Edinburgh*
28	1784–1803	*Chemische Annalen für die Freunde der Naturlehre Arzneygelahrtheit, Haushaltungskunst, und Manufacturen*
29	1785–1795	*Beiträge zu den chemischen Annalen von Lorenz Crell*
30	1785–1787	*Magazin für Apotheker, Chemisten, und Materialisten* (+ No. 33)
31	1786–1804	*Mémoires de l'académie royale sciences et belles-lettres* (+ No. 55)
32	1787–1802	*Bibliothek der neuesten physisch-chemischen, metallurgischen, technologischen, und pharmaceutischen Literatur*
33	1788–1790	*Repertorium für Chemie, Pharmacie, und Arzneimittelkunde*
34	1788–1803	*Sammlung der deutschen Abhandlungen der königlischen Akademie der Wissenschaften zu Berlin*
35	1790–1802	*Annali di chimica e storia naturale, ovvero raccolta di memorie sulle scienza, arti, e manufatture ad esse relative*
36	1790–1794	*Journal der Physik* (+ No. 41)
37	1793–1817	*Journal der Pharmacie für Aerzte und Apotheker* (+No. 70)

treatise has its index, accompanied usually with a list of the periodicals covered. The current abstracting journals are probably unsurpassed in the quality of their indexes, and each occasionally publishes lists of the periodicals covered. In brief, the problem remaining is to discover any lack of coverage of the periodicals by these organizing agencies and then to determine what indexes are available for such periodicals.

First of all one needs a complete list of all present and discontinued periodicals having any possible chemical interest. This would include those devoted entirely

Selected Early Periodicals

to entry number of superseding periodical)

No.	*Date*	*Title*
38	1794–1815	*Journal des mines* (+ No. 67)
39	1795–1840	*Berlinisches Jahrbuch für die Pharmacie*
40	1795–	*Journal de l'école polytechnique*
41	1795–1797	*Neues Journal der Physik* (+ No. 50)
42	1796–1815	*Bibliothèque Brittannique. Sciences et arts* (+ No. 66)
43	1797–	*Journal des savants*
44	1797–1813	*Journal of Natural Philosophy, Chemistry, and the Arts*
45	1797–1806	*Magazin für den neuesten Zustand der Naturkunde*
46	1798–1803	*Allgemeines Journal der Chemie* (+ No. 52)
47	1798–1815	*Mémoires de l'institut national des sciences et arts* (+ No. 68)
48	1792–1798	*Neuestes chemisches Archiv*
49	1798–	*Philosophical Magazine*
50	1799–	*Annalen der Physik*
51	1802–1813	*Annales de muséum d'histoire naturelle* (+ No. 64)
52	1803–1806	*Neues allgemeines Journal der Chemie* (+ No. 56)
53	1803–1818	*Archiv der Agriculturchemie für denkende Landwirthe*
54	1803–1822	*Mémoires de l'académie imperiale des sciences de St. Petersbourg*
55	1804–	*Abhandlungen der königlichen Akademie der Wissenschaften in Berlin*
56	1806–1809	*Journal für die Chemie, Physik, und Mineralogie* (+ No. 62)
57	1806–1818	*Afhandlingar i Fysik, Kemi, oc Mineralogi*
58	1807–1817	*Mémoires de physique et de chimie de la société d'Arcueil*
59	1808–1827	*Giornale di fisica, chimica, et storia naturale*
60	1810–1814	*American Mineralogical Journal*
61	1810–	*Memoirs of the Connecticut Academy of Arts and Sciences*
62	1811–1833	*Journal für Chemie und Physik*
63	1813–1826	*Annals of Philosophy*
64	1815–1832	*Mémoires de muséum nationale d'histoire naturelle*
65	1816–1830	*Quarterly Journal of Science, Literature, and Art*
66	1816–1835	*Bibliothèque universelle des sciences, belles-lettres, et arts*
67	1816–	*Annales des mines*
68	1816–	*Mémoires de l'académie royale des science de l'institut de France*
69	1817–1822	*Allgemeine Nordische Annalen der Chemie für die Freunde der Naturkunde und Arzneiwissenschaft* (+ No. 77)
70	1817–1834	*Neues Journal der Pharmacie*
71	1818–	*American Journal of Science*
72	1819–1826	*Edinburgh Philosophical Journal* (+ No. 82)
73	1820–1928	*Transactions of the Cambridge Philosophical Society*
74	1821–1849	*Jahresbericht über die Fortschritte der Chemie und Mineralogie*
75	1821–1851	*Arsberättelse om Framstegen i Fysik och Kemi till Kongligsche Vetenskaps-Akademien*
76	1822–	*Archiv der Pharmacie und Berichte der deutschen pharmazeutischen Gesellschaft*
77	1823–1831	*Magazin für Pharmacie*
78	1824–1832	*Edinburgh Journal of Science*
79	1824–1835	*Archiv für die gesammte Naturlehre*
80	1825–1876	*Journal de chimie médicale, de pharmacie et de toxicologie*
81	1826–1864	*Edinburgh New Philosophical Journal*
82	1826–	*Journal of the Franklin Institute*
83	1826–	*Bulletin de la société industrielle de Mulhouse*
84	1828–1833	*Journal für technische und ökonomische Chemie*
85	1829–	*American Journal of Pharmacy*

Table III. Number of Periodicals Abstracted by Different Abstracting Periodicals at Different Dates

Chemisches Zentralblatt		*British Abstracts*[a]		*Chemical Abstracts*	
Date	*No.*	*Date*	*No.*	*Date*	*No.*
1890	115	..	..	..	..
1900	145	..	..	..	..
1910	162	1910	222	1910	435
1915	153	1916	264	1915	671
1920	306	1920	464	1920	959
1926	480	1926	406	1926	1246
1930	839	1931	474	1931	1996
..	..	1936	715	1936	2808
1952	4925	..	..	1942	3740
		1946	1317	1946	4318
				1951	5236

[a] Prior to 1926 divided between *J. Chem. Soc.* and *J. Soc. Chem. Ind.*

Table IV. Periodicals

1633–1876. Catalogue of Scientific Serials, by S. H. Scudder.
The 4390 entries include transactions of learned societies in the natural, physical, and mathematical sciences. The titles are listed by countries and sublisted by place. Separate indexes cover places (towns), titles, and certain subjects, such as chemistry.

1665–1895. A Catalogue of Scientific and Technical Periodicals, by H. C. Bolton.
This great compilation was "intended to contain the principal independent periodicals of every branch of pure and applied science published in all countries from the rise of this literature to the present time" (1895). The 8600 titles are arranged alphabetically. Included also are chronological tables, a classified subject index, and American library holdings.

1665–1800. Repertorium Commentationum a Societatibus Litterariis Editarium Secundum Disciplinarium Ordinem Digessit, by J. D. Reuss.
Of the 16 volumes of this work the third, Scientia Naturalis, deals with chemistry and metallurgy. It functions as a precursor to the Catalog of Scientific Papers, listed next.

1800–1900. Catalog of Scientific Papers, by Royal Society of London.
The 19 volumes of this indexing serial contain entries from 1555 periodicals. Our interest is the list of many periodicals covered. The number varies, there being 1400 in Vol. 1 and 1865 in Vol. 13.

1800–1916. Mezhenko, IU. A., bibliograficheskii ukazatel. Russkaia tekhnicheskaia periodika, Izd-vo Akademii Nauk S.S.S.R., Moskva, 1955. 299 pp.
Annotated descriptive bibliography, with subject and other indexes, of 415 Russian periodicals in technological fields, published between 1800 and 1916.

1901–1914. International Catalogue of Scientific Literature, by Royal Society of London.
This publication, a continuation of Catalog of Scientific Papers, is divided into 17 sections, chemistry being D. The first volume for chemistry lists 116 periodicals, which increased to 417 in the fourteenth volume. The total of journals for 1903–04 contains 5546 entries.

1802–1907. Index to Periodical Literature, by W. F. Poole.
The 470 periodicals indexed are in the English language and are of a general nature. The entries concerning chemical subjects are relatively small in number.

1823–1908. Repertorium der technischen Journal-Literature, by E. L. Schubarth *et al.*
This serial began as Repertorium der technischen Literature and in 1909 became Fortschritte der Technik. During the 85 years shown more than 400 periodicals were covered at some time.

*–1866. Catalogue of Publications of Societies and of Periodical Works Belonging to the Smithsonian Institution.
The alphabetical list, by country and city, includes publications of more than 25 countries.

*–1888. Bibliographie des travaux scientifiques publiés par les sociétés savantes de la France, by J. Deniker and R. Descharmes.
This set, completed thus far only to the heading "Sarthe," lists the publications of French scientific societies. The arrangement is by departments, then by towns, and finally by societies.

1879–1934. Bibliographie der deutschen Zeitschriftenliteratur.
This work is especially useful as an indexing serial for German periodicals. The number of journals covered ranges from 275 in the first volume to over 4500 at the peak of the 55-year period.

Table IV. Periodicals *(Continued)*

1884– Engineering Index.
The periodicals covered in this indexing serial, now in the neighborhood of 2000, concern primarily engineering and allied technical fields.

1889– Experiment Station Record.
This digest of current agricultural literature serves practically as an index in this field prior to the start of Agricultural Index in 1916.

*–1898. Publications of Societies, by R. R. Bowker.
Over 1000 American societies issuing publications of general or technical interest are listed.

1900– . Readers' Guide to Periodical Literature.
This index is of possible use for general or popular articles in a limited number of periodicals.

*–1914. Die wissenschaftlichen Vereine und Gesellschaften Deutschlands im neunzehnten Jahrhundert.
A list is given of German societies and periodicals.

*–1938. Hand-List of Titles of Current Periodicals in the Science Library. His Majesty's Stationery Office.
This list contains titles of the publications, together with details of the holdings.

*–1900. British Museum Catalogue of Printed Books.
Volume 1, Academies, lists academy publications in the library of the British Museum prior to 1885. Volume 41, Periodical Publications, includes periodicals prior to 1900. Listing is by place of issue, with sublisting by societies.

1879–1926. Index Medicus (Quarterly Cumulative Index Medicus after 1926).
This is an indexing serial covering medical publications in all the principal languages.

1880– Index Catalogue of the Library of the Surgeon-General's Office.
This is an index of our great medical library, with various lists of the serials covered in the several series. Thus, Volume 10, 4th Series, lists 6776 serial publications.

1900–1950. World List of Scientific Periodicals.
Over 36,000 periodicals are listed for the publication period shown. All details are included for checking, such as changes of name, and library holdings.

1907– . International Index to Periodicals.
This list covers several hundred periodicals not included in sources such as Engineering Index, Industrial Arts Index, and Agricultural Index.

1911– . Bibliographie der fremdsprachigen Zeitschriftenliteratur.
Here are indexed some 1400 non-German periodicals. It is said to be valuable for French and Italian publications.

1913–1957. Industrial Arts Index (followed by Applied Science & Technology Index, 1958–).
Because of its nonscientific emphasis, this work is probably of less value for our purpose than various other lists.

*–1949. Union List of Serials in Libraries of the United States and Canada, by W. Gregory.
Since this vast collection lists more than 115,000 titles, it includes many relatively unimportant entries. However, it does undoubtedly cover some of our less familiar works.

* These publications are supposed to be complete to the dates shown.

to chemical information; those devoted either to general science or to a nonchemical field but containing incidental chemical items; and those devoted to borderline fields, some of the information of which has some bearing on some chemical problems.

Such a list should give the inclusive dates covered by each periodical. Along with the date should appear notations to show which treatises and which abstracting journals have covered the periodical, with inclusive dates if the whole period of the periodical was not covered. We shall assume for the present purpose that coverage by a treatise and/or an abstracting journal is adequate.

When there is not such coverage, the following cases might arise: The periodical was completely overlooked or disregarded by editor and/or abstractor; there was no organizing agency during the period of the periodical, or some part of it; and the abstracting journal began later than the periodical to be abstracted.

To the best of the authors' knowledge, there is no annotated list of uncovered periodicals, such as that suggested. Until its possible compilation, we seem to be dependent largely upon a collection of other lists arranged for various purposes. Special attention was given to including works listing the early publications. Journals published prior to 1900 are most difficult to locate and least likely to be available except in very large libraries.

Having in hand the possible residue of uncovered or partially covered periodicals, one can then turn to whatever means are available for searching the publications concerned. Lacking organizing agencies, about the only alternatives remaining are the indexes for the individual periodicals. Most likely they are annual indexes, with some cumulative indexes covering either specified intervals of time or the entire run of the periodical. As a final entry, then, for each periodical in our projected list there should be notations on the availability of such indexes.

The authors know of no general list of the available cumulative indexes for all periodicals of interest. However, some help may be had, as in Haskell's check list (*11*). Also during the past three decades Columbia University has issued a number of such lists covering its own acquisitions. An example is *Bibliographic Index* (*3*) for the period 1951–55.

Perhaps mention should be made here of the occasional help of comprehensive historical articles, especially if their aim was to present a complete survey of a subject. An American example is the paper by Silliman (*21*) on "American Contributions to Chemistry" which covers over 60 pages. In this review of the work of the century 1774 to 1874 one finds not only the names of now familiar periodicals, such as the *Journal of the Franklin Institute* and *American Journal of Science,* but also less familiar ones, such as *New York Medical Repository, Boston Journal of Chemistry, New York Medical and Philosophical Journal, Thomson's Annals of Philosophy, Mémoire des savants étrangers,* and *Memoiri degli spectroscopisti italiani.*

House organs and trade journals constitute part of our periodical problem. Mention was made of the difference in number of publications abstracted by *Metals and Alloys,* a metallurgical journal, and by the Metallurgical section of *Chemical Abstracts,* a general abstracting journal. As the editor of the latter periodical endeavors to abstract from every original source which contains new chemical information, one may assume that any unmentioned house organs and trade journals contain little that is new. In fact, many items therein are intended to be of only passing interest or for advertising purposes.

In this connection, a work of possible value is the "Directory of House Organs" (*20*), a work listing more than 6329 titles in 1954. The arrangement is by title (alphabetical) and by sponsor (both alphabetical and geographical). A symbol indicates the user as internal, external, or both. Titles of special chemical interest must be inferred from the name or the sponsor. An earlier work by Groves (*10*) dealt with British house organs.

Conclusion

If one has at hand the journals, house organs, and any other like periodicals, together with their indexes, it remains only to use the works. This involves chiefly subject indexes and there is nothing peculiar about those concerned here. Perhaps the chief point to remember is that many of them are in no way comparable in usefulness to the present expertly constructed subject indexes of *Chemical Abstracts.* If one can live through the experience, page-by-page examination of the periodical is the last resort for searching an inadequately indexed publication. In a recent book (*5*) the authors report use of such means to locate every reference to boron trifluoride and its derivatives.

Literature Cited

(1) Beilstein, "Handbuch der organischen Chemie," G. E. Stechert & Co., New York.
(2) Berl-Lunge, "Chemische-technische Untersuchungsmethoden," Julius Springer, Berlin.
(3) *Bibliographic Index* 4 (1955).
(4) Bolton, H. C., "Select Bibliography of Chemistry," Smithsonian Misc. Collections, Nos. **851** (1893), **1170** (1899), and **1440** (1904).
(5) Booth, H. S., Martin, D. R., "Boron Trifluoride and Its Derivatives," p. vii, Wiley, New York, 1949.
(6) Crane, E. J., Patterson, A. M. "The Literature of Chemistry," Wiley, New York, 1957.
(7) Friend, J. N., "Textbook of Inorganic Chemistry," Griffin & Co., London, 1937.
(8) Gmelin, "Handbuch der anorganischen Chemie."
(9) Grignard, Victor, "Traité de chimie organique," Masson & Cie., Paris, 1936.
(10) Groves, F. R., "House Organ Handbook and Review," Institute of House Organ Editors, London, 1939.
(11) Haskell, D. C., "Check List of Cumulative Indexes to Individual Publications in the New York Public Library," New York Public Library, New York, 1942.
(12) Hoffmann, M. K., "Lexikon der anorganischen Verbindungen," J. A. Barth, Leipzig.
(13) Houben-Weyl, "Die Methoden der organischen Chemie," G. Thieme, Leipzig, 1925.
(14) Howe, J. L., "Bibliography of the Metals of the Platinum Group," Smithsonian Misc. Collections, No. **1084** (1897).
(15) Kirk, R. E., Othmer, D. E., "Encylopedia of Chemical Technology," Interscience, New York, 1947.
(16) Landolt-Bornstein, "Physikalisch-chemische Tabellen," 5th Aufl., 1951.
(17) Marie, Charles, "Tables annuelles de constants et données numériques,"
(18) Mellon, M. G., "Chemical Publications," p. 106, McGraw-Hill, New York, 1958.
(19) Pascal, Blaise, "Traité de chimie minerale."
(20) *Printer's Ink*, "Directory of House Organs," Printer's Ink Publishing Co., New York, 1947.
(21) Silliman, Benjamin, *Am. Chemist* **5**, 70, 195, 327 (1875).
(22) Thorpe, J. F., Whiteley, M. A., "Dictionary of Applied Chemistry," Longmans, Green & Co., New York, 1926.
(23) Ullmann, "Enzyklopädie der technischen Chemie," Urban & Schwarzenberg, Berlin, 1934.
(24) Washburn, E. W., ed., "International Critical Tables," McGraw-Hill, New York, 1926.
(25) West, C. J., Berolzheimer, D. D., "Bibliography of Bibliographies on Chemistry and Chemical Technology," National Research Council, Washington, D. C., 1925; two supplements, 1924–1931.

BASED on paper presented before the Division of Chemical Literature, Symposium on Searching the Chemical Literature, 117th Meeting, ACS, Detroit, Mich., April 1950. Revised 1960.

Identification of Less Common Forms of Abbreviations for Chemical Journal Titles

TERESA GNASSO LABOV
Closter, N. J.
Revised by **JAMES L. WOOD**
Librarian, Chemical Abstracts Service, Columbus, Ohio

Journal abbreviations are unwelcomed by the literature searcher only when they tend to obscure rather than to disclose the actual title. Confusion in such a citation may arise from a change in the normal word order, such as inversion; addition of extra words, such as the society name, place of imprint, or founder; unusual contractions or abbreviations of individual words; and the complete omission of certain words appearing in the full title. Standard abbreviations have been established from time to time, but as yet no one system of constructing abbreviations may be considered to be truly international.

To the chemical worker, references to periodicals, books, and patents are the means by which the wealth of published scientific knowledge is made accessible. Without the elaborate network of abstract journals, bibliographies, reviews, and indexes which exist today, the research worker would be little better off than the first man who discovered the use of fire. An important phase of locating any article is the identification of the periodical in which it appeared, or, as is more often the case, the abbreviations of its title.

General Forms of Abbreviation

Few literature searches can remain within the *Chemical Abstracts* system of abbreviations for any length of time. Even within the confines of *Chemical Abstracts*, Beilstein, *British Abstracts* (which discontinued in 1953), *Chemisches Zentralblatt*, and the *Referativnyĭ Zhurnal, Khimiya* the abbreviation of Justus Liebig's *Annalen der Chemie* will vary from *Ann.* to *A* to *Annalen* to *Liebig's Ann. Chem.*, or *Liebigs Ann. Chem.* Other examples could easily be appended.

One question arises immediately: Is there not at least one standard list of abbreviations of journal titles? In 1922, the abbreviations used in the "List of Periodicals Abstracted by *Chemical Abstracts*" (7) were adopted as a standard by the International Union of Pure and Applied Chemistry. Crane and Patterson (*12*) commented in 1927 that these abbreviations "have not been accepted universally, but their use is increasing," and Soule (*42*) added in 1938 that the adoption of the "List of Periodicals Abstracted by *Chemical Abstracts*" by the International Union of Chemistry "gives the list a definite status and increases the probability of its wider adoption in the near future."

Since the acceptance by the International Union of Pure and Applied Chemistry of journal abbreviations used by *Chemical Abstracts,* it is encouraging to note that these abbreviations are gaining increasing recognition and usage. In the 1951 revision of the "List of Periodicals" a few abbreviations were altered to conform with recommendations made by the International Federation of the National Standardizing Associations, as suggested by UNESCO, and some other alterations were made at the request of the American Institute of Physics, which had adopted the *CA* abbreviations for use in its journals and in the field of physics. In 1960 the Committee on Form and Style of the Conference of Biological Editors adopted the *CA* journal title word abbreviations that were published in the 1956 edition of the "List of Periodicals" for inclusion in its "Style Manual for Biological Journals" (*9*). The *CA* abbreviations are also used by *Nuclear Science Abstracts* and in many other scientific and technical journals published both in this country and abroad.

Another list of abbreviations is offered by the "Word List of Scientific Periodicals" (*44–45*). The third edition of this work, published in 1952, contains abbreviations that follow the system recommended at an international conference of the International Institute of Intellectual Cooperation. The original World List abbreviations, published in 1927, required only slight modifications to comply with this system.

The whole problem of abbreviated titles is aptly reviewed by Mitchell in his preface to the second edition of the World List, where he states that "the use of abbreviated titles is a necessity in scientific literature, but unless the abbreviations have been devised so that each one indicates only one periodical and also unless they are in general use, they fail of their purpose." The Royal Society Scientific Information Conference, held in London from June 21 to July 2, 1948, recommended that the World List abbreviations be adopted by abstracting agencies.

Pflücke and Hawelek in 1952 (*31*) mention that the *Chemisches Zentralblatt* abbreviations are based on the World List and the rules of the International Institute of Intellectual Cooperation, as set forth in German Standard No. 1502: however, the list of journal title word abbreviations used by *CZ* and published in "Periodica Chimica" (*31*) shows considerable variation from the German Standard No. 1502.

Thus there are two sets of abbreviations which have attained, at the very minimum, the nominal status of international standards. A comparison of the two lists—i.e., "List of Periodicals Abstracted by *Chemical Abstracts,*" most recently revised in 1956 with annual supplements for 1957, 1958, 1959, and 1960, and the "World List of Scientific Periodicals, 1900–1950"—discloses the followink data:

Chemical Abstracts	20,155 entries including 9700 titles in current usage and 7500 earlier titles with references to succeeding ones
World List	50,000 titles listed (*46*)

In general, the citations in the World List are slightly longer than those in *Chemical Abstracts.*

Chemical Abstracts	*World List*	*Title*
Ber.	*Ber. dtsch. chem. Ges.*	*Berichte der deutschen chemischen Gesellschaft*
Compt. rend.	*C. R. Acad. Sci., Paris*	*Comptes rendus hebdomadaires des séances de l'académie des sciences*
Monatsh.	*Mh. Chem.*	*Monatshefte für Chemie und verwandte Teile anderer Wissenschaften*
Rec. trav. chim.	*Rec. Trav. chim. Pays-Bas*	*Recueil des travaux chimiques des Pays-Bas*

This difference in length of citation would be expected, because the World List must distinguish among nearly two and one half times as many journals as *Chemical Abstracts.*

Another system of abbreviations, which also has a world-wide perspective, is utilized in the "International Catalogue of Scientific Literature" (*21*). This work, a continuation of the "Catalogue of Scientific Papers" that will cover the literature of the nineteenth century, is issued annually in 17 volumes, the fourth of which deals with chemistry. The rules for periodical abbreviations which are given in the "Instructions for Use of Regional Bureaus" (1903) are most brief. The first two commonly accepted rules state general principles:

1. Abbreviated titles must be intelligible without a key.
2. Words in abbreviated titles must follow each other in the same order as the original title.

The remaining two rules presuppose a little more than what is common knowledge of the histories of various journals.

3. Titles of proceedings, reports, or scientific periodicals in general, which are edited or published by learned societies, academies, etc., must begin with the name of the place where the society resides.
4. When the society does not reside in a fixed place, the publication must be dealt with as stated in Rule 2, the place of present publication being added at the end of the abbreviation.

Chemical Abstracts periodical title abbreviations are based on the following rules (*5*). In general, the normal word order of the title is preserved.

1. Prepositions and conjunctions are omitted except where required for identity or differentiation of journals with similar names.
2. Abbreviations, with the exception of the often used J. (Journal) and Z. (Zeitschrift), are of sufficient length to enable recognition of the word.
3. Only words in the *principal* technical languages are abbreviated, or at least extensively abbreviated, with some exceptions for less used languages such as Dutch, Finnish, Celtic, Czech, etc., where the word is of the same generic origin as that of an accepted abbreviation.
4. In general, for journals with single-word names no abbreviating has been done.
5. Colloquial expressions are permitted where no confusion would arise. See second paragraph below.
6. Exceptions to the general rules are obvious as they occur; for instance, "Ind." is used for "Industrial" or "Industry"; hence neither India nor Indiana is abbreviated. To differentiate between similar titles such as *J. Chem. Phys.* and *J. Chem. and Physics* the "and" may be required.

The recognition of so-called colloquial abbreviations is an innovation, considered acceptable for our specific field when indicated by "chem.," as in the example *Ber. deut. chem. Ges.* (*colloq. chem.: Ber.*), which means that in chemical journals *Ber.* may be used, but elsewhere the longer abbreviation is probably desirable. Another example, this time for the engineering field, is *Proc. Inst. Radio Engrs.* (*colloq. eng., Proc. IRE*).

In each of the prefaces of the three editions of the World List, a special description of the rules employed in constructing the abbreviations is given. The rules of the "International Code of Periodicals" (1930) and its supplement (1932) were utilized in revising the directions given in the first edition (22). These rules, as they now exist, may be summarized as follows:

1. Contractions are differentiated from abbreviations by omission of full stop. Thus if *Engineering* is contracted to *Engng*, no period follows the abbreviation, whereas if *Engineering* is shortened to *Eng.*, a period is used.
2. Nouns have capital initial letters, adjectives small.
3. Prepositions, articles, and connectives are generally omitted.
4. Singular and plural words are not distinguished.
5. Places of imprint are omitted except where a question of the language used, or the need to distinguish two periodicals with the same title, arises.
6. In Germanic and Scandinavian languages, different parts of complex words are abbreviated as if distinct. For example, *Kunstseide* might be abbreviated *Kt.-sd.*, but never *Kunst.*

Similar problems arise when one attempts to define the most general forms used in citing journals in other sciences. The question of standard abbreviations for titles of periodicals in botany was discussed recently by Little (25). The confusion within this science exists in part because each of the four main botanical indexes—i.e., *Bulletin of the Torrey Botanical Club, Agricultural Index, Biological Index,* and *Bibliography of Agriculture*— stoutly adheres to its own system of abbreviating periodical titles. The suggestion was made by Little that an attempt to eliminate these differences be made at the Seventh International Botanical Congress at Stockholm.

Various schemes for standardization of abbreviations have met with partial success. Additional proposals for solving abbreviation problems have been made. One suggestion that has been presented from time to time is to assign a number to every periodical and use these numbers in place of word abbreviations. Whereas such a scheme would eliminate the confusion that now exists between the same or similarly titled periodicals, it would create problems when periodicals change titles or cease publication, or when new periodicals are initiated. Also the numbers would give little indication of the subject matter or type of journals cited.

A more feasible plan was proposed by the International Institute of Intellectual Cooperation and, more recently, by the Royal Society. Let it be the responsibility of the periodical published to obtain an abbreviation that has the approval of either *Chemical Abstracts* or the World List (preferably both). This abbreviation would then appear printed on the covers and at the bottom of each page of the journal. Such a plan would make abbreviation problems a thing of the past.

Currently the American Standards Association Sectional Committee Z39 on Library Work and Documentation, Subcommittee on Abbreviations for Periodicals, is working on a standard which will serve as a guide for abbreviating periodical titles. In 1954 the International Standards Organization issued the first edition of "ISO Recommendation R4, International Code for the Abbreviation of Titles of Periodicals." This standard was rejected by the American Standards Association on the basis that the general principles established by it were too broad and would lead to varying interpretations and would not achieve the standardization desired. Since ISO R4 became an international standard it has been the subject of several changes or amendments which have been proposed at the ISO Technical Committee meetings. These go far to indicate a good deal of dissatisfaction with this set of periodical title abbreviation rules.

Less Common Forms of Abbreviation

There seem to be logically only four types of word order which can be used in abbreviating the name of a journal.

1. Exact title order, as appears in the periodical.
2. Name of issuing society, followed by the title.
3. Place of imprint, followed by the title.
4. Founder or successive editors of journal, followed by title.

Thus, for the *Journal of the American Chemical Society*, there would be:

1. *J. Am. Chem. Soc.*
2. *Am. Chem. Soc., J.*
3. *Washington, J. Am. Chem. Soc.*
4. *Lamb, J. Am. Chem. Soc.*

In addition to the problem of which word order is to be used, there is the question of which words or parts of words shall be omitted or retained. For instance, the word *American* might appear as *A*, *Am.*, *Amer.*, or *Amern.* Abbreviations for the word *Journal* are similarly varied. The letter *A* might also stand for *Annalen, annaler, annales, annali, Annalen der Chemie, abstracts, age,* or even *British Abstracts,* Section A.

Generally no difficulty arises in the case of a periodical abbreviation given in exact title order, provided that the individual word abbreviations chosen are long and distinct enough. The abbreviation Z. *an.* follows the principle of strict order, but its parsimony leads to a possible confounding of the following:

Z. anal. Chem.
Z. anal. Entwichlungsgeschichte
Z. angew. Chem.
Z. angew. Mikroskop. u. Klin. Chem.
Z. angew. Mineral.
Z. angew. Phot. Wiss. u. Tech.
Z. anorg. Chem.
Z. anorg. u. allgem. Chem.

Similarly, the Russian word *Trudy* as an abbreviation would lead to the possible confusion of 604 citations in "Ukazatel Sokrashchennykh i Polnykh Nazvaniĭ Nauchnoĭ i Tekhnicheskoĭ Literatury" (29) and 464 citations in the 1961 edition of the "List of Periodicals Abstracted by *Chemical Abstracts*."

By beginning an abbreviation with the name of the issuing society, as in the case of *Am. Chem. Soc., J.*, one benefit is procured: Most libraries index and shelve society or institutional periodicals and pamphlets under the name of the society issuing them. Whereas *Deutsche chemische Gesellschaft, Berichte* may be logical to a librarian, it may be more difficult for the research worker to remember.

An ingenious variation for the abbreviation of an important Italian journal can be found by considering *Atti della reale accademia nazionale dei Lincei, Rendiconti Classe di scienze fisiche, matematiche e naturali. Chemical Abstracts* accords one of its lengthiest abbreviations to this journal, maintaining, however the normal word order—*Atti accad. nazl. Lincei, Rend., Classe sci. fis. mat. e nat. Chemisches Zentralblatt* also conforms to the logical word order in using *Atti R. Accad naz. Lincei, Rend.* However, Beilstein and *British Abstracts* invert the order and place the society first so as to produce *R.A.L.*, and *Real. Acc. Lincei,* respectively.

The third arrangement of abbreviations, with the place of imprint first, is exemplified by *Wash., J. Am. Chem. Soc.* Thus *Berichte der deutschen chemischen Gesellschaft* is sometimes cited as *Berliner Ber.,* or even *Ber. Ber.*

The methods in which the society or place of imprint is placed first in citing journals are not too common, and such systems can be recognized without too much difficulty.

The last type of word order to be considered consists in placing first the name of the founder or one of the successive editors of the journal. A list of the most common of such abbreviations includes the following:

Crell J., Journal für die reine und angewandte Mathematik
Dingl, J., Dingler's Polytechnisches Journal
Drude, Annalen der Physik
Erdmann's J., Journal für praktische Chemie
Fr., Zeitschrift für analytische Chemie (Fresenius)
Gilb. Ann., Annalen der Physik (Gilbert)
H.-S., Zeitschrift für physiologische Chemie (Hoppe-Seyler)
Liebig's, Annalen der Chemie
Pogg. Ann., Annalen der Physik (Poggendorf)
Pflüger Arch., Archiv für die gesamte Physiologie
Sill. J., The American Journal of Science (Silliman)
Wiedermann's Ann., Annalen der Physik

An extensive list of older periodicals, including their editors, is given by Dyson (*14*).

Given an abbreviated citation that is not immediately recognizable, how then is one to proceed to identify it?

The shorter and seemingly more obscure abbreviations are generally those given to the most widely used journals within any one field. It is more likely that *A.*, *B.*, and *C.* will refer to *Annalen der Chemie, Berichte der deutschen chemischen Gesellschaft*, and *Comptes rendus hebdomadaires des séances de l'académie des sciences*, than to periodicals such as *Allgemeine Textile-Zeitschrift, Bulletin of Pharmacy*, and *Coal Age.*

A first step in locating the obscure citation is to place it in one of the four categories just described. Thus *Lond., P.R.S.* is obviously a case of the place of imprint preceding the title, whereas *S.C.I.J.* is probably an example of the issuing society placed first. By omitting the place or society name, the remaining parts of words may be found by using any of the periodical lists giving abbreviations. The location of some of these sources is given in the bibliography.

If it is suspected that an editor's or founder's name has been utilized—for example, *Lamb, J. Am. Chem. Soc.*—the abbreviations shown above should be considered, as well as descriptions of the history of chemical periodicals such as those of Crane and Patterson (*12*), Mellon (*26*), or Soule (*42*). The various sources of lists of abbreviations may aid in discovering the journal name.

If the citation is seemingly given in normal title order, clues to the subject matter considered may help to identify the journal. The subject matter might be deduced from such key words as *Bot.* (Botany) or *Anal.* (Analytical) or from the content of the reference itself. The data of the reference and the language in which the reference is published may also be valuable; these would aid in placing the journal within definite time and space limits. Again, such guides to the chemical literature as Crane and Patterson (*12*) or Mellon (*26*) should be utilized. Perhaps even the synchronistic tables as found in Lange (*24*) may be of value.

This discussion is by no means complete. No attempt has been made to consider the problems which arise when it is necessary to transliterate other alphabets into the Roman. This problem arises especially with the Slavic language, Chinese, Japanese, and Hebrew. Generally, such citations tend to be lengthy, and hence are more easily deciphered.

No complete scheme can or should be proposed for identifying obscure journal citations. An outline is suggested which may be valuable at times, and at other times totally useless. In this problem, as in all others considered in this symposium, the searcher needs a good general knowledge of chemical literature, plus intuition and the proverbial grain of skepticism to produce the desired results.

Selected Bibliography of References on Journal Citations

(1) Abstracting Service Consultative Committee, "List of Periodicals and Bulletins Containing Abstracts Published in Great Britain," Royal Society, London, 1949.

(2) Allen, E. F., "Dictionary of Abbreviations and Symbols," Coward-McCann, New York, 1946.

(3) *Am. Scientist* **35,** 306, 308, 310, 312–14, 316, 318 (1947). Editors: Relax, Please.

(4) Barrows, F. E., *Chem. Met. Eng.* **24,** 423–8, 477–9, 517–21 (1921). Investigations of the Chemical Literature.

(5) Bureau of Abstracts, London, "Principles of Abstracts," 1949.

(6) Cameron, G. R., "Manual of the Literature of Chemistry," Louisiana State University Press, Baton Rouge, 1940.

(7) Chemical Abstracts Service, "List of Periodicals Abstracted by *Chemical Abstracts*," 1956 with Supplements for 1957, 1958, 1959, and 1960.

(8) Clapp, V. W., *Library of Congress Information Bulletin*, Appendix, pp. 1–3 (July 12–18, 1949). International Conference on Science Abstracting, Paris, June 20 to 25, 1949.

(9) Conference of Biological Editors, Committee on Form and Style, "Style Manual for Biological Journals," American Institute of Biological Sciences, Washington, 1960.

(10) Crane, E. J., *Chem. Eng. News* **25,** 2075 (1947). Periodical List of Publications.

(11) Crane, E. J., *Ind. Eng. Chem., News Ed.* **14,** 447 (1936). Twenty-eight Hundred Periodicals of Chemical Interest.

(12) Crane, E. J., Patterson, A. M., Marr, E. B., "Guide to the Literature of Chemistry," 2nd ed., Wiley, New York, 1957.

(13) Davidson, A., "Periodica Technica Abbreviata," Series *Tekniska Litteratursällskapets, Handbok Nr. 1,* Victor Pettersons Bokindustriaktiebolag, Stockholm, 1946.

(14) Dyson, G. M., ADVANCES IN CHEM. SERIES No. 4, 96 (1950). Searching the Older Chemical Literature.

(15) Ellis, A., *Sci. Monthly* **66,** 427–30 (1948). Application of Scientific Principles to Scientific Publications.

(16) Frank, O., *Intern. Fed. Doc., Trans.* **14,** C111–13 (1938). Normung und Dokumentation in Deutschland.

(17) Grivet, T., "Present State of Science Abstracting Service and Possible Improvements," UNESCO/NS/SAC/ 1, Paris (April 15, 1949).

(18) Heilbron, I. M., "Dictionary of Organic Compounds," Oxford University Press, New York, 1934–38.

(19) Heinrich, A., "Aküschlü, Abkürzüngsschüssel herausgegeben und bearbeitet vom Verlag," Brunnen, Berlin, 1935.

(20) Hollmann, W., "Die Zeitschriften der exakten Naturwissenschaften in Deutschland," Series *Zeitung und Leben, Bd. 39,* Zeitungswissenschaftliche Vereinigung, Munich, 1937.

(21) International Council, "International Catalogue of Scientific Literature, List of Journals with Abbreviations Used in the Catalogue as References," Royal Society, London, 1903; Supplement, 1904.

(22) International Institute of Intellectual Cooperation, "International Code of Abbreviations for Titles of Periodicals," International Institute of Intellectual Cooperation, Paris; 1930; Supplement, 1932.

(23) John Crerar Library, Chicago, *Ref. List* 39–42 (1938). Abbreviations by Initial Letters.

(24) Lange, N. A., "Handbook of Chemistry," 7th ed., 1820–3, Handbook Publishers, Sandusky, Ohio, 1949.

(25) Little, E. L., *Science* **110,** 666–8 (1949). Citations of Botanical References.

(26) Mellon, M. G., "Chemical Publications, Their Nature and Use," 3rd ed., McGraw-Hill, New York, 1958.

(27) Merril, E. D., *Science* **62,** 419–20 (1925). Appeal for Simplified Literature Citations.

(28) Mummendey, R., "Bibliographie der Gesamt-Zeitschriften-Verzeichnisse," Series *Kölner Bibliographische Arbeiten,* Bd. **4,** Baldwin Pick, Köln, 1939.

(29) Nikitin, P. I., ed., "Ukazatel Sokrashchennykh i Polnykh Nazvaniĭ Nauchnoĭ i Tekhnicheskoĭ Literatury," Izdatel'stvo Akademii Nauk SSSR, Moscow, 1957.

(30) Pflücke, M., Z. *angew. Chem.* **48**, 25–8 (1935). Normungsfragen der deutschen chemischen Literatur.
(31) Pflücke, M., Hawelek, A., "Periodica Chimica, Verzeichnis der im Chemischen Zentralblatt referierten Zeitschriften mit den entsprechenden genormten Titelabkürzungen," Verlag Chemie, Berlin, 1952.
(32) Prinzhorn, F., *Intern. Fed. Doc., Trans.* **14,** C108–10 (1938). Nationale und Internationale Normen auf dem Gebiet des Bibliothek-, Buch- und Zeitschriftenwesens.
(33) Prinzhorn, F., *Zentr. Bibliothek.* **45,** 522–33 (1928). Normung für Bibliothek-, Buch- und Zeitschriftenwesen.
(34) Royal Society, "Royal Society Scientific Information Conference, 21 June–2 July 1948, Report and Papers Submitted," London, 1948.
(35) Rust, W., *Intern. Fed. Doc., Trans.* **14,** C110–11 (1938). Regelung der Zitierformen von Wissenschaftlichen Zeitschriften.
(36) Rust, W., "Verzeichnis von unklaren Titelkürzungen deutscher und ausländischer Zeitschriften," Harrassowitz, Leipzig, 1927.
(37) Rust, W., *Zentr. Bibliothek.* **44,** 503–14 (1927). Vorschlag zur Regelung der Zitierform.
(38) Serralach, M., "Bibliografía Química," Claraso, Barcelona, 1946.
(39) Shankle, G. E., "Current Abbreviations," H. W. Wilson Co., New York, 1945.
(40) Shull, C. A., *Science* **73,** 363–4 (1931). Erroneous Citations and Titles of Scientific Papers.
(41) Singer, T. E. R., *News Ed. (Am. Chem. Soc.)* **18,** 541–2 (1940). Current Abstract and Index Periodicals of Interest to Chemists.
(42) Soule, B. A., "Library Guide for the Chemist," McGraw-Hill, New York, 1938.
(43) Stephenson, H. J., "Abbrevs. (a Dictionary of Abbreviations)," Macmillan, New York, 1943.
(44) World List of Scientific Periodicals Published in the Years 1900–1921, Vol. 1, Abbreviated Titles and Location of Sets, 1925; Vol. 2, 1927, Oxford University Press, London.
(45) World List of Scientific Periodicals Published in the Years 1900–1933, Oxford University Press, London, 1934.
(46) "World List of Scientific Periodicals Published in the Years 1900–1950," 3rd ed., Butterworths Scientific Publications, London, 1952.
(47) Zimmerman, O. T., Lavine, I., "Scientific and Technical Abbreviations, Signs and Symbols," Industrial Research Service, Dover, N. H., 1948.

BASED on paper presented before Division of Chemical Literature, Symposium on Searching the Chemical Literature, 117th Meeting, ACS, Detroit, Mich., April 1950. Revised 1961.

Searching for Theses, Dissertations, and Unpublished Data

IRLENE ROEMER STEPHENS[1]
Celanese Corp., Summit, N. J.

Theses and dissertations are indexed in standard abstract journals and books only after they are published in current periodicals, where they usually appear in abbreviated form. Published research reports are not the only source of valuable information; scientific meetings, preprints, abstracts, and publications of limited circulation are often of interest. Lists of sources of dissertations by country and by individual institution and suggested ways of tracing unpublished data are presented.

THE searcher of chemical literature has at his disposal a large collection of sources and, to be sure, a number of tools which appear to be adequate aids for tracing specified subject information. Yet, the individual who searches for information which he knows he has seen published somewhere, soon becomes aware of the fact that "the artisan is only as efficient as his tools," and, when the source of the data cannot be traced, the tools seem inadequate.

Recently, I wanted to refer to an account of some calculations made by Harlow Shapley, the eminent American astronomer, which showed very clearly the huge number of molecules in any small parcel of matter. The story was based on the fact that in any volume of air, four fifths of the particles are molecules of nitrogen and that when a deep breath is exhaled, the nitrogen molecules in it are rapidly dispersed. After a certain period, probably not more than a few years, perhaps less, they will be equally distributed throughout the atmosphere. By this time, each unit volume of air at the surface of the earth will contain between two and three of the nitrogen molecules that were present in the original volume exhaled. To make it more dramatic, the author of this account selected the breath that Shakespeare exhaled as he wrote the first line of the second act of Hamlet. As you inhale a breath today it will contain two of the actual molecules exhaled by Shakespeare at that particular moment. You would be most unlucky were you to get only one molecule; were you to capture three, you would belong to a fortunate minority.

I remembered the details of the story. It was not written by Dr. Shapley himself, it was among several related and unrelated accounts given by someone who

[1] Present address, Maplewood, N. J.

prefaced this and other illustrative stories with "may I be pardoned by the cognoscenti . . ." and who concluded his article by offering "humble apologies for the attempt to cover so many topics, and so inadequately." I enjoyed reading what the author said, and recalled I had read it at home and not at business.

Had I read it over someone's shoulder on the subway train? Probably not, for it would be unusual, indeed, to have read so much under such circumstances. How could I trace this reference? The article had been published, to be sure, but I remembered details which were not sufficiently important to have been indexed in standard tools. There was the possibility, too, that the publication was too new to have been picked up by these tools.

It certainly was not important, but I was subconsciously irked by my inability to recall the source when I remembered the story. I thought that this incident was typical of many of the problems in searching for information which chemists and literature people, alike, meet daily.

Shortly after being plagued by not having recalled the source of this "breathing story," I remembered that it was told by Sir Robert Robinson and then found out that it was in his 1955 Presidential Address to the Society of Chemical Industry (*13*). The human mind does not always react logically. We are not always fortunate enough to remember the key information used in indexing articles for which we search.

The tools available to search the chemical literature are good. We know they are. And so we proceed with reasonable assurance that we will trace some of the references relating to our problem and that we won't miss too much pertinent information. We preface the report of search results with a list of tools used and may state that in so far as these tools cover the literature, the search was exhaustive. In certain cases, we may even consider it desirable to specify the subject approach used for particular tools. In so doing we recognize the shortcomings of available tools in the subject control of published literature. Much that is published is not indexed in available indexing and abstracting periodicals; some of the published literature which is indexed may be missed because of differences in subject approaches.

But what of unpublished data? When would searching for unpublished data be in order? What kinds of unpublished literature might contribute to our work in chemistry? How can we know that unpublished data exist on a specific subject, how can we trace them, and what determines their accessibility?

In an exhaustive survey, any source of information which has even the slightest possibility of being productive should be consulted. There are several advantages which might result. It is to be understood, however, that the very nature of unpublished literature makes the search a time-consuming one. The mechanics of searching such literature are not well established as are the approaches to searching in *Chemical Abstracts* or *Chemisches Zentralblatt*. The direct subject approach is often impossible; the search, therefore, is prolonged.

Academic Dissertations

There are several kinds of unpublished literature which might well be considered. These are among them, although they are often used principally as a means of developing research initiative. Yet, the final product often reflects original thinking and concentrated effort (*7*). Dissertations are not always required at the master's level, and master's degrees, as such, are not granted in many European universities; consequently most theses are doctoral theses. Granting these facts, one can accept unhesitatingly the possibility that theses would report data which might contribute to research-in-progress. There seems to be a popular misconception that theses are classified as published literature and as such are indexed in standard indexing and abstracting journals and books. Only if academic dissertations are published in current periodicals will they be indexed in the standard tools. Dissertations are rarely printed in full in scientific journals; consequently, a thoroughgoing search would require obtaining and reviewing the thesis itself. Some dissertations are published in obscure journals not covered by the indexing tools at our disposal. The situation is further complicated by the fact that present abstracting tools in chemistry do not indicate that the version of the dissertation published is actually a portion of a dissertation available in complete form from the university where the work was done. Occasionally, a searcher may be able to guess this fact from the affiliation listed in the abstract, but this is not a foolproof method. The affiliation, as included in the abstracting tool, may be the present industrial affiliation of the scientist whose Ph.D. thesis, accepted some time in the past, is only now being published.

Unfortunately, many dissertations are never published. If the quality of the research were the only determining factor in deciding nonpublication of theses, the problem would be well in hand.

Lists of Titles of Academic Dissertations

There have been a number of scholarly attempts at listing dissertation titles so that reported research would not be lost. Many of these are noteworthy. It is helpful to know of their existence so that one may refer to them selectively.

Australia

Marshall, M. J. M., ed., "Union List of Higher Degree Theses in Australian University Libraries," University of Tasmania Library, Hobart, Tasmania, Australia, 1959.

Austria

Faculty of Philosophy, University of Vienna. "Verzeichnis über die seit dem Jahre 1872 und der philosophischen Facultät der Universität in Wien, eingereichten und approbierten Dissertationen," 4 volumes, University of Vienna, Austria, 1935–1937. Volume 4 contains the basic list for Innsbruck.

Canada

Association of Research Libraries, "Doctoral Dissertations Accepted by American Universities," H. W. Wilson, New York, 1933–1957. D. B. Gilchrist, E. A. Henry, A. H. Trotier, and M. Harman, editors. Gives titles for dissertations. Appendix shows which publications of universities in the United States contain abstracts. Information on availability of photostats and microfilms is listed. In 1957, "Doctoral Dissertations Accepted by American Universities" was absorbed by *Dissertation Abstracts.*

Palfrey, T. R., and Coleman, H. E., "Guide to Bibliographies of Theses, United States and Canada," 2nd ed., American Library Association, Chicago, 1940.

Rosenberg, R. P., "Bibliography on Theses in America," *Bull. Bibliography,* **18,** 181, 203 (1946). Additions to and corrections of Palfrey and Coleman cited above.

"Canadian Graduate Theses in the Humanities and Social Sciences," 1921–1946, Ottawa, 1951.

Denmark

"Dissertations," University of Copenhagen, Denmark, since 1897. Annual listing of dissertations in pamphlet form. Beginning in 1897, this listing has been issued each year and is continuing at present.

France

Bolton, H. C., "Selected Bibliography of Chemistry," Smithsonian Institution, Washington, D. C., 1901–1904. Section 8 lists older unpublished dissertations in chemistry, excluding analytical chemistry, for the period of 1492 to 1902. French dissertations are included.

Ministry of Education, Paris, "Catalogue des thèses et éscrits académique," Paris, 1884 +. Annual listing of academic dissertations, classified with author, subject, and title indexes. Dissertations from all French universities are included.

French Cultural Services in New York, "French Doctoral Theses, Science, 1951–1953" (1955). An issue of the *French Bibliographical Digest* (No. 1, series III) prepared and distributed as a guide to advanced researchers. Covers biology, botany, biochemistry, logic and philosophy of science, hygiene, etc. Subject index is included. "French Doctoral Theses—Pharmacy and Medicine, 1951–1954" is also available.

Germany

"Jahresverzeichnis der deutschen Hochschulschriften," publishers vary, Berlin and Leipzig, 1885–1934.

"Jahresverzeichnis der an deutschen Universitäten erschienen Schriften," 1935 +. Issued annually, under normal conditions, with author and subject indexes. Official listing of dissertations from all German universities.

Bolton, H. C., "Selected Bibliography of Chemistry," Washington, D. C., Smithsonian Institution, 1901–1904. Section 8 includes German dissertations.

Great Britain

No national listing of academic dissertations is at present prepared. L. Newcombe, in a report of the *Proceedings of the Sixteenth Conference of the Association of Special Libraries and Information Bureaux*, discusses the accessibility of British university thesis literature in 1939. England, Wales, Ireland, and Scotland are covered. Newcombe lists British universities together with names of publications which list titles or give abstracts of university dissertations.

Newcombe, L., "Accessibility of British University Thesis Literature," *Association of Special Libraries and Information Bureaux Proceedings* (1939), pages 21–30.

Association of Special Libraries and Information Bureaux, "Index to Theses Accepted for Higher Degrees in the Universities of Great Britain and Ireland," London, 1955–56 (1958); 1956–57 (1959); 1957–58 (1960).

India

Inter-University Board of India, "Bibliography of Doctorate Theses in Science and Arts, Accepted by Indian Universities of Different Years," Bangalore Press, Bangalore, India, 1949.

Netherlands

"Catalogus van academische geschriften in Nederlandsch–Indie verschenen," 1924 +. Utrecht, 1925–present.

Russia

Bolton, H. C., "Selected Bibliography of Chemistry," Smithsonian Institution, Washington, D. C., 1901–1904. Section 8 lists Russian dissertations.

South Africa

Robinson, A. M. L., "Catalog of Theses and Dissertations Accepted for Degrees by South African Universities, 1918–1941," Capetown, South Africa, 1943.

Potchefstroom University for Christian Higher Education, "Union Catalogue of Theses and Dissertations of the South African Universities, 1942–1958," Potchefstroom, South Africa, 1959.

Sweden

Nelson, A., "Akademiska avhandlingar vid Sveriges universitet och högskolor, läsären 1890 to 1909–10," A. B. Akademiska Bokhandeln, Uppsala, Sweden, 1911.

Tuneld, J., "Akademiska avhandlingar vid Sveriges universitet och högskolor, läsären 1910–11 to 1939–40," Ohlssons', Lund, Sweden, 1945.

Ottervik, G., and Lundberg, S. G., editors, "Swedish Books and Publications on Science, Medicine and Humanities, 1937–1947," Swedish Institute, Stockholm, 1949. Survey of important works published in Sweden. Academic dissertations of Swedish universities are included.

Switzerland

"Jahresverzeichnis der schweizischen Universität Schriften," Verlag der Universität Bibliotek, Basel, Switzerland, 1897 +.

United States

1. National Listings

American Chemical Society, Committee on Professional Training, "ACS Directory of Graduate Research," Washington, D. C., 1959. Faculties, publications, and doctoral theses in departments of chemistry, biochemistry and chemical engineering at United States universities are listed. In each section, institutions are arranged alphabetically. For each department, the degrees offered are indicated, together with a statement of fields in which doctoral degrees are granted. Following this, the instructional staff is listed alphabetically, and summarized for each member are brief biographical information, statement of major field of research interest, and a list of references covering most recent research publications.
This is a biennial publication and was preceded by editions of 1957 and 1955 by the same title and with same coverage except for biochemistry in 1955. Predecessors were: "Faculties, Publications, and Doctoral Theses in Chemistry and Chemical Engineering at U. S. Universities" (1953) and "Titles of Theses Submitted for Doctoral Degrees in Chemistry and Chemical Engineering at American Educational Institutions" (1952), both published by the committee, and "Doctors of Philosophy Degrees in Chemistry and Chemical Engineering Granted in the United States from June 1951 through December 1951" compiled by the staff of *Chemical & Engineering News*, and "Ph.D. Theses in Chemistry

and Chemical Engineering" (1951), 13 compilations on individual universities published from Aug. 20, 1951, through Jan. 14, 1952, in *Chem. & Eng. News*, **29**, 3368, 3470, 3876, 4003, 4182, 4184, 4289, 4693, 5163; **30**, 178.

American Institute of Chemical Engineers lists in each January issue of *Chemical and Engineering Progress* since 1952 Ph.D. theses in chemical engineering granted during the prior year. List is classified by subject and includes information on length and where copies can be obtained.

Association of Research Libraries, "Doctoral Dissertations Accepted by American Universities," H. W. Wilson, New York, 1933–57. Gives titles of dissertations; appendix shows which publications of universities in the United States contain abstracts. Information on availability of photoprints and microfilms is listed. Absorbed in 1957 by *Dissertation Abstracts.*

Bledsoe, B., editor, "Master's Theses in Science, 1952," Biblio Press, Washington, D. C., 1954.

Bolton, H. C., "Selected Bibliography of Chemistry," Smithsonian Institution, Washington, D. C., 1901–1904. Section 8 lists United States dissertations.

Danton, J. P., and Tauber, M. F., editors, "Graduate Theses and Dissertations, 1894–1940," Sullivan Memorial Library, Temple University, Philadelphia, 1940.

Engineering College Research Council, American Society for Engineering Education, "Engineering College Research Review," 9th edition, Urbana, Ill., 1959. First edition published 1944 as "Directory of Member Institutions and Their Principal Fields of Research." Biennial.

Library of Congress, "List of American Doctoral Dissertations Printed in 1912–1938," Government Printing Office, Washington, D. C., 1913–1940. Includes only printed academic dissertations received by the Library of Congress. Most dissertations are unpublished; some are in journal reprint form, others are mimeographed copies.

National Academy of Sciences–National Research Council, "Doctorates conferred in Chemistry by American Universities, 1922–1925," *J. Chem. Educ.*, **3**, 77–99 (1956).

National Academy of Sciences–National Research Council, "Doctorates Conferred in Medical Sciences by American Universities, 1922–1925," *Arch. Pathol. Lab. Med.*, **1**, 259–62 (1926). Lists many dissertations in biochemistry.

National Academy of Sciences–National Research Council, Research Information Service, "Doctorates Conferred in Science by American Universities," Reprint and Circular Series, **12** (1919–1920); **26** (1920–1921); **42** (1921–1922); **75** (1925–1926); **80** (1926–1927); **86** (1927–1928); **91** (1928–1929); **95** (1929–1930); **101** (1930–1931); **104** (1931–1932); **105** (1932–1933).

National Academy of Sciences–National Research Council, Office of Scientific Personnel, "Doctorate Production in United States Universities, 1936–56, with Baccalaureate Origins of Doctorates in Sciences, Arts, and Humanities," Publication 582, Washington, D. C., 1958.

Palfrey, T. R., and Coleman, H. E., "Guide to Bibliographies of Theses, United States and Canada," 2nd ed., American Library Association, Chicago, 1940. Most of the theses listed are unpublished M. A. theses.

Rosenberg, R. P., "Bibliography on Theses in America," *Bull. Bibliography*, **18**, 181, 203 (1946). Additions to and corrections of Palfrey and Coleman, listed above.

Sampey, J. R., "Chemical Research in Liberal Arts Colleges, 1952–1959," *J. Chem. Educ.*, **37**, 316 (1960).

Trytten, M. H., and Harmon, L. R., "Doctorate Production in U. S. Universities 1936 to 1956 with Baccalaureate Origins of Doctorates in Sciences, Arts, and

Humanities." Publication 582, National Academy of Sciences–National Research Council, Washington, D. C., 1958. Includes all fields in which third level research degrees are granted.

University of Michigan, "Microfilm Abstracts"; a collection of abstracts of doctoral dissertations and monographs available in complete form on microfilm, University Microfilms, Ann Arbor, Mich., 1939–1948. Issued irregularly during this period.

"Doctorates Conferred in Sciences by American Universities." Published annually in *Science,* 1898–1915. Published in *School and Society,* 1916.

2. **Lists for Individual Institutions.**

Annual listings of academic dissertations accepted and issued by universities have not gained wide circulation. Indeed, their inclusion in standard indexing and abstracting tools is somewhat of a chance matter. These annual listings are sometimes published in book form, more often in pamphlet form, and sometimes in form of an article in an education journal, a society journal, or a university periodical. Whatever the case may be, the circulation of these lists is most often limited.

If one is interested in reviewing academic dissertations coming from a specific source, it is useful to know certain general bibliographic aids through which one can determine which university publications list dissertatons or abstracts. Bibliographies of dissertations can also be traced by the use of such general tools (*1–3, 8, 9, 13, 16*). Some listings of academic dissertations of individual institutions can be traced through standard indexing tools in chemical and applied sciences.

California

California State College, "Master of Arts and Master of Science Theses and Projects, 1950–57 (proc.)," San Diego State College Library, San Diego, Calif., 1959.

Stanford University, "Abstracts of Dissertations," Stanford University Libraries, Stanford, Calif., issued annually.

Iowa

University of Iowa, "Doctoral Dissertations: Abstracts and References" (1937–1939), University of Iowa Press, Iowa City, Iowa. Intended as an annual listing. Title varies—often issued as "Graduate Theses." Usually listed as an issue of *Aims and Progress of Research;* 1939 listing appeared in 1943.

Massachusetts

Massachusetts Institute of Technology, "Publications of the Institute and Theses for Advanced Degrees for the Year Ending June 30, 1959," Cambridge, Mass., 1959.

Minnesota

University of Minnesota, "Register of Ph.D. Degrees Conferred by the University of Minnesota, 1888 through June, 1938," *Univ. Minnesota Bull.* **42,** No. 31, 1–276 (1939).

Nebraska

University of Nebraska, "*Abstracts of Doctoral Dissertations, 1941,*" Lincoln, Neb., 1942.

New York

Sabine, G. H., editor, "Abstracts of Theses Accepted in Partial Satisfaction of the Requirements for the Doctor's Degree, 1940," Cornell University Press, Ithaca, N. Y., 1941. List of titles of theses accepted in 1940 for the master's degree is appended.

North Carolina

Cantrell, C. H., editor, "Graduate Degrees Awarded and Titles of Theses, 1894–1940," D. H. Hill Library, North Carolina State College of Agriculture and Engineering, University of North Carolina, Raleigh, N. C., 1941.

Ohio

Ohio State University, "Abstracts of Dissertations Presented by Candidates for the Degree of Doctor of Philosophy, Autumn Quarter, Winter Quarter, 1940–1941," Graduate School, Ohio State University, Columbus, Ohio, 1941.

Ohio University Graduate College, "Abstracts of Masters' Theses," Ohio University, Athens, Ohio, 1958.

Pennsylvania

Ruffin, B., editor, "Graduate Theses and Dissertations, 1892–1937" (Library Studies No. 1), Pennsylvania State College Library, State College, Pa., 1938.

University of Pennsylvania, graduation programs (winter and spring) carry titles of theses with names of graduates.

Virginia

University of Virginia, "Abstracts of Dissertations Accepted in Partial Fulfillment of the Requirements for the Degree of Doctor of Philosophy, 1945–1947," University of Virginia, Charlottesville, Va., 1948.

Washington

University of Washington, "Abstracts of Theses, Faculty Bibliography, and Research Progress," 1937–1941, Seattle, Wash.

Wisconsin

University of Wisconsin, "Summaries of Doctoral Dissertations, July 1938–June 1939," Madison, Wis., 1940.

3. **Lists in Specialized Areas.**

In some fields of the natural sciences, individual listings are published annually. The field of chemical engineering is noteworthy (5).

Accessibility of Academic Dissertations

After selectively searching through one, several, or all of the tools listing academic dissertations, and exhausting task in itself, one is faced with the problem of obtaining a copy of individual theses which seem of interest. Unfortunately, no library in the United States has a complete file of dissertations from American colleges and universities. It is known that the library of the institution where the degree was earned holds a copy of the dissertation. Occasionally, one may borrow the thesis through a library. If such an arrangement cannot be set up, it is sometimes possible to find a nearby library with the specified thesis in its collection, because many American universities exchange dissertations and have built up large collections of material from different universities.

If one tries to get a dissertation issued by an American university during the period prior to 1947, one may be able to trace it through use of *Special Library Resources* (*15*) which surveys collections of dissertations in research libraries in the United States and Canada.

But the problems of locating and referring to dissertations prepared in universities in this country are small, compared to those concerned with foreign dissertations. *Special Library Resources* sometimes lists the number of foreign dissertations in the collection of a particular research library, but that is all. Some universities have foreign dissertations in their collections, but there are no published listings of these holdings. The accessibility of university thesis literature in the United States, Great Britain, and France has been studied and the surveys published (*1, 4, 6, 12*). An international depository of dissertations would be a help, but it does not exist. There are some national centers; France has her Bibliothèque Nationale in Paris, and Germany had a collection at the University of Berlin. The currency of these collections is now questionable. The collection of the Bibliothèque Nationale is increased by an active exchange system carried out by the French Ministry of Education. There are collections—incomplete, to be sure—in government libraries in Washington, D. C., the British Museum, and Oxford University, England. If a dissertation is located, an interlibrary loan or a photoprint can be obtained.

Once in a while time can be saved in obtaining copies of academic dissertations by operating through documentation centers. There is no international cooperation, and the organization of these centers is such that services are limited, but they may help. Any one of the following centers might provide needed service: The American Documentation Institute, Washington, D. C.; The Chemical Society, London; Department of Scientific and Industrial Research, London; Association of Special Libraries and Information Bureaux, London; Centre National de Recherche Scientifique, Paris; UNESCO Library, Paris; Specia, Paris; Société de Chimie Industrielle, Paris; Netherlands Instituut voor Documentatie en Registratuur, The Hague; Consiglio Nazionale delle Ricerche, Rome; Kekulé Bibliothek, Farbenfabriken Bayer, Leverkusen; Deutsche Gesellschaft für Dokumentation, Frankfurt am Main.

An international listing and depository would help, to be sure, but the world situation would indicate that there is much to be desired where international cooperation is concerned. Such international cooperation is not too much to hope for, but immediate success in such a venture is not likely. It is apparent that thesis literature seldom appears in bibliographies appended to research reports because academic dissertations are not readily accessible even in this country. The academy of science of an individual country may be able to help in tracing theses. It is well to be aware of the activities of the academies in various countries. In 1956, A. Vucinich, San Jose State College, described the Soviet Academy of Sciences which had been reorganized with the aim of centralizing scientific research (*16*).

Reports for Limited Circulation

Academic dissertations are presumably traceable and available with more or less difficulty. There are other unpublished literature materials which may contribute to research in progress and which should be considered by the searcher for reported data. Unclassified reports of the Atomic Energy Commission are conspicuous examples of limited circulation reports. They no longer require security control and their titles are published in lists of documents by the Atomic Energy Commission, available through the Office of Technical Service, U. S. Department of Commerce, and the Government Printing Office. *Nuclear Science Abstracts,* issued monthly, not only lists titles but provides abstracts of the literature on nuclear science and engineering as well as immediate and detailed indexes to that literature. *Nuclear Science Abstracts* covers: (1) research reports of the United States Atomic Energy Commission and its contractors; (2) research reports of government agencies, universities, and industrial research organizations on a world-wide basis; and (3) translations, patents, books, and articles appearing in technical and scientific journals.

Consultant groups run surveys for industrial organizations. Often these surveys are later made available to interested subscribers. The economic surveys of Arthur D. Little, Inc., Stanford Research Institute, Foster D. Snell, Roger Williams, and other consultants are noteworthy.

Scholarly societies and societies in the applied sciences often issue reports to member organizations or individuals. These reports are usually published later, but one can often make use of data prior to publication. It is useful to consult the National Research Council's "Scientific and Technical Societies of the United States" (*11*) for subjects when searching for the name of societies in a particular field. "The Encyclopedia of American Associations" is also a helpful tool.

Reports for Very Limited Circulation

It is well not to overlook checking what has been done within one's own organization on the problem in question. It is helpful to have a good data department at one's disposal, one which has all company reports and correspondence carefully and assiduously indexed. At any rate, company report files should be considered as sources of time-saving data. One cannot just trust Miss Typewriter's memory, even though she has been secretary to the director of research since the opening of the research division, or Joe's recollections, although he has been the most respected research scientist in the research division as far back as anyone can remember.

Scientific Meetings

The value of programs presented at scientific meetings has been discussed *ad infinitum*. They are undeniably valuable and can be used in a number of ways.

The program, listed prior to the meeting, enables one to review paper titles and request preprints. Here, at last, is a source of unpublished data which is painless. Abstracts of meeting papers provide a more detailed insight into the papers to be presented and like preprints can be used as a basis to gage whether attendance at meetings will be desirable. Attendance has added advantages over and beyond reading a copy of the paper. Discussion periods usually follow presentation of papers and they are seldom incorporated in the published paper. It is possible that valuable information may be brought to light in such discussion.

Scientific meetings bring together people who are working in the same and allied fields. General and specific discussion among such individuals can be invaluable in bringing to light solutions to old problems, and, indeed, in stimulating new ideas.

Even when scientists are unable to attend meetings, they may review abstracts of meeting papers before or after meetings. Several divisions of the American Chemical Society issue preprints of meeting papers. The Federation of American Societies for Experimental Biology issues extensive abstracts prior to annual meetings. Preprints and abstracts of meeting papers of these and other societies are a source of research information which may not be published anywhere else.

It is well to remember the fact that published reports of research are not the only source of valuable literature. Each situation demands individual attention. The amount of time spent in searching out unpublished literature will depend upon the specific case in point. The important thing, it would seem, is to be aware of all possible sources of literature and then make use of them selectively, depending on the individual circumstance.

In conclusion, we have many sources of unpublished data which are important in literature searching. In many instances, this searching will be time-consuming and unrewarding and many times not worth the effort.

These considerations recall another value of unpublished literature not considered as data. This value is as a source of thoughts and ideas. Even a superficial look into the use of unpublished writings for ideas is an interesting one—think of folklore. But this is a topic beyond the scope of this discussion.

Bibliography

(1) American Council on Education, Washington, D. C., "Universities of the World Outside of U.S.A.," 1950.
(2) Basterman, T., "A World List of Bibliographies," 2nd ed., Oxford University Press, London, 1947–1949.
(3) *Bibliographic Index,* H. W. Wilson, New York, 1938+.
(4) Cain, J., *ASLIB* (Association of Special Libraries and Information Bureaux, London) **1939,** 35. Thesis literature in France.
(5) *Chem. Eng. Progr.* **57,** 81–84 (1961). Research roundup for 1960.
(6) Davis, W., *ASLIB* **1939,** 31–34. "Accessibility of thesis literature of the United States."
(7) Dawley, E. R., *J. Chem. Educ.* **29,** 902–7 (1939). Undergraduate theses as a means of developing research initiative among faculty and students.
(8) *Education Index,* H. W. Wilson, New York, 1929+.
(9) Gale Research Co., Detroit, Mich., "Encyclopedia of American Associations," 2nd ed., 1959.
(10) *Library Literature,* H. W Wilson, New York, 1921+.
(11) National Academy of Science–National Research Council, "Scientific and Technical Societies of the United States and Canada," 7th ed., National Research Council, Washington, D. C., 1961.
(12) Newcombe, L., Pafford, J. H. P., *J. Document.* **7,** 119–22 (1951). University theses; review of accessibility of British university thesis literature.
(13) Robinson, R., *Chem. & Ind.* (London) **26,** 1094–101 (Sept. 3, 1955). Science and the scientist.
(14) Schneider, G., "Handbuch der Bibliographie," 4th ed. pp. 422–37, Hiersmann, Leipzig, 1937.
(15) Special Library Association, New York, "Special Library Resources," 4 vols., 1941–1947.
(16) Vucinich, A., "The Soviet Academy of Sciences," Hoover Institute Studies, Series E.: Institutions, No. **3,** Stanford University Press, Stanford, Calif., 1956.
(17) Winchell, C. M., "Guide to Reference Books," 7th ed., American Library Association, Chicago, 1951; 1st suppl. (1950–1952) 1954; 2nd suppl. (1953–1955) 1956; 3rd suppl. (1956–1958) 1960.

BASED on paper presented before Division of Chemical Literature, Symposium on Searching the Chemical Literature, 130th Meeting, ACS, Atlantic City, N. J., September 1956. Revised 1960.

Searching Medicinal Chemical Literature

C. R. ADDINALL and P. G. STECHER
Merck & Co., Inc., Rahway, N. J.

The technical information department of the research and development division of a manufacturer of fine chemicals has many interesting problems in searching for information in the medicinal chemical literature and that of pertinent and allied fields. Three such representative problems have been selected for presentation.

Knowledge of somewhat obscure sources of botanical drug information is necessary in answering such queries as those concerned with a folk remedy known only by its vernacular name, the determination of the scientific nomenclature of a popular plant name in some dialect or foreign language, the active pharmacological principles of a specific drug, or the occurrence in plant materials of certain active principles of a predetermined chemical or biological character.

Searching the Botanical Drug Literature

Many suggestions of folk remedies known only by vernacular names have been inspired by awakened interest in synthetic organicals with activity in the treatment of rheumatoid arthritis. One such example was the report that a local drug named *bawang* is valued in the Philippines for the treatment of rheumatism. Books have been published on the folk remedies of almost every country and geographical area in the world, and the Philippines are no exception. In 1901, Tavero (*15*) published an interesting but now out-of-date volume on the medicinal plants of the Philippines. Often an old compilation of this kind is far more valuable for such a search than new publications written when the old knowledge is lost in the splendor of the new, and for this reason they should be jealously guarded and treasured. In Tavero's work *bawang*, under a slightly different spelling, is described, and the miracle drug is exposed as ordinary garlic.

Often, however, the information available is so indefinite that the search is hopeless from the beginning. The folklore that rheumatism can be cured by infusion of "rheumatism root" or "rheumatism weed" suggests the identification of this herb with a view to further investigation. Clute (*3*) has listed all such vernacular descriptive plant designations. Rheumatism root may be *Chelone glabra* (Scrophulariaceae), *Chimaphila maculata* (Ericaceae), *Apocynum cannabinum* (Apocynaceae), *Jeffersonia diphylla* (Berberidaceae), or even *Dioscorea villosa* (Dioscoreaceae), whereas the name rheumatism weed has been assigned to another species of *Apocynum.*

Clute's invaluable compilation is restricted to American usage. There are, however, many polyglot compilations of this type. Thus, in Lyons' book (*9*), Latin, English, French, German, and Spanish are represented. Even more comprehensive is the illustrated polyglotic dictionary by Bedevian (*1*).

After definite identification of a supposed drug plant, it is necessary to determine the active principles known to occur in the drug and to consider the known biological activity of these principles with reference to the alleged curative properties. For such a search Wehmer's three-volume work (*16*) is invaluable. In condensed style, consisting mainly of literature references and cross references, this magnificent compilation lists the content of plants and the source of the information. Thus (Volume 1, page 327), *Jeffersonia diphylla,* one of the above-mentioned rheumatism roots, contains berberine, as was shown by Gordin (*5*). Wehmer covers the literature up to 1934 only and a similar up-to-date compilation would be a welcome addition to the library files.

Wehmer also gives preliminary answers to the question of what species might be suitable sources of a definite compound or product—the type of question that arises when substitute raw materials must be found in times of economic stress or dislocation. Thus, he gives 31 references to the occurrence of berberine in different plants. Apart from sources familiar to all chemists, such as abstract journals, additional references for information of this type can be found in monographs on alkaloids (*6, 12*).

Considerably more difficult than the search for a definite compound such as berberine is that for plants yielding a material with given definite biological activity, because the required effect may be provided by various substances of like or unlike chemical nature. Thus, compiling a list of drug plants having digitalis-like physiological activity might be required. Much preliminary information can be gleaned from texts dealing with the chemical class of compound under investigation. Its steroid and glycosidal nature suggests a study of the many available texts on steroids, particularly that by Fieser and Fieser (*4*) and of monographs on glycosides (*14*) or the chapter on glycosides by Lebeau and Courtois (*7*). In continuation of the search, reference would then be made to books on medicinal plants with indexes of therapeutic applications. Thus, Madaus (*11*) lists seven species alleged to have digitalis-like action on the heart, one such plant being the beautiful mountain laurel, *Kalmia latifolia* L. Finally, purely medical compilations will be consulted. Thus, the "Cumulative Quarterly Index Medicus" lists numerous papers on "heart insufficiency" and some of these deal with vegetable drugs other than those of the digitalis species. Sufficient information, however, may be gleaned to round out this most difficult of all searches into the botanical drug literature.

Interpreting the Foreign Prescription

The postwar scarcity of drugs in Europe, particularly of previously well-established specialties of the prewar drug concerns, the shifting of large populations, and the entry of many displaced persons into the United States made the tracking down and identification of prescription specialties, and of chemicals indicated in obscurely written foreign prescriptions, a matter of much concern and significance.

As many European countries do not insist on prescription forms with printed letterheads, initial difficulty in deciphering the text prior to its translation may be due to doubt as to the country of origin. Once a clear text has been obtained, the problems that interest the worker in the chemical literature field are mainly those of the identification of a European specialty or drug, the establishment of its correct chemical name, and the identification of its American equivalent. To illustrate these problems, a recent Polish prescription is given:

Asthma! 7–1–49r
Rp.
Coramini liq. 50,0

Jurasthmol, scat. orig. VI

Dehydrit vel Euphyllin, amp XV
Ad manus medici!
Dr. Adelmann

Because this prescription for asthma is Polish in origin (as suggested by the date line), the European specialties prescribed must be sought in the various excellent repertoria and codices of medicinal drugs. According to Ludwig (*8*), Coramin (Ciba) (pyridin-β-karbonsäure-diäthylamid) is made available in Europe as a 25% aqueous solution for oral use. In the index of *Chemical Abstracts* Coramine is listed under *N,N*-diethylnicotinamide, and from "New and Nonofficial Remedies" we learn that the compound is officially designated as Nikethamide in the United States and is sold by numerous companies under the official designation "Solution Nikethamide 25% w/v."

Although the index of *Chemical Abstracts* is extremely helpful in giving the chemical name of Coramine and thus immediately making the search for an American equivalent of the European drug relatively simple, it would not have been so simple to identify the well known drug, Caronamide (now Carinamide®). In the index to *Chemical Abstracts,* Volume 42 (1948), several references are given under the heading Caronamide. The same references are given under the heading Benzoic acid, *p*-(benzylsulfonamido), but the references are not cross-indexed.

According to Bernoulli and Lehmann (*2*), Jurasthmol is a powder for the treatment of bronchial asthma and contains antipyrine, acetanilide, citrated caffeine, and lobeline sulfate, together with minute amounts of digitalin and strophanthin. By reference to the "Modern Drug Encyclopedia" (*13*), the pharmacist can select a corresponding American proprietary remedy and adjust the prescription to fit the number of powders to the requirement of the demand for six original packages (of 15 powders each).

The Polish proprietary medicine Dehydrit is described in Gehe's Codex (3rd supplement, 1950) as the sodium salt of *o*-[(3-hydroxymercuri-2-methoxypropyl) carbamyl]phenoxyacetic acid dissolved in aqueous theophylline solution. This preparation is known in the U. S. Pharmacopeia as Mersalyl and theophylline injection, and in the U. S. Dispensatory (page 700, 24th edition) the pharmacist is informed of the United States equivalent in the form of Salyrgan-Theophylline Ampuls (Winthrop).

The compendia cited give the composition of drugs and the chemical identity of their ingredients. Especially useful for this purpose are "The American Drug Index" and "The Merck Index," the latter being international in scope.

Another source is the monthly publication *Unlisted Drugs,* edited by the Pharmaceutical Section of the Special Libraries Association. This listing attempts to be truly international in scope and has become a trustworthy tool for workers in the field of medicinal chemical literature whose labors carry them into the field of prescription translation.

Identifying Merck References

A somewhat difficult problem encountered by librarians of pharmaceutical houses and other institutions concerned with research on medicinal problems is that of tracing and identifying references to Merck literature.

Heinrich Emanuel Merck, intimate friend of Justus von Liebig, and founder of the first factory of the enterprise, E. Merck, Darmstadt (Germany), had as his main objective the preparation of pure alkaloids. His many achievements included the original commercial manufacture of morphine (1827), codeine (1836), and cocaine (1862).

Following the scientific tradition established by the founder, the Chemical Works of E. Merck, Darmstadt, up to the beginning of World War II, serially issued various types of pharmaceutical publications including, among others, the following important reference material:

"*E. Merck's Jahresbericht*" (1887–1946; Vols. 1 to 60). In German, though some early issues appeared in English. Originally intended as a report on E. Merck's products, it began publication of original communications on natural products with the article "Neue Alkaloide aus Sabadillsamen," Vol. 4 (1890). Contains many valuable communications, particularly on alkaloidal investigations, not elsewhere available.

"E. Merck's Annual Report on the Advancements of Pharmaceutical Chemistry and Therapeutics" (1887–1940). English, French, Spanish, Portuguese, and Italian (1930) editions. Contains original articles of general and scientific interest, a pharmacotherapeutic review, and medical opinions regarding E. Merck products. Originally a translation of *E. Merck's Jahresbericht* but later a different and more popular publication.

"E. Merck's Wissenschaftliche Abhandlungen aus den Gebieten der Pharmakotherapie, Pharmazie und verwandter Disziplinen" (Nos. 1–42; 1890–1929). No translations or foreign editions known. Published to provide the busy practitioner with information not readily available in the international literature concerning old and new therapeutic or diagnostic useful preparations. Includes monograph No. 22, "Nicht offizinelle Alkaloide" (480 pages).

"Merck's Index" [1897, 1902, 1910, 1914 (in French), 1927, 1928 (in 1930 in Spanish), 1935 (in French)]. A collective index of preparations, drugs, and minerals listed by E. Merck with descriptions of their chemical composition, physical properties, and medical, technical, and other uses.

"Merck's Reagenzien-Verzeichnis" (1903, 1907, 1913. 1916, 1924, 1928, 1932, 1936), in German. Useful reagents and reactions listed according to author's name. Afterwards appeared serially in translation in American Merck's Report and Merck Report and reproduced in Merck Index (5th edition).

The American house of Merck, established in 1887 in New York and organized in 1891 as Merck & Co. by George Merck, grandson of Heinrich Emanuel Merck, was incorporated in 1908 in New York and in 1919 became an independent American enterprise, consolidated with Powers-Weightman-Rosengarten Co. of Philadelphia, Pa., in 1927 to form Merck & Co., Inc.

During the gradual development from an offshoot of E. Merck, Darmstadt, to the present independent American corporation, the enterprise published works with titles originally identical and later more or less similar to those of the publications of E. Merck, Darmstadt. In the course of time, these publications became entirely different and individually distinct works. A brief résumé is accordingly given of the publications of Merck & Co. and of Merck & Co., Inc., to lighten the difficulties arising from the similarity of their titles to those of the original and often contemporaneous publications of the entirely distinct German organization.

Merck's Bulletin (Merck & Co., 1888–1891). A periodical record of new discoveries, introductions, or applications of medicinal chemicals.

Merck's Archives of the Materia Medica and Its Uses (Merck & Co., 1899–1901; Vols. 1–3).

The Merck Report (1892–, issued quarterly). *Merck's Market Report and Pharmaceutical Journal* (Merck & Co.), (1892–96; Vols. I to V). *Merck's Report* (Merck & Co., 1897–1927; Merck & Co., Inc., 1927–34). A practical journal of pharmacy, materia medica, and chemistry, with a section of each quarterly devoted to current price lists. *The Merck Report* (Merck & Co., Inc., 1934–, Vol. 43–). For many years Theo. Holm contributed a series of articles on "Medicinal Plants of North America" with figures drawn from nature. This extensive series, covering 99 plants, has never been reproduced elsewhere and is often cited by botanists and pharmacognosists.

"The Merck Index." First American edition (E. Merck, 1889); Merck's 1896 Index (Merck & Co.); Merck's 1907 Index (Merck & Co.); Merck's Index, 4th ed. (Merck & Co., Inc., 1930); The Merck Index, 5th ed. (Merck & Co., Inc., 1940); The Merck Index, 6th ed. (Merck & Co., Inc., 1952); The Merck Index 7th ed. (Merck & Co., Inc., 1960). An encyclopedia for the chemist, pharmacist, physician, dentist, and veterinarian.

"The Merck Manual." "Merck's Manual of Materia Medica" (1st English ed., E. Merck, 1899); "Merck's 1901 Manual" (Merck & Co.); "Merck's Manual" (Merck & Co., 1905, 1911, and 1923); "The Merck Manual" (Merck & Co., Inc., 1934, 1940, 1950, 1956; 6th, 7th, 8th, and 9th eds.). First five editions were counterparts of the original first English edition prepared for British physicians. No German edition seems to exist and no translation of the original E. Merck publication of 1899 is known. In 1934, "The Merck Manual" appeared as a newly revised sixth edition, and extensive revision and enlargements were continued in the subsequent editions.

Conclusions

Although the problems discussed are but a few of those facing workers in the literature of the fine chemical field, they are probably of concern to many others because of the widespread interest due to recent advances in medicinal chemistry. The discussion of the Merck literature seems of particular importance at this time, because no study has previously been published of this source of so many papers in the fields of alkaloid chemistry, pharmacognosy, and related disciplines.

Bibliography of Drug Compendia

American Drug Index, C. O. Wilson and T. E. Jones, eds., Lippincott, Philadelphia. Published annually.

"American Druggist Blue Book," American Druggist, 250 West 55th St., New York 19, N. Y. Published every spring.

"Apotekens Register över Standardförpackade Läkemedel," Apotekarsocietetens Informationsavdelning, Stockholm, Sweden. Published annually.

"Apotekens Specialitetsregister," Apotekens Kontrol-laboratorium, Kronobergsgatan 27, Stockholm, Sweden. Published annually.

"Austria Codex," Österreichischer Apothekenverlag, Vienna IX, Austria, 1959.

Bernoulli, E., Lehmann, H., "Übersicht der gebräuchlichen und neueren Arzneimittel," 9th Auflage, Benno Schwabe & Co., Basel, Switzerland, 1959. 555 pages. Revised every 2 to 3 years.

Council on Pharmacy and Chemistry, American Medical Association, "New and Nonofficial Drugs," J. B. Lippincott Co., Philadelphia, Pa. Annual publication containing descriptions of articles accepted by council.

"Drug Topics Red Book," Topics Publishing Co., Inc., 10 East 15th St., New York 3, N. Y. Published annually.

Fumi, R., "Repertorio Terapeutico" (Elenco Generale delle Specialità Medicinali Commerciale in Italia), Aracne, Milan, Italy. Annual publication.

"Gehes Codex der pharmazeutischen Spezialpräparate mit Angaben über Zusammensetzung, Indikationen, Zubereitungsformen und Hersteller." 9th edition. Wissenschaftliche Verlagsgesellschaft, Stuttgart, 1960.

Helwig, B., "Moderne Arzneimittel," Wissenschaftliche Verlagsgesellschaft, Stuttgart, 1956. 772 pages. Supplement 1958.

Jalander, Y. W., Helsinki, Finland, "Farmaseutisia ja kemiallisia Synonymeja," 1948. 570 pages plus 1949 supplement of 47 pages.

Kaplan, A., "Manual de Especialidades Medicinales," Lopez & Etchegoyen, S.R.L., Junin 863, Buenos Aires, 1951. 777 pages and supplements.

Ludwig, H., "Repertorium pharmazeutischer Spezialpräparate, Sera und Impfstoffe," 1st Ausgabe, Verlagsgesellschaft Beobachter A.G., Basel, Switzerland, 1946. 1308 pages. Supplement, Ausgabe 1947, 331 pages. 2nd supplement, 1950.

Martindale, "The Extra Pharmacopoeia," Vol. I, 24th edition, 1958; Vol. II, 23rd edition, 1955. Pharmaceutical Press, 17 Bloomsbury Square, London W.C. 1.
"The Merck Index," P. G. Stecher, M. J. Finkel, O. H. Siegmund, B. M. Szafranski, eds., 7th ed., Merck & Co., Inc., Rahway, N. J., 1960. 1642 pages.
"Modern Drug Encyclopedia and Therapeutic Index," 7th ed., Drug Publications, Inc., 11 East 36th St., New York 16, N. Y. Published every 3 years. Publishers issue supplementary service every 2 months under title of "Modern Drugs," which contains descriptions of new preparations as they appear on the market.
Negwer, M., "Organisch-Chemische Arzneimittel und ihre Synonyma," Akademie-Verlag, Berlin, 1959.
"Österreichisches Spezialitätenverzeichnis," Hauptverband der österreichischen Sozialversicherungsträger, Hegelgasse 8, Vienna.
Osol, A., *et al.*, "Dispensatory of the United States of America," 25th ed., J. B. Lippincott Co., Philadelphia, 1955. 2134 pages.
"Physicians' Desk Reference to Pharmaceutical Specialties and Biologicals," Medical Economics, Inc., Oradell, N. J. Published annually.
"Rote Liste Verzeichnis pharmazeutscher Spezialpräparate," Herausgeber: "Bundesverband der Pharmazeutische Industrie," Editio Cantor, Aulendorf in Württemberg, Germany.
Vidal, L., "Dictionnaire des spécialités pharmaceutiques," Office de Vulgarisation pharmaceutique, 11, rue Quentin-Bauchart, Paris (VIIIe). Published annually.

Literature Cited

(1) Bedevian, A. K., "Illustrated Polyglotic Dictionary of Plant Names in the Latin, Arabic, Armenian, English, French, German, Italian, and Turkish Languages," Cairo, Egypt, 1936. Published by the author, represented in the United States exclusively by Stechert-Hafner, Inc., 31 East 10th St., New York 3, N. Y.
(2) Bernoulli, E., Lehmann, H., "Übersicht der Gebräuchlichen und Neueren Arzneimittel," Benno Schwabe & Co., Basel, 1959.
(3) Clute, W. N., "American Plant Names," Willard N. Clute & Co., Indianapolis, Ind., 1940.
(4) Fieser, L. F., Fieser, M., "Chemistry of Natural Products Related to Phenanthrene," 3rd ed., Reinhold, New York, 1949. New edition named "Steroids" (1959) omits phenanthrene.
(5) Gordin, H. M., *Arch. Pharm.* **239**, 638 (1901).
(6) Henry T. A., "Plant Alkaloids," 4th ed., J. & A. Churchill, London, 1949.
(7) Lebeau, P., Courtois, G., "Traité de Pharmacie chimique," 4th ed., Masson & Cie., Paris, 1955–56. 5 vols.
(8) Ludwig, H., "Repertorium pharmazeutischer Spezialpräparate," Verlagsgesellschaft Beobachter A.G., Basel, Switzerland, 1946. 2 supplements, 1947 and 1950.
(9) Lyons, A. B., "Plant Names, Scientific and Popular," Nelson, Baker & Co., Detroit, Mich, 1900.
(10) McIlroy, R. J., "The Plant Glycosides," Edwin Arnold, London, 1951.
(11) Madaus, Gerhard, "Lehrbuch der biologischen Heilmittel," G. Thieme, Leipzig, 1938.
(12) Manske, R. H. F., Holmes, H. L., "The Alkaloids," Academic Press, New York, 1949–55. 5 vols. Two supplemental vols. published in 1960.
(13) "Modern Drug Encyclopedia." See above bibliography.
(14) Rijn, J. J. L. van, "Die Glykoside," Gebrüder Borntraeger, Berlin, 1931.
(15) Tavero, Pardo de, "Medicinal Plants of the Philippines," Blakiston's, Philadelphia, 1901.
(16) Wehmer, C., "Die Pflanzenstoffe," Gustav Fischer, Jena, J. W. Edwards, Ann Arbor, Mich., 1946 (reprint).

Based on paper presented before the Division of Chemical Literature, Symposium on Searching the Chemical Literature, 117th Meeting, ACS, Detroit, Mich., April 1950. Revised 1960.

House Organs and Trade Publications as Information Sources

ELLA MAE BAER and HERMAN SKOLNIK

Research Center, Hercules Powder Co., Wilmington, Del.

House organs and trade publications are a large and important body of useful information, much of which is not duplicated elsewhere. Although their primary objective is to sell products or enhance prestige, they are an excellent source of the latest technical information on specifications, physical and physiological properties, reactions, and uses of commercial chemicals. The chief problems associated with this literature are how to get it and how to handle it. Several solutions to these and other problems are suggested. A list of house organs of interest to the chemical industry is given.

House organs and trade publications lie within the uncharted area of chemical literature. House organs have the appearance and many of the characteristics of journals. They are, with few exceptions such as *Chemist Analyst*, not considered technical periodicals by abstracting services or journals (*3, 6, 13, 14*). By and large, therefore, the monthly printing of an estimated 50,000,000 copies of the many house organs issued by nearly 6000 American companies is a flood without a Noah's Ark (*9*). Even within the category of chemical industry, there is no established service specifically designed to cover the information aspect of house organs. Compounding this flood is a tidal wave of trade publications advertising and promoting the thousands of products of American industry. This paper discusses these two types of industrial publications.

Purpose of House Organs and Trade Publications

First, let us consider what house organs and trade publications are. Their primary objective is to sell products. They are a method of selling by providing a point of contact with a prospective customer. This point of contact, if successful, provides the prospective customer with information. In this sense, house organs and trade publications must be considered as advertisements. Basically, we are concerned with two categories of advertisements: "action" and "good will." The "action advertisement" attempts to induce an immediate response from the reader—to have him make inquiries. Trade publications, in general, and a good share of house organs belong in this category. The "good will advertisement" attempts to instill in the reader a friendly feeling toward, respect for, and confidence in the company and its products. The more elaborate house organs and trade publications belong in this category.

Advertising Viewpoint

From the advertising viewpoint, the information communicated by house organs and trade publications may be classified in four types:

1. **Introduction.** A new product is introduced to possible consumers. Various properties may be listed, and probable uses and applications suggested.
2. **Announcement.** An established product with existing markets is introduced by a company making it for the first time and in competition with established manufacturers. The purpose here is to direct demand to the announced product on the basis of merits, such as purity, and certain advantages, such as technical service facilities and delivery schedules.
3. **Reminder.** This type of information is designed to retain customers and to maintain demand for products. The purpose is to induce action.
4. **Company Prestige.** Publications under this category are commonly known as institutional advertising and have as their primary objective the molding of prestige for, good will toward, and confidence in the company and its products. This type of advertising is the most productive as an information source.

The Information Viewpoint

From the information viewpoint, house organs and trade publications are potentially important sources (*4–8*). Yet many scientists and librarians regard this segment of the chemical literature with the impatience and doubt best described by the doggerel verse:

> So tell me quick and tell me true
> —Or else, my friend, the heck with you!—
> Not what this blasted thing is meant to be
> But what *will the darn thing do for me?*

Suppose we let the answer come from a leading chemical company's advertisement: ". . . technical literature is written to help you . . . technical booklets, for example, are written—and constantly revised—to give you the latest technical information on uses, physical properties, specifications and physiological data" (*2*). Trade publications often are the first publication of data on the properties and applications of commercial products. Many house organs, such as *Research Today,* publish original articles of high scientific merit. Some house organs, such as *The Paper Maker,* are famous for their historical articles. Many analytical procedures and testing methods are first published in house organs. House organs directed to employees constitute an excellent source for learning about companies—their new products, end uses of products, and expansion plans. Information is where you find it, and there's plenty in house organs and trade publications.

The Librarian's Problem

If house organs and trade publications are valuable and important information sources, why have they been relegated to an inconsequential position in so many libraries? The real problems posed by house organs and trade publications are how to get them, and what to do with them once they are received.

There is no agent to whom we can turn for ordering the house organs and trade publications useful in our work. There is no source that will delineate and describe the house organs and trade publications that we might need. It would be impractical, to say the least, to write to every company that publishes house organs and trade publications and ask for everything pouring forth from the printing presses. And, even if we should be so bold, who among us has the time to process the thousands of publications that would be forthcoming?

House organs and trade publications, even when ordered selectively and judiciously, do not constitute an information source until a logical processing system is adopted and a key is provided for the valuable or useful part of the contents.

How to Get House Organs

Our first problem, of course, is how to learn about the house organs of possible interest to our particular needs. Unfortunately, there is no easy answer. There are several directories, however, which we can consult. *Printer's Ink* "Directory of House Organs" lists 6329 house organ titles in its 1954 edition (*10*); but the house organs, listed alphabetically by title and by issuing company, are classified as internal, external, or combined, and not by subject content. Despite the list of 6329 titles, a few excellent house organs—for example, *Chemist Analyst*—are omitted. "House Magazine Directory" (*7*) indexes its listing of 3000 house organs by subject, but from the free lance writer's or editor's viewpoint. Because directories are not published at frequent intervals, they are perforce unreliable to the degree that new house organs appear and established ones leave the scene.

An excellent discussion and evaluation of house organs issued by pharmaceutical companies was published by Maurice (*9*). Lederman's list of house organs of interest to the chemical industry, broken down by subject interest and by type of house organ—for example, review or abstract—provides the chemical field with a nucleus for starting a file of house organs. The list appended to this paper is based on the Lederman list with revision and extensions in several areas.

Another helpful list, given by Royer (*12*), is based on the house organs received by the Technology Division of the Cleveland Public Library. A useful feature of Royer's list is that the house organs which have been of greatest help in answering reference questions are noted with an asterisk.

Other ways by which we can learn of new house organs are good communication among libraries and between librarians and scientists within a given environment. A good system for spotting trade publications also uncovers leads to new house organs.

We should approach the obtaining of house organs, however, with a subdued enthusiasm. There is no merit in obtaining them all. Furthermore, both house organs and trade publications are expensive to produce. Many issuing companies have an understandable reluctance to distribute these publications to "squirrels." On the other hand, they are extremely happy to send them where, from the advertiser's viewpoint, they will do some good.

What to Do with House Organs

The responsibility for obtaining, processing, and circulating house organs should be assigned to a librarian, preferably one educated in the subject knowledge most important to the environment. This qualification is necessary if house organs are to be evaluated against the needs of the scientists served by the library. Placing responsibility on the librarian permits control of the orderly acquisition of all needed house organs through the proper channels of the companies issuing them, and assures the companies issuing house organs that their communications will reach the largest number of people with the fewest number of copies.

Several alternative procedures can be used for processing house organs. Since house organs are serial publications and are usually issued with some degree of regularity, the librarian may categorically treat them as journals. In this event, house organs must be chosen with the same selectivity as journals. Otherwise, journal holdings will be diluted by the house organs and the relative importance of the journals be depreciated by sheer weight of numbers, space requirements in the library, and demand of the librarian's time to process and circulate the collection.

An efficient approach to this problem is to separate the house organs worthy of consideration into those equivalent to journals and those equivalent to trade publications in terms of content. The house organs considered equivalent to journals then should be given the necessary time and attention. They should be included with the journals in evaluation of articles for the internal literature abstracting service and for the file of articles of importance to a company's products, processes, and fields of interest. Retention schedules must be established in much the same manner as for journals. A few house organs will be bound. The important articles in those not bound should, of course, be clipped and retained in some accessible form. House organs adjudged to be equivalent to trade publications should be so treated.

How to Get Trade Publications

If there is a commercial product, there is a trade publication extolling its virtues and usefulness. Among several excellent sources listing manufacturers under product headings and vice versa are:

Chemical Week Buyer's Guide
Oil Paint and Drug Reporter Green Book
Reinhold's Chemical Materials Catalog
Thomas' Register of American Manufacturers

These sources make an effort to cross-refer trade-marks, but not always successfully. However, when a trade-mark is the only fact known, various dictionaries (*1, 5, 11, 16*) and journal articles on specialized fields can be consulted, such as McCutcheon's articles on wetting agents in *Soap and Chemical Specialties,* and the series of articles in *Chemical Week* highlighting selective fields. Many special libraries maintain a file of trade-marks of products important to their particular operations and research. This file obviously would then be the first place to consult to relate a trade-mark to its manufacturer.

There are two ways for keeping up to date on new trade publications. Once you are on the mailing list for such material, the companies issuing the trade publication will automatically send you the new issues and, in some cases, will inform you which ones they supersede. It is not possible nor desirable to be on the mailing list of every company. The best way to be aware of new products and the existence of trade publications describing them is to scan a certain number of trade and technical new journals routinely for advertisements and announcements. The following journals, for example, provide a relatively broad and complete coverage:

Chemical and Engineering News
Chemical Engineering
Chemical Week
Industrial and Engineering Chemistry

What to Do with Trade Publications

As with house organs, the responsibility for obtaining, processing, and circulating trade publications should be assigned to the librarian. In this way we can be assured of a complete file of all needed material and one which is controlled for the best interests of all. A convenient way to file trade publications is by company, and, if necessary, further classification of each company by department or division. To afford the circulation librarian a convenient system for charging out trade publications, each publication of a company should be assigned an accessions number.

Trade publications, on receipt, should be circulated immediately to all those who might have an interest in the products, their uses and applications, and their physical or physiological properties. Those who maintain a trade-mark file should be on the circulation list. If the library issues a list of acquisitions, the trade publications received should be listed in it by company. This is an excellent communication medium for informing many people of the existence of such information.

Generally speaking, there is no need to catalog or index trade publications. Exceptions would be those containing good bibliographies, comprehensive physical or physiological data, or an unusual treatment of chemical reactions not to be found elsewhere. A few trade publications are important enough to be considered as equivalent to books—for example, Wyandotte's "Chlorine" (*15*).

Selected House Organs

The house organs in this list are classified in three general categories: I, those equivalent to journals; II, those containing mainly advertising material; and III, those primarily published for employees and stockholders. The list is submitted as a guide and not as a comprehensive compilation.

Company	*House Organ*	*Frequency of Publication*
	I. Equivalent to Journals	
Abbott Laboratories	*What's New*	Not stated
Allied Chemical and Dye Corp., National Aniline Division	*Dyestuffs*	Quarterly
American Cyanamid	*Cyanograms*	Quarterly
Lederle Laboratory Division	*Lederle Bulletin*	6 issues per year
J. T. Baker Chemical Co.	*Chemist Analyst*	Quarterly
Baldwin-Lima-Hamilton Corp.	*Testing Topics*	Quarterly
Beckman Instruments, Inc., Scientific and Process Instruments Division	*The Analyzer*	Quarterly
Borden Co.	*Borden's Review of Nutrition Research*	Monthly except July and August
Burrell Corp.	*Burrell Announcer*	Not stated
Central Scientific Co.	*Cenco News Chats*	Not stated
Ciba Co., Inc.	*Ciba Review*	Bimonthly
Denver Equipment Co.	*Deco Trefoil*	Bimonthly
Dow Chemical Co.	*Down to Earth*	Not stated
Allen B. Du Mont Laboratories, Inc.	*Du Mont Oscillographer*	Quarterly
E. I. du Pont de Nemours & Co., Inc.	*Agricultural News Letter*	Not stated
Elastomers Division	*Neoprene Notebook*	Quarterly
Eastman Kodak Co.	*Organic Chemical Bulletin*	Not stated
Eberback and Son Co.	*Announcer of Scientific Equipment*	Not stated

Company	*House Organ*	*Frequency of Publication*
	I. Equivalent to Journals (*continued*)	
Esso Standard Oil Co.	*Esso OilWays*	Monthly
Evans Research and Development Corp.	*Research Comments, Facts and Trends*	Not stated
Fisher Scientific Co.	*The Laboratory*	Not stated
Fritzsche Brothers, Inc.	*Fritzsche Library Bulletin*	Monthly
Geigy Chemical Corp.	*Technica*	Not stated
General Mills, Inc.	*Progress Thru Research*	Quarterly
Givaudan-Delawanna, Inc.	*Givaudanian*	Monthly
Givaudan Flavors, Inc., Associated with Givaudan-Delawanna, Inc.	*The Givaudan Flavorist*	Not stated
Hercules Powder Co.	*Explosives Engineer*	Bimonthly
	Hercules Chemist	Not stated
	Paper Maker	Not stated
Imperial Chemical Industries, Ltd.	*Endeavour*	Quarterly
Interchemical Corp., Printing Ink Division	*IPI Quarterly*	Quarterly
International Business Machines Corp.	*IBM Journal of Research and Development*	Quarterly
International Nickel Co.	*Nickel Bulletin*	Monthly
Johnson, Matthey and Co., Ltd.	*Platinum Metals Review*	Quarterly
Eli Lilly and Co.	*Research Today*	Not stated
Arthur D. Little, Inc.	*Industrial Bulletin*	Monthly
LKB-Produkter Fabrieksaktiebolag	*Science Tools*	Not stated
Merck & Co., Inc.	*Merck Report*	Quarterly
Merck, Sharp and Dohme	*Seminar Report*	Not stated
Minneapolis-Honeywell Regulator Co.	*Instrumentation*	Quarterly
Oakite Products, Inc.	*Oakite News Service*	Not stated
Pennsylvania Salt Manufacturing Co.	*Laundry Bundle*	Not stated
Radio Corp. of America	*Electronic Age*	Quarterly
Reichhold Chemicals, Inc.	*By Gum*	Bimonthly
Reynolds Metals Co.	*Aluminum Digest*	Monthly
Rohm and Haas Co.	*Rohm and Haas Reporter*	Bimonthly
Resinous Products Division	*Amber-hi-Lites*	Not stated
E. H. Sargent and Co.	*Scientific Apparatus and Methods*	Not stated
Texas Co.	*Lubrication*	Monthly
Vanadium Corp. of America	*Vancoram Review*	Quarterly
Wallace and Tiernan	*Chlorination Topics*	Not stated
Wallerstein Co., Division of Baxter Laboratories, Inc.	*Wallerstein Laboratories Communications*	Three times a year
West Virginia Pulp and Paper Co.	*Taste and Odor Control Journal*	Monthly
Whitin Machine Works	*Whitin Review*	Not stated
Witco Chemical Co.	*Witcombings*	Not stated
Worthington Corp.	*Power and Fluids*	Quarterly
	Worthite News	Quarterly
Wyeth, Inc.	*Pulse of Pharmacy*	Not stated
	II. Predominantly Advertising	
Acheson Colloids Co.	*Dag Dispersions*	Not stated
Air Reduction, Inc.	*Airco News*	Not stated
American Cyanamid Co.	*Acrylo News*	Not stated
American Instrument Co.	*Aminco Laboratory News*	Not stated
Ansul Chemical Co.	*Ansul News Notes*	Quarterly
Archer-Daniels-Midland Co.	*ADM Kaleidoscope*	Not stated
Armour and Co., Armour Chemical Division	*Ideas in Development*	Not stated
Armstrong Machine Works	*Armstrong Trap Magazine*	Not stated
Atlas Powder Co.	*Chemmunique*	Not stated
Barber-Coleman Co., Wheelco Instruments Division	*Wheelco Comments*	Not stated
Beckman Instruments, Inc.	*Beckman Infrared Notes*	Not stated
	Beckman Bulletin	Not stated
Bensing Brothers and Deeney Sales Co.	*News and Tips*	Monthly

Company	House Organ	Frequency of Publication
II. Predominantly Advertising (*continued*)		
Celanese Corp. of America	*Celanese Plastics*	Monthly
Columbia-Southern Chemical Corp.	*Columbia-Southern Chemicals*	Quarterly
Consolidated Engineering Corp.	*Recordings*	Quarterly
Crown Cork and Seal Co.	*Crown*	Monthly
E. I. du Pont de Nemours & Co., Inc.	*Du Pont Magazine*	Bimonthly
Dyes and Chemicals Division	*Technical Bulletin*	Quarterly
Electrochemicals Dept.	*Modern Metal Finishing*	Not stated
Engineering Dept.	*Engineering News*	Not stated
Fabrics and Finishes Dept.	*Finishes First*	Monthly
Industrial and Biochemicals Dept.	*Chemical Briefs for Industry*	Not stated
Ethyl Corp.	*Ethyl News*	Not stated
Fansteel Metallurgical Corp., Chemical Equipment Division	*Corrosionomics*	Not stated
Foote Mineral Co.	*Foote Prints*	Not stated
Foster Wheeler Corp.	*Heat Engineering*	Bimonthly
Geigy Chemical Corp.	*What's Doing*	Not stated
Glidden Co.	*Glidden Industrial Review*	Not stated
B. F. Goodrich Chemical Co.	*GoodChemCo News*	Monthly
Goodyear Tire and Rubber Co.	*Goodyear Chemical Review*	Quarterly
Hooker-Electrochemical Co., Durez Plastics Division	*Durez Molder*	Monthly
	Durez Plastics News	Monthly
	Shell Molding News	Not stated
Rodney Hunt Machine Co.	*Orange Peal*	Not stated
Interchemical Corp., RBH Dispersions Division	*RBH Trends*	Monthly
International Nickel Co.	*Mechanical Topics*	Quarterly
	Process Industries Quarterly	Quarterly
Jarrell-Ash Co.	*JAco News Letter*	Not stated
Leeds and Northrup Co.	*Modern Precision*	Not stated
Minerals and Chemical Corp. of America	*Attaclay Pesticide Digest*	Not stated
National Lead Co.	*Dutch Boy Paint Dealer*	Not stated
New Jersey Zinc Co.	*Alloy Pot*	Not stated
	Metal Powder Press	Not stated
	Paint Progress	Not stated
Nopco Chemical Co.	*Nopco News*	Not stated
Perkin-Elmer Corp.	*Perkin-Elmer Instrument News for Science and Industry*	Quarterly
Perkins Glue Co.	*Perkins Glue Line*	Not stated
Pfaudler Co.	*Corrosioneering News*	Not stated
Philadelphia Quartz Co.	*Silicate P's and Q's*	Monthly
Pittsburgh Plate Glass Co.	*PPG Products*	Bimonthly
Reynolds Metals Co.	*Reynolds Technical Advisor*	Not stated
Rockwell Manufacturing Co., Nordstrom Valve Division	*Flow Line*	Not stated
Rohm and Haas Co., Resinous Products Division	*Resin Review*	4 issues per year
Schaar and Co.	*Lab-Oratory*	Not stated
Scientific Glass Apparatus Co.	*What's New for the Laboratory*	Not stated
Sindar Corp.	*Sindar Reporter*	Not stated
Socony Mobil Oil Co., Inc.	*Oil Power*	Not stated
Standard Oil Co. of California	*Bulletin*	Quarterly
Thiokol Chemical Corp.	*Thiokol Facts*	Not stated
Union Carbide Corp.		
Union Carbide Chemicals Co.	*Chemical Progress, News of Applied Chemistry*	Not stated
Union Carbide Metals Co.	*Union Carbide Metals Review*	Not stated

Company	House Organ	Frequency of Publication
II. Predominantly Advertising (*continued*)		
Union Carbide Plastics Co.	*Bakelite Extruderitems*	Not stated
U. S. Industrial Chemicals Co.	*U. S. I. Chemical News*	Not stated
R. T. Vanderbilt Co.	*Vanderbilt News*	Not stated
Whitmoyer Laboratory	*Lab Fax*	Not stated
Will Corp.	*Lablog*	Not stated
III. Primarily for Employees and Stockholders		
Abbott Laboratories	*PharmAgraph*	Not stated
American Cyanamid Co.	*Monthly News Bulletin*	Not stated
Babcock and Wilcox Co.	*Generator*	Bimonthly
Champion Paper and Fibre Co.	*The Log*	Monthly
Dow Chemical Co.	*Dow Diamond*	Bimonthly
E. I. du Pont de Nemours & Co., Inc.	*Better Living*	Bimonthly
Food Machinery and Chemical Co.	*FMC Flask*	Bimonthly
General Aniline and Film Corp.	*The Rainbow*	Not stated
Gulf Oil Corp.	*Orange Disc*	Bimonthly
Hercules Powder Co.	*Hercules Mixer*	Monthly
Humble Oil and Refining Co.	*The Humble Way*	Bimonthly
Eli Lilly and Co.	*The Lilly Review*	Not stated
Merck & Co., Inc.	*Merck Review*	Not stated
Monsanto Chemical Co.	*Monsanto Magazine*	Bimonthly
Shell Oil Co.	*Shell News*	Bimonthly
Standard Oil Co. of California	*The Standard Oiler*	Monthly
Standard Oil Co. (New Jersey)	*The Lamp*	Quarterly
Sunray Oil Corp.	*Sunray News*	Monthly
Texas Co.	*The Texaco Star*	Not stated

Conclusion

House organs and trade publications constitute a large and important body of useful information not duplicated in other sources. Although their primary objective is to sell products or enhance a company's prestige, they successfully communicate the "latest technical information on uses, physical properties, specifications, and physiological data" (2). The chief problems in this area are how to get this literature and what to do with it once obtained. This paper has provided answers to these two questions. No list of trade publications has been compiled, as it is impossible to make a selection in accord with the interests of more than one company.

Literature Cited

(1) Bennett, H., ed., "Concise Chemical and Technical Dictionary," Chemical Publishing Co., New York, 1947.
(2) Carbide and Carbon Chemicals Co., *Chem. Week* **78,** No. 22, 49 (1956).
(3) Chemical Abstracts Service, private communication.
(4) Cheyney, L. E., Advances in Chem. Ser., No. **4,** 126–31 (1951).
(5) Gardner, W., "Chemical Synonyms and Trade Synonyms," 2nd ed., Van Nostrand, Princeton, N. J., 1955.
(6) Gebbie Press, New York, private communication.
(7) "House Magazine Directory," Gebbie Press, New York, 1954.
(8) Lederman, L. F., Advances in Chem. Ser., No. **4,** 104–11 (1951).
(9) Maurice, Jewell, *Med. Library Assoc. Bull.* **40,** 341–7 (1952).
(10) Printers' Ink, "Directory of House Organs," Printers' Ink Publishing Co., New York, 1954.
(11) Rose, A., Rose, E., eds., "Condensed Chemical Dictionary," 5th ed., Reinhold, New York, 1956.
(12) Royer, M. H., "Descriptive List of House Organs in the United States Selected for Use in the Medium Sized Library," thesis, Western Reserve University, 1949.
(13) Technical Survey, 650 Newark Ave., Elizabeth, N. J., private communication.

(14) Wilson, W. H., Co., New York, private communication.
(15) Wyandotte Chemicals Corp., Wyandotte, Mich., "Chlorine," 1956.
(16) Zimmermann, O. T., Lavine, I., "Handbook of Material Trade Names," with Supplements I-III, Industrial Research Service, Dover, N. H., 1953, 1956, 1957, 1960.

BASED on paper presented before Division of Chemical Literature, Symposium on Searching the Chemical Literature, 130th Meeting, ACS, Atlantic City, N. J., September 1956. Revised 1960.

The Chemical Literature of Germany

ERNEST F. SPITZER

Chas. Pfizer & Co., Inc., Groton, Conn.

Revised by

VLADIMIR SLAMECKA

Columbia University, New York, N. Y.

Since the appearance of the *Chemisches Journal* in 1778, the German chemical literature has represented a sizable segment of the literature of chemistry as a whole. *Chemisches Zentralblatt,* the earliest of the abstract journals, was widened in scope in 1949 to cover the chemical literature of the world. Aside from language difficulties, a search of German chemical literature involves no essential change in methods employed for search of any other area of chemical literature.

The extensive and rapid recovery of the postwar German economy, at least for West Germany, has been fully shared by the German chemical industry, and the German chemical literature has also participated in the general upswing. The objective of this paper is to bring earlier information (*24*) up to date, to provide a broad view of the current picture with regard to German chemical literature, and to detail some of the major sources of chemical literature now available in West and East Germany.

Periodicals

The trend toward a general reduction of German periodical output during the 1939–1945 period, which was the inevitable outgrowth of a wartime economy, has been definitely reversed. "Deutsche Bibliographie der Zeitschriften 1945–1952" (*6*) lists 11,408 periodicals appearing in that period in the German language. Of the 1077 scientific periodicals appearing in West Germany in 1959 (*16*), the majority were of chemical interest; in 1956, *Chemical Abstracts* already covered 473 West German serials (*15*). The German Democratic Republic (East Germany), where once most of the chemical journals were published, accounts for a smaller fraction of German chemical publication.

Aside from "Deutsche Bibliographie der Zeitschriften 1945–1952," the second (1952) edition of "Periodica Chimica" (*18*) is a reliable source of information on German periodicals up to 1952. Corresponding to the "List of Periodicals Abstracted by *Chemical Abstracts,*" "Periodica Chimica" lists titles, abbreviations, title changes, mergers, suspensions, and publishers' addresses for periodicals abstracted in *Chemisches Zentralblatt,* but does not indicate library locations, nor is it brought up to date by annual supplements.

Until the fourth edition of the "World List of Scientific Periodicals" is published, a good source of information on newer German periodicals is the annual amendments to the third edition, published since 1953 in *Chemistry & Industry* (London).

A location list of the holdings of scientific and technical periodicals in West German libraries has been completed since 1945 by the Arbeitsgemeinschaft technisch-wissenschaftlicher Bibliotheken in Essen, Germany. One may write to this organization with regard to the location of chemical periodicals in West German libraries (*23*). One of the largest chemical libraries in the world, the Kekulé-Bibliothek of the Bayer concern in Leverkusen, receives currently over 2200 periodical titles; its holdings number about 190,000 volumes and some 50,000 dissertations in the fields of pure and applied chemistry (*14*).

A union list of periodicals abstracted by major American abstracting and indexing services is being prepared (*21*); when completed, this guide will be most useful in locating German periodicals in U. S. libraries.

The basic and well-known German periodicals in the field of general chemistry, such as *Justus Liebigs Annalen der Chemie, Chemische Berichte,* and *Angewandte Chemie,* have been back with us for some time. *Chemische Berichte,* which is the continuation of *Berichte der Deutschen Chemischen Gesellschaft,* never published volumes 78 (1945) and 79 (1946).

Zeitschrift für physikalische Chemie, founded by Ostwald, which prior to World War II was published by Akademische Verlagsgesellschaft in Leipzig, has undergone some turbulent days. Its publishing house was seized first by the Hitler government, then by the communists; at the present time an East German edition is published by this Leipzig publisher under the old title. In 1954, the original owners began publishing a West German edition called *Zeitschrift für physikalische Chemie (Neue Folge)*; by 1960, a total of 22 volumes of this new series had appeared in print.

Started in 1947, *Makromolekulare Chemie* was meant to succeed the *Journal für praktische Chemie* which had stopped in 1943 with volume 162, and which was then continued by *Journal für makromolekulare Chemie*; of the latter title, however, only two volumes were published. In 1954, *Journal für praktische Chemie* was started again in the East Zone of Germany, where it has been published since. *Makromolekulare Chemie* may be considered the West German successor of the prewar *Journal für praktische Chemie.*

Naturwissenschaften resumed publication in 1946.

Zeitschrift für Naturforschung, an important West German scientific serial published since 1946, offers broad coverage of astrophysics, physics, and physical chemistry (Section A), and of chemistry, biochemistry, biophysics, biology, and allied fields (Section B). The two sections appear as separate issues twelve times a year.

The growing volume of scientific work and publishing has undoubtedly fostered the development of scientific and technological documentation in both zones of Germany. At least two West German documentation journals appeared in the early fifties: *Nachrichten für Dokumentation,* the leading periodical of this field, has been published since 1950, while the less scholarly *Dokumentation-Fach-*

bibliothek-Werksbücherei made its bow in 1952. The representative East German counterpart is *Dokumentation* (1953–).

Abstracting Services

Now in its 130th year, *Chemisches Zentralblatt* processes annually some 30,000 individual periodical issues from 50 countries, in 35 languages. In 1959, about 100,000 abstracts appeared on 18,400 pages of *Chemisches Zentralblatt*, exclusive of indexes (*14*).

The oldest major chemical abstracting service in the world suffered a lapse in publication in 1945; shortly after the end of World War II, two editions were published, one in the Western and one in the Eastern Zone of divided Germany. The West German edition stopped in the middle of 1949, whereas the East Zone edition continued until the end of that year. As of January 1950, only one edition of *Chemisches Zentralblatt* was published jointly by the following four societies: Deutsche Akademie der Wissenschaften zu Berlin, Chemische Gesellschaft in der Deutschen Demokratischen Republik (both in the German Democratic Republic), Akademie der Wissenschaften zu Göttingen, and Gesellschaft Deutscher Chemiker (both in West Germany).

While the division of *Chemisches Zentralblatt* into six sections was abandoned, after six months of existence, in January, 1950, its division into Parts I and II lasted until 1952: Starting with volume 132 there is continuous pagination for the entire calendar year, and only one (annual) index.

When the Western and Eastern Zone editions were combined in 1950, it was decided to include only abstracts of new and most recent chemical papers. Accordingly, the editors chose to publish supplementary volumes (*Ergänzungsbände*) covering work published during and after the war through 1949 and not abstracted in *Chemisches Zentralblatt* before. With the exception of the last (tenth) volume for 1949, this plan was to be completed by mid-1960 with the publication of 26 *Ergänzungsbände* totaling 16,640 pages.

Abstracts of chemical literature from the 1950–1954 period which were not included in the *Chemisches Zentralblatt* volumes covering this period are now available in the supplementary set of 10 (out of 13 projected) *Sonderband 1950/54* parts.

Having almost finished the remarkable work of closing the war and postwar gap in coverage of chemical literature, the editors of *Chemisches Zentralblatt* are now preparing the publication of several cumulative indexes, indexes to the *Ergänzungsbände* and the *Sonderband 1950/54*, and indexes to the more recent volumes. No cumulative index has been available in 1960 for the period since 1944, and the 1940–1944 volumes have only one cumulative (author) index. Annual subject indexing of *Chemisches Zentralblatt* is some three to four years behind in publication.

A brief account of the history of *Chemisches Zentralblatt* is given by Pflücke (*17*).

In the absence, at the present time, of any subject indexing of the current issues of chemical abstracting journals of the world, *Chemisches Zentralblatt—Das System* is the first device providing a unilateral subject approach to the weekly issues of *Chemisches Zentralblatt*. Published in 1958, *Das System* (*4*) is a listing of 8662 "system numbers" allotted to chemical subject terms; since the sequence of abstracts in each weekly issue of the journal is numerical, one may determine—by looking up pertinent system numbers—whether that issue carries any abstracts of interest. However, since each abstract has only one system number, *Das System* does not permit any cross- or multisubject indexing of that abstract.

Like its American and Russian counterparts, *Chemisches Zentralblatt* remains a permanent, general record of the progress of chemistry, not necessarily satisfying specialized demands or narrower viewpoints of a more restricted audience. As in other countries of the world, such demands have brought about specialized abstracting services also in Germany; the trend is particularly pronounced in East Germany whose government-organized network of documentation centers emphasizes prompt evaluation of scientific publications for specialized areas. ZWL-Dokumentationsdienste, for example, provides subscribers with rapidly mimeographed abstract cards available for a rather narrow delimitation of subject areas (information on services currently available is supplied by Institut für Dokumentation der Deutschen Akademie der Wissenschaften, Berlin).

The monthly *Inhaltsverzeichnisse sowjetischer Fachliteratur* is another example of East German abstracting services, appearing in several subject series since 1953 (Reihe III/B covers chemistry and biology). Each monthly issue abstracts totally, in German, well over 20 top Soviet chemical and biological journals (the list of these titles remains standard) published not more than 4 months before. Annual subject and author indexes to *Inhaltsverzeichnisse* are usually available within a year—which is sometimes earlier than the appearance of the subject indexes of the original Russian journals.

Reference Works

In 1958, having completed the Second Supplement to "Beilsteins Handbuch der organischen Chemie," the Beilstein-Institut für Literatur der organischen Chemie began publishing the Third Supplement covering the literature of organic chemistry for the 20-year period 1930–1949. This supplement is to be completed in some 10 to 12 years; it will total about 32,000 pages. By 1960, three parts of the first volume were published.

The Third Supplement of Beilstein may be the last ever published in book form. Writing on the occasion of the 75-year history of this treatise, its editor, Friedrich Richter, suggests that other forms of publication may be more appropriate in the future (punched cards, etc.), because of time lag in publication and other reasons (*20*).

Volumes 28 and 29 of the Second Supplement are, respectively, the subject and formula indexes to the entire "Beilsteins Handbuch"; the three-part cumulative formula index, arranged by the Hill system, is the only index recording the known formulas of organic compounds from the beginnings of organic chemistry through 1929. (The *Chemical Abstracts* cumulative formula index extends this period to 1946.)

The Beilstein-Institut also took over the publication of "Elsevier's Encyclopaedia of Organic Chemistry." Following the publication of four parts of Supplement V of the fourteenth volume of Elsevier on steroids and triterpenes (in English, but under the auspices of the Beilstein-Institut), further volumes will appear in the "Beilstein Handbuch" series.

The standard treatise of inorganic chemistry, "Gumelins Handbuch der anorganischen Chemie," is now in its eighth edition. The previous literature deadline of January 1, 1950, was extended to cover the 1950–1960 decade, and special volumes covering this period are to be published, starting in 1963; their sequence will be based on the state of the art of individual elements. At the same time, the program calling for supplements to individual volumes published before 1950 is being implemented.

The extension of the literature-coverage deadline to 1960 was made possible by constant reviewing of current literature of inorganic chemistry by the Gmelin-Institut, whose archives contained over 1,500,000 literature cards as of January 1960. Based on these archives is the Gmelin Information Service, designed to provide literature reviews on individual topics; its task is greatly facilitated by the decision to code all literature published after 1950 for machine searching.

In the absence of subject and formula indexes of individual volumes, many non-German users welcome the bilingual feature introduced in "Gmelins Handbuch" in January 1959: German and English tables of contents, and English headings and subheadings on the margins of the text. Another useful device, the so-called alphabetic series (a supplement to the systematic subject index), was published in 1959.

The history of "Gmelins Handbuch der anorganischen Chemie" and the plans and services of the Gmelin-Institut were described by Pietsch (*19*) on the occasion of the 100th anniversary of Gmelin's death.

Whereas "Beilsteins Handbuch der organischen Chemie" describes individual compounds, "Houben-Weyl's Methoden der organischen Chemie" deals with methods of preparation and rearrangement of classes of compounds. The fourth edition, scheduled to be completed by 1964 in 16 volumes, strives for a critical presentation of the useful methods of preparative organic chemistry; its most substantial departure from the previous edition is the extensive coverage of patent literature and industry archives.

The final volume of Houben-Weyl—the author and subject index—promises to present a new, generally applicable system of organic chemical reactions which will facilitate the use of the whole set.

Under the editorship of A. Eucken, the sixth edition of "Landolt-Börnsteins Zahlenwerte und Funktionen aus Physik, Chemie, Astronomie, Geophysik und Technik" began appearing in 1950. Volumes I and II together form the new edition of the old (1936) set: Volume I deals with atomic and molecular physics; Volume II, with macrophysics and chemistry. (Volume I, in five parts, was published by 1955; three parts of Volume II were available by 1960.) Publication of Volumes III and IV proceeds more slowly.

Books

The compilation by Cummings and Vince of German chemical book titles published between 1939 and 1950 proved especially useful in taking up the information gap left during and after World War II. A supplement (*5*), listing German chemical books published from 1950 to 1953, appeared in 1954.

The national bibliographies of West and East Germany provide information on the more current publications. In West Germany, "Bibliographie der deutschen Bibliothek, Reihe A" is a listing of new books published in that zone. The East German counterpart is "Deutsche Nationalbibliographie," appearing in two series covering trade and noncommercial publications, respectively.

The classified book catalogs of several German publishers and booksellers offer a comprehensive view of German chemical publications reaching the book market. Harrassowitz publishes an annotated *Zeitschrift für Chemie Neuerscheinungen,* and a monthly classified *German Book Digest* of new books published in both zones of Germany, Austria, and Switzerland. The annotated *Nova,* published monthly by Deutscher Buch-Export und -Import in Leipzig, is a selective listing of East German monographs and other books.

Various German chemical periodicals regularly carry book news and book reviews.

West German doctoral theses are listed selectively in the supplement to *Angewandte Chemie;* this regular list includes titles from the East German national bibliography (Reihe B). Swiss dissertations appear in an annual listing in *Chimia;* West German chemical engineering dissertations are listed once a year in *Chemie-Ingenieur-Technik.*

Biographical Information

A current directory of German chemists is the 1960 publication "Das Adressbuch deutscher Chemiker 1959/60" (*1*), for the first time including a listing of German university chemical institutes.

"Kürschners deutscher Gelehrten Kalender," a biographical guide to scientists using the German language for all or part of their publications, with pertinent scholarly and biographical data, has long served as an important source of information. The eighth edition is dated 1954.

Another old stand-by in the field of German science biography, "Poggendorffs Biographisch-literarisches Handwörterbuch der exakten Naturwissenschaften," has a new series in progress. Volume 7A contains biographies of scientists from Germany, Austria, and Switzerland.

The periodically revised "Minerva" handbook covers universities, learned institutions, and their staffs in all Europe (*12*).

Patent Literature

In recent years, the West German Patent Office (Deutsches Patentamt) in Munich has received some 55,000 patent applications annually, and it grants between 18,000 and 20,000 letters patent a year. About 50% of the applications were made public (German patent applications are required to be open for inspection for three months in the Public Display Room of the Deutsches Patentamt) (*3*).

The system of classes and subclasses of the Deutsches Patentamt has remained fundamentally unchanged since 1933: Its 89 classes comprise industrial and trade subject fields, the numerical arrangement following the alphabet (from "Aufbereitung" to "Zucker"). Each class is further subdivided into subclasses, groups, etc. (*7*). Starting with applications made public on January 1, 1957, a new patent numbering system has gone into effect: If granted, a patent has the same number as its application (the numbering began with 1,000,001). Published patents also indicate whether any textual changes were made in the applications.

A number of publications are useful in locating and searching West German patents. Deutsches Patentamt publishes several journals.

Patentblatt, a weekly published in two editions, lists patent applications filed (by number, class and subclass, group and subgroup, file reference, name of applicant, name of inventor, title of application, and date of application), patents granted (again all pertinent information), applications withdrawn, applications denied, changes and corrections, terminations, and useful-model patents (Gebrauchsmuster).

Blatt für Patent-, Muster- und Zeichenwesen is a patent law monthly which lists new regulations, official rules, orders, agreements, rulings, treaties of interest, and other legal data for patent lawyers; it covers legal matters both inside and outside of Germany.

Warenzeichenblatt, also issued in two editions, is a semimonthly journal dealing with trade-marks and their uses.

Deutsches Patentamt also publishes *Vierteljährliches Namensverzeichnis,* a quarterly compilation of names of patentees listed in *Patentblatt.*

Since none of these official journals contains any annotations of abstracts or contents of either the applications or the patents granted, a private Munich firm began publishing the weekly *Auszüge aus den Patentanmeldungen* containing abstracts of all patent applications made public by the Deutsches Patentamt (*2*). A broadside publication, it consists of one major claim from each application (whichever the abstractor considered to be the most significant), sketches, and drawings; its information is thus supplemental to that given in *Patentblatt.*

A weekly English-language journal, published by Technical Information Co. of Liverpool under the title *German Patents Gazette,* contains "summaries in the English language of the specifications" of West German patent applications. While *Auszüge aus den Patentanmeldungen* costs about $6.00 per year, the English-language publication is offered at $95.00 per year.

In 1958, the Wila Verlag für Wirtschaftswerbung in Munich began publishing a monthly classified guide to patent application titles, at about $5.00 per three months. Each application title is entered under several catch words in three separate parts of the guide: by subject, process, and use. In addition, each issue contains an index of authors and an alphabetical index of titles with class and application numbers. Considering the promptness with which each title is listed (two to six weeks after it was made public by the Patent Office), this *Monatsregister deutscher Patentanmeldungen* (*13*) is a most useful tool in subject and name searches of West German patent applications.

Although there is at present no periodical publication devoted specifically to abstracts of German patents when granted and published, both *Chemisches Zentralblatt* and *Chemical Abstracts* pay attention to published German patents. *Chemisches Zentralblatt* used to refer, in its annual patent index, from duplicate patents to those originally granted in other countries; since 1945, however, equivalent patents are referred to in the abstracts themselves (as is done by *Chemical Abstracts*).

Of the various German journals carrying regular listings of patent application titles, the classified list in *Chemiker-Zeitung* is most comprehensive, and particularly useful because of the coverage of both West and East German patents.

With regard to East German patents, White and Ravenscroft (*27*) state:

> The patent law of September 6, 1950, provides for granting of patents for 18 years from the filing date. Patents are divided into industrial and exclusive patents. In the case of an industrial patent, the right to use the invention shall belong to the patentee and also to such persons as shall be determined by the Office for Inventions and Patents of Soviet Germany. An exclusive patent invests the right to use the invention exclusively in the patentee, but the Government may retract or revoke a patent at any time upon the payment of adequate remuneration to the patentee.

In searching German patent literature, certain special features and peculiarities should be borne in mind. The remarks of Horwitz and Robbins (*10*) are equally applicable to German and to other foreign patents.

A good yet brief German-language guide to the patents of West Germany was published in 1958 (*26*); and the German-English and English-German dictionary of patent terms, "Wörterbuch der Patentfachsprache" (*11*), is most helpful to anyone working in that area.

Conclusion

Reference should be made to a few recent papers useful to chemists translating or searching in German chemical literature: Fischbach's paper is concerned with suggestions on translating chemical German (*9*) and with biochemical and pharmaceutical terminology (*8*). Smith and Singer discuss the problem of translating foreign-language patents (*22*); the fourth (1959) edition of the UNESCO bibliography of scientific dictionaries lists several good monolingual dictionaries (*28*); Stevens gives information on the chemical literature of Eastern Germany and other Soviet-bloc countries (*25*).

Literature Cited

(1) "Adressbuch deutscher Chemiker 1959/60," Verlag Chemie, Weinheim, 1960.
(2) "Auszüge aus den Patentanmeldungen," Wila Verlag für Wirtschaftswerbung, Munich, 1955–.
(3) Beil, W., *Chem.-Ing.-Tech.* **31**, 485 (1959).
(4) *"Chemisches Zentralblatt—Das System,"* Akademie-Verlag, Berlin, 1958.
(5) Cummings, A. E., Vince, S., "German Books on Chemical and Cognate Subjects Published 1950–1953," Lange, Maxwell, and Springer, London, 1954.
(6) Deutsche Bibliothek (Frankfurt/Main), "Deutsche Bibliographie der Zeitschriften 1945–1952," Buchhändler Vereinigung, Frankfurt am Main, 1958.
(7) Deutsches Patentamt, "Gruppeneinteilung der Patentklassen," 7th ed., Heymanns Verlag, Munich, 1958.
(8) Fischbach, H., ADVANCES IN CHEM. SER., No. **10**, 510–19 (1954).
(9) Fischbach, H., *J. Chem. Educ.* **30**, 388–93 (1953).
(10) Horwitz, L., *Chem. Eng. News*, **38**, 102–6, 108 (May 23, 1960).
(11) Klaften, B., Allison, F. C., "Wörterbuch der Patentfachsprache," Wila Verlag für Wirtschaftwerbung, 2nd ed., Munich, 1959.
(12) "Minerva—Jahrbuch der gelehrten Welt," 35th ed., DeGruyter, Berlin, 1956.
(13) "Monatsregister deutscher Patentanmeldungen," Wila Verlag für Wirtschaftswerbung, Munich, 1958–.
(14) Mueller, F., *Chem.-Ztg.* **84**, 289 (1954).
(15) *Nachrichten Chem. Tech.* (suppl. to *Angew. Chem.*) **5**, 230 (1957).
(16) *Ibid.*, **7**, 167 (1959).
(17) Pfluecke, M., *Chem. Tech.* **6**, 125–6 (1954).
(18) Pfluecke, M., Hawelek, A., "Periodica Chimica," 2nd ed., Akademie Verlag, Berlin, 1952.
(19) Pietsch, E. H., *Chimia (Switz.)* **7**, 49–57 (1953).
(20) Richter, F., *Angew. Chem.* **70**, 279–84 (1958).
(21) *Science* **130**, 689 (1959).
(22) Smith, J. F., Singer, T. E. R., *J. Chem. Educ.* **32**, 461–2 (1955).
(23) Southern, W. A., *Library Quart.* **25**, 235 (1955).
(24) Spitzer, E. F., ADVANCES IN CHEM. SER., No. **4**, 30–6 (1954).
(25) Stevens, L. J., "Abstracts of Papers," 135th meeting, ACS, p. 8G, April 1959.
(26) Weisse, E. F., "Erfindungen—Patente—Lizenzen," VID-Verlag, Düsseldorf, 1958.
(27) White, W. W., Ravenscroft, B., "Patents throughout the World," Trade Activities, Inc., New York, 1956.
(28) Wuester, E., "Bibliography of Monolingual Scientific and Technical Glossaries," UNESCO, Paris, 1955, 1959. 2 vols.

BASED on paper presented before Division of Chemical Literature, Symposium on Searching the Chemical Literature, 117th Meeting, ACS, Detroit, Mich., April 1950. Revised version presented before Division of Chemical Literature, 130th Meeting, ACS, Atlantic City, N. J., September 1956. Revised 1960.

Scientific and Technical Literature of the USSR

MORDECAI HOSEH

Chemical Abstracts, Washington, D. C.

A large volume of scientific and technical material is published in the USSR. Some of it is very good, some of it is average, and some is indifferent. Most of the scientific and technical literature published in the Soviet Union is now available in this country. Information services are thus charged with the twin tasks of obtaining all that is of value and screening out the gangue. To do this effectively it is necessary to have a good knowledge of pertinent bibliography, of the organization of Soviet publications, its publication practices, the distribution of published material in the Soviet Union, and other information relating to publishing practices in the Soviet Union.

Since 1956 the procurement of scientific and technical literature from the USSR has undergone great changes; bibliographic information concerning this literature can no longer be called scarce. The literature, as well as information concerning it, is now available and it is up to us to acquire it and to process it. Indeed, because of the relative ease of acquisition it now becomes necessary to winnow the grain and free it of chaff, if we wish to avoid trifling and excessive scattering of effort. The rather extensive treatment of the scientific and technical literature of one country is motivated by the fact that this large volume of literature reports results of a vast research activity through channels unlike the ones with which we are familiar, in a language very few of us know. In addition, the publications are hard to obtain.

In the Soviet Union are currently published around 2300 titles with over 12,500 issues annually. These embrace mathematical and natural sciences, engineering, technology, agriculture, and medicine. In this output of printed matter are included periodicals (publications appearing at scheduled intervals) and serials (sequentially numbered publications appearing at variable intervals). Not included are books, monographs, commemorative volumes (Festschriften), collections of papers presented at meetings, conferences, congresses, etc., and special publications appearing adventitiously. The figures given include all levels of material from theoretical research to instructions for ship foremen. Not all of it is of interest to the American scientist, engineer, or physician. It is the task of the literature specialist to select the pertinent material and convey it in the best possible form to the user. No attempt is made here to evaluate the quality of the printed matter; the discussion is limited to the formal status of the publications.

Publications and Publishers

Organization of a Publication. Each Soviet periodical publication has three distinct bodies connected with it: sponsoring body, editorial board, and publisher. Obviously, each publication also has a printer.

The sponsoring body is an institution or organization which officially is responsible for the publication, takes credit for it, and presumably carries its cost.

The sponsoring body is usually identified at the top of the title page or just below the name of the publication. The first form is usually followed in publications having a general title like *Zhurnal, Trudy, Vestnik,* or *Uchenye Zapiski.* The second form–i.e.,the name of the sponsor following the title–is given on publications having a specific name, such as *Ugol, Stal, Khimicheskaya Promyshlennost,* and *Stanki i Instrument.* The title is indicative not merely of the content of a publication but also of its background, and thus the location of the sponsor's name is to some extent specific.

EDITORIAL BOARD. United States publications usually have an editor; they may also have an executive editor (the fellow who does the work), and in society publications an advisory board which functions in a more or less perfunctory manner.

Soviet periodical publications have an editorial board, Redaktsionnaya kollegiya, usually abbreviated Redkollegiya. The board or collegium consists of the editor-in-chief, Glavnyĭ redaktor, his deputy, Zamestitel' glavnogo redaktora, secretary, Uchenyĭ sekretar, and several board members. The editorial board is apparently appointed by the sponsoring body and is responsible for the content and quality of the publication. The members of editorial boards, particularly of academy and university publications, are men outstanding in their fields. Many publications have a technical editor, Tekhnicheskiĭ redaktor, whose name is often, but not always, printed on the back page along with the name of the proofreader, Korrektor.

PUBLISHERS. Publishers of scientific periodic literature in the Soviet Union can be divided into two groups; the academies and universities form one group, while all the others belong in the second group. The distinguishing mark of the first group is that the publisher is synonymous with the sponsoring body. Thus, when the sponsor is Akademiya Nauk SSSR, the publisher is Izdatel'stvo Akademii Nauk SSSR; publications of the Moscow State University are issued by the Izdatel'stvo Moskovskogo Gosudarstvennogo Universiteta. The publishers of this group usually have their own printing establishments. Some of the provincial universities print their publications in the printing houses of other universities.

The second group publishes the various journals, serials, and monographs sponsored by the different ministries and sovnarkhozy. The publishers of this group are numerous and go under a variety of names: Gizlegprom (literature on light industry), Medgiz (medical and health publications in the widest sense), Gostoptekhizdat (petroleum and coal mining literature), Sel'khozgiz (literature on agriculture), etc. The name of the publishing house, the approved abbreviation, as here given denotes the type of material which it handles. These publishing houses seem to farm out their printing jobs.

Sponsoring Bodies. ACADEMIES. Under the Soviet system the entire publishing program of scientific and technical literature is directly sponsored by the government, as is all other publishing. The actual sponsors are distinct bodies clearly identified on the publication.

The most important sponsor by far, with respect to quantity and quality of scientific material, is the Academy of Sciences of the USSR, Akademiya Nauk SSSR, together with its several branches, Filialy Akademii Nauk SSSR (Ural'skiĭ Filial, Karelo-Finskiĭ Filial, Kazanskiĭ Filial, Moldavskiĭ Filial, etc.); there are 15 or more such branches. By the decree of April 12, 1961, the academy branches and some of its institutes were detached from the academy and transferred to other jurisdictions: Council of Ministers' Committees, Ministries, Departments, and to the Council of Ministers of the R.S.F.S.R. [Russian Federated Republic].

The academy issues a most impressive list of publications. These can be divided into two classes: those published by the academy as a whole and publications issued by the departments into which the academy is subdivided. Into the first group fall: *Doklady, Vestnik,* and such important journals as *Zhurnal Fizicheskoĭ Khimii, Zhurnal Obshcheĭ Khimii, Zhurnal Prikladnoĭ Khimii, Zhurnal Analiticheskoĭ Khimii, Uspekhi Khimii, Kolloidnyĭ Zhurnal, Radiokhimiya, Geokhimiya, Zhurnal Eksperimental'noĭ i Teoreticheskoĭ Fiziki, Fizika Tverdogo Tela, Kristallografiya, Zhurnal Tekhnicheskoĭ Fiziki, Biokhimiya, Mikrobiologiya,* and *Uspekhi Sovremennoĭ Biologii,* to mention only some of the journals. The publications of the departments of the academy are called *Izvestiya Akademii Nauk SSSR* and are modified by the name of the respective department, such as *Otdelenie Khimicheskikh Nauk, Otdelenie Tekhnicheskikh Nauk, Seriya Biologicheskaya, Seriya Fizicheskaya,* and so on. A large department, such as *Otdelenie Khimicheskikh Nauk* may comprise several divisions and these in turn issue their own publications. Thus, Institut Obscheĭ i Neorganicheskoĭ Khimiĭ (General and Inorganic Chemistry) which is further divided into "sectors" publishes *Izvestiya Sektora Fiziko-Khimicheskogo Analiza* and *Investiya Sektora Platiny i Drugikh Blagorodnykh Metallov,* both remarkable publications, the first dealing primarily with phase rule and the geometry of chemistry, and the second with coordination compounds. (These two publications ceased in 1956 and 1955, respectively. The kind of material they used to publish now appears in *Zhurnal Neorganicheskoĭ Khimii,* which started in 1956.) The *Vestnik, Doklady, Zhurnal,* and the several *Izvestiya* are periodicals—i.e., they are issued at definite intervals. The *Izvestiya* of the two previously mentioned sectors are serials issued at no specific intervals; there are usually one to three volumes a year. Each issue is referred to as volume (tom) and numbered consecutively. Occasionally, one volume appears in several parts.

In addition to the publications of the central academy, its various branches or Filial's have their own publications. The extent of their publishing activity varies greatly. In this respect, the Ural'skii Filial is the most important; it publishes among others *Trudy Gorno-Geologicheskogo Instituta, Trudy Instituta Biologii,* and *Trudy Instituta Fiziki Metallov.*

Besides the regular departments and their subdivisions, the regional branches and their subdivisions (not to be confused with the regional academies), a large number of research institutes are connected with and directed by the academy. Among these institutes are: Institut Fizicheskoĭ Khimii, Fizicheskiĭ Institut, Institut Kristallografii, Institut Nefti, Pochvennyĭ Institut im. V. V. Dokuchaeva, Institut Geologicheskikh Nauk (publishing several series), Institut Fiziologii Rasteniĭ im. K. A. Timiryazeva, Institut Mikrobiologii, as well as a number of research laboratories, such as Biogeokhimicheskaya Laboratoriya and Laboratoriya

Sapropelevykh Otlozhenii. All of these institutes publish their own *Trudy.*

The academy publications discussed hitherto, periodicals or serials, are scheduled publications. In addition to these the academy issues occasional volumes dealing with specific topics: a conference called to discuss spectroscopic methods, or flotation problems, or the theory of chemical bonds. The papers presented at such conferences and the discussion of these papers will appear in one or more volumes, usually called *Trudy Konferentsii po . . .* or *Trudy Soveshchaniya po . . .* followed by the name of the topic of the conference. A similar type of material is presented by the work of a committee appointed by the academy to study a certain field or problem. The work of the committee may extend over several years. Papers written by members and papers invited by them appear in one or more volumes, usually as *Trudy Komissii po . . .* followed by the subject of the investigation, such as *Analiticheskoĭ Khimii.*

The academy also publishes numerous monographs on a variety of scientific and industrial problems, such as metallo-organic compounds, mine safety, and many others.

Another type of academy publication is a memorial volume honoring one of their great scientists—e.g., *Sbornik posvyashchennyĭ semidesyatiletiyu akademika A. E. Ioffe,* 1950, *Voprosy mineralogii, geokhimii i petrografii,* issued as the Fersman memorial volume in 1946, and the Belyankin memorial volume of the same year.

ACADEMIES OF FEDERATED REPUBLICS. Most of the federated republics of the Soviet Union have their own Academies of Sciences which, for the sake of convenience, will be referred to as republic academies. A republic academy usually starts out as a branch of the Akademiya Nauk SSSR. Its first task is to train research personnel from among the respective nationalities to staff the laboratories and institutes. As qualified personnel becomes available, it gradually takes over administrative and research duties. When the local staff is of such quality and quantity that it can initiate and carry out a research program on a proper level, and when its training program is developed to a point where it is assured of a continuous supply of scientific personnel, the branch is transformed into an independent academy.

At present there are the following republic academies: (1) Akademiya Nauk Armyanskoĭ SSR (Armenian), (2) Akademiya Nauk Azerbaĭdzhanskoĭ SSR (Azerbaidzhan), (3), Akademiya Nauk Belorusskoĭ SSR (Belorussian), (4) Akademiya Nauk Estonskoĭ SSR (Estonian), (5) Akademiya Nauk Gruzinskoĭ SSR (Georgian), (6) Akademiya Nauk Kazakhskoĭ SSR (Kazakh), (7) Akademiya Nauk Kirgizskoĭ SSR (Kirgiz), (8) Akademiya Nauk Latviĭskoĭ SSR (Latvian), Akademiya Nauk Litovskoĭ SSR (Lithuanian), (10) Akademiya Nauk Tadzhikskoĭ SSR (Tadzik), (11) Akademiya Nauk Turkmenskoĭ SSR (Turkman), (12) Akademiya Nauk Ukrainskoĭ SSR (Ukrainian), and (13) Akademiya Nauk Uzbekskoĭ SSR (Uzbek).

The organization of the republic academies parallels that of the Akademiya Nauk SSSR, but the extent to which they follow the research program of the National Academy varies. Quite naturally, the republic academies devote most of their effort to research problems peculiar to their regions. The USSR Academy may study the theory of metal structure, but the Kazakh Academy will investigate the dressing of polymetal nonferrous ores, while the Ukrainian Academy will investigate the treatment of ferruginous ores. The USSR Academy will conduct research in plant physiology, but the Armenian Academy is more likely to study disease prevention and fertilization of fruit trees and vines, and the Turkman

Academy will study similar problems applied to cotton. The Kirgiz and Tadzhik Academies are more likely to emphasize animal husbandry, the Azerbaĭdzhan Academy, petroleum, and the Belorussian Academy, peat.

Even as the organization of the republic academies is fashioned after that of the USSR Academy of Sciences, so is their publication program, but on a much reduced scale.

Every one of the republic academies publishes a *Vestnik*, many publish one or more *Izvestiya* and *Trudy* of their own subdivisions, and a few publish *Doklady*.

Since the avowed aim is to have the native or local language dominant in the cultural activities of the region, all of the titles and at least part of the text are given in the native tongue. A Russian translation of the title usually, but not always, follows. Thus we have: *Zyegwoihtzner* (*Doklady*) and *Delegakir* (*Izvestiya*) published by the Armenian Academy. The Kazakh Academy issues *Khabarlary* (*Izvestiya*) and *Khabarshysy* (*Vestnik*), the Latvian, *Vestis* (*Izvestiya*) and *Raksti* (*Trudy*), the Uzbek, *Dokladlari* (*Doklady*) and *Akhboroti* (*Izvestiya*), and so on. The Ukrainian Academy publishes *Dopovidi* and *Visnik* (in 1960 combined with *Doklady*) (corresponding to *Doklady* and *Vestnik*) wholly in Ukrainian, while the Georgian Academy issues *Moambe* and *Shrometi* in Georgian and the corresponding *Soobshcheniya* and *Trudy* in Russian.

Of the republic academies the most prolific publisher is the Ukrainian Academy, Akademiya Nauk Ukrains'koĭ RSR. In addition to *Dopovidi* mentioned above, the institutes of the Ukrainian Academy publish regularly: (1) *Ukrains'kyĭ Botanichnyi Zhurnal* (in Ukrainian), (2) *Geologichnyĭ Zhurnal* (in Ukrainian), (3) *Mikrobiologichnyĭ Zhurnal* (in Ukrainian), (4) *Ukrains'kyĭ Biokhimichnyĭ Zhurnal* (in Ukrainian), (5) *Avtomaticheskaya Svarka* (in Russian), (6) *Medichnyĭ Zhurnal* (in Ukrainian), (7) *Ukrainskiĭ Matematicheskiĭ Zhurnal* (in Russian), (8) *Ukrainskiĭ Khimicheskiĭ Zhurnal* (in Russian), and (9) *Ukrains'kyĭ Fizychnyĭ Zhurnal* (in Ukrainian).

In addition to the above, the departments of the Ukrainian Academy publish serials, such as *Trudy Instituta Chernoĭ Metallurgii, Trudy Instituta Gidrobiologii,* and many others.

Besides the USSR Academy and the republic academies there are also the Lenin Academy of Agricultural Sciences, Vsesoyuznaya Akademiya Sel'skokhozyaĭstvennykh Nauk im. V. I. Lenina, which sponors *Doklady* published by Sel'khozgiz and the Academy of Medical Sciences, Akademiya Meditsinskikh Nauk SSSR, sponsoring *Vestnik* published by Medgiz.

UNIVERSITIES. The other bodies in the sponsor-publisher group are the universities. In the Soviet Union as in the rest of continental Europe universities are state institutions coming within the jurisdiction of the Ministry of Higher Education. Therefore, every university is a "Gosudarstvennyĭ Universitet"—a state university. A university is usually identified by the city in which it is located: Moskovskiĭ, Kievskiĭ, Tomskiĭ, or Khar'kovskiĭ Gosudarstvennyĭ Universitet. Often, there is the name of a patron attached to it—e.g., Leningradskiĭ Gosudarstvennyi Universitet im. A. A. Zhdanova—but it is of little importance, as patrons come and go while the institution remains. On its publications the name of the sponsoring university appears at the top of the cover and at the head of the title page.

The title of a university periodical is usually *Uchenye Zapiski* or *Nauchnye Zapiski;* thus: *Uchenye Zapiski, Kazanskiĭ Gosudarstvenniyĭ Universitet im. Ul'yanova-Lenina, Naukovi Zapysky, Kyivskyĭ Derzhavnyĭ Universitet im. T. G. Shevchenka,* and so on. The larger universities, such as Moscow, Leningrad, and Kiev, also publish a *Vestnik.* The Leningrad University issues in addition a *Nauchnyĭ*

Byulleten (discontinued in 1955). Most university publications are serials rather than regular periodicals. An exception is the *Vestnik* of the Moscow University, which now appears bimonthly in ten series: physics and astronomy, chemistry, geology, biology and pedology, geography, engineering and mathematics, history, philology and journalism, philosophy and economics, and law.

The *Vestnik* of the Leningrad University appears in six series—physics and chemistry; biology; geology and geography; mathematics, engineering, and astronomy; history, language, and literature; and economics, philosophy, and law—each of which appears four times a year.

The *Uchenye Zapiski* and *Nauchnye Zapiski,* being serials, are numbered consecutively. One issue may be given over to the work of one of the university departments and in that case will carry two numbers: the consecutive number in the whole series and the consecutive number of issues devoted to the work of the particular department, Fakultet. Thus: *Uchenye Zapiski, Moskovskiĭ Gosudarstvennyĭ Pedagogicheskiĭ Institut im. V. I. Lenina, Kafedra Obshcheĭ i Analiticheskoĭ Khimii,* and *Uchenye Zapiski, Leningradskiĭ Gosudarstvennyĭ Universitet im. A. A. Zhdanova, Seriya Khimicheskikh Nauk.*

The Moscow and Leningrad Universities have the largest publication programs among Soviet universities. Other universities with significant publication programs are those of Kiev, Kazan, Lviv, Kharkov, and Odessa. The Tomsk University, the Central-Asia University in Tashkent, the Karelo-Finnish University in Petrozavodsk, and the Riga University are worth notice. Other universities also publish, but their publications usually are issued in small numbers and are difficult to obtain.

In 1957 the Ministry of Higher Education started the *Izvestiya Vysshikh Uchebnykh Zavedeniĭ.* This title appears in 22 series, each of which is published at some university or school of engineering with a frequency of one, two, or three months. They all carry the general title and a specific subtitle which identifies the series—*Izvestiya Vysshikh Uchebnykh Zavedeniĭ Ministerstva Vysshego i Srednego Spetsial'nogo Obrazovaniya—Fizika,* a bimonthly published by Tomskiĭ Gosudarstvennyĭ Universitet in Tomsk—or the same general title of the series followed by *Tsvetnaya Metallurgiya* (*Nonferrous Metallurgy*) a bimonthly published by Severo-Kavkazskiĭ Gorno-Metallurgicheskiĭ Institut in Ordzhonikidze. Another publication, *Nauchnye Doklady Vyssheĭ Shkoly,* was started in 1958. This general title comprises 16 quarterlies: biological sciences, mining, forestry, metallurgy, construction, radio and electronics, physicomathematical sciences, chemistry and chemical technology, etc., all published in Moscow.

Besides universities, other schools of higher education, such as schools of engineering, Politekhniki or Politekhnicheskie Instituty, schools of mining, Gornye Instituty, and other specialized schools issue their own publications—e.g., *Nauchnye Trudy, Moskovskiĭ Gornyĭ Institut im. I. V. Stalina, Naukovi Zapysky, L'vivskyĭ Politekhnichnyĭ Institut,* and *Uchenye Zapiski, Leningradskiĭ Godsudarstvennyĭ Pedagogicheskiĭ Institut im. P. N. Pokrovskogo.*

Organizations with No Publishing Establishments. Hitherto were discussed sponsoring bodies which are simultaneously their own publishers. The other group of sponsoring bodies is made up of organizations which have no publishing establishments of their own, or which are at least directly identified as such. This includes such government bodies as ministries, bureaus, and boards

In the Soviet Union each major phase of activity and each major industry was up to 1957 headed by a ministry: a ministry of health, agriculture, food, chemical industry, metallurgy, coal, petroleum, building materials, etc. Each ministry sponsored one or more periodicals, which will be referred to as trade journals, in its field of activity.

Since the decentralization of the administrative branch of the government in 1957 and elimination of many ministries, the sponsorship of most trade journals as well as of most publishing houses formerly controlled by the ministries was transferred to the Gosudarstvennyĭ Nauchno-Tekhnicheskiĭ Komitet Soveta Ministrov SSSR (State Science and Technology Committee of the Council of Ministers, USSR) abbreviated GNTK. The GNTK sponsored 40 to 50 periodicals. [The GNTK was abolished by the decree of the Council of Ministers on April 12, 1961 (cf. *Pravda,* April 12, 1961). Its functions were turned over to the newly established State Committee for Coordination of Research.]

The sponsors of trade journals are identified on the title page, usually on the masthead, by a statement "organ" of such and such a body—e.g., *Organ* (or *Zhurnal*) *Gosudarstvennogo Komiteta Soveta Ministrov SSSR po Khimii, Zhurnal Gosudarstvennogo Nauchno-Tekhnicheskogo Komiteta Soveta Ministrov SSSR, Organ Gosudarstvennogo Komiteta Soveta Ministrov SSSR po Delam Stroitel'stva, Organ Ministerstva Sel'skogo Khozyaĭstva SSSR.* There can be joint sponsorship—e.g., for *Gazovaya Promyshlennost'* the sponsors are Glavnoe Upravlenie Gazovoĭ Promyshlennosti pri Sovete Ministrov SSSR (Gas Industry Administration of the Council of Ministers USSR), Ministerstvo Kommunal'nogo Khozyaĭstva RSFSR (Ministry of Communal Affairs of RSFSR), and Nauchno-Tekhnicheskoe Obshchestvo Energeticheskoĭ Promyshlennosti (Scientific and Technical Association of the Power Generating Industry).

The publishers of the trade journals are distinct from the sponsors and have their own names. Some of these were mentioned above.

INDUSTRIAL INSTITUTES. The trade journals are industry-wide and deal only with general organizational and production topics. Industrial research is carried on in industrial research institutes.

Most of these institutes publish serials more or less frequently. They are usually called *Trudy, Sbornik Rabot,* or *Sbornik Stateĭ,* modified by the name of the institute—*Trudy, Gosudarstvennyĭ Naucho-Issledovatel'skiĭ Institut Tsementnoĭ Promyshlennosti* (State Institute of Cement Technology); *Sbornik Stateĭ, Vsesoyuznyĭ Nauchno-Issledovatel'skiĭ Institut Khimicheskogo Mashinostroeniya* (All-Union Institute of Chemical Equipment Building); and *Sbornik Rabot, Gosudarstvennyĭ Institut Prikladnoĭ Khimii* (State Institute of Applied Chemistry).

Some material can have more than one use and is thus likely to be the subject of study by more than one institute. For example, steel is studied by the Ural'skiĭ Industrial'nyĭ Institut im. S. N. Kirova, which publishes *Trudy* and is sponsored by the Ministry of Metallurgy. It is also studied by the Tsentral'nyĭ Nauchno-Issledovatel'skiĭ Institut, which also publishes its work as *Trudy* and is sponsored by the Shipbuilding Ministry, by the Institute of the Ministry of Equipment and Apparatus Building, and so on.

Government agencies other than GNTK also sponsor publications. *Standartizatsiya* is sponsored by the Standardization Administration, Upravlenie po Standartizatsii pri Gosplane SSSR. Another is *Byulleten' Izobreteniĭ* (*Bulletin of Inventions*) sponsored by the Komitet po Delam Izobreteniĭ i Otkrytiĭ pri Sovete Ministrov SSSR (Committee on Inventions and Discoveries of the Council of Ministers USSR).

SOCIETIES. Learned societies in the Soviet Union also sponsor publications, but these are underwritten and published by the academy, a university, or a ministry.

So the All-Union Mineralogical Society, Vsesoyuznoe Mineralogicheskoe Obshchestvo, sponsors *Zapiski,* which is published by the USSR Academy of Sciences. The Leningrad Society of Naturalists, Leningradskoe Obshchestvo Estestvoispitateleĭ, sponsors *Trudy,* which is published by the Leningrad University, while the Pirogov Surgical Society, Khirurgicheskoe Obshchestvo Pirogova, sponsors *Vestnik Khirurgii im. Grekova,* published by the Ministry of Health.

There are other publications in the same category, such as the Moscow Society of Naturalists, Moskovskoe Obshchestvo Ispitateleĭ Prirody, sponsoring *Byulleten'* in two series—biology and geology—all published by the Moscow University.

OTHER SPONSORING BODIES. Museums, botanical gardens, biological field stations, observatories, and similar establishments issue serials in their respective fields.

Significance of Titles. The name or title of a periodical publication is indicative of its sponsor. *Zhurnal* is reserved for regular periodicals published by the USSR Academy and the Ukrainian Academy. *Doklady* and *Vestnik* are used for the main publications of the various academies; *Izvestiya* is used for publications of academy departments. Institute publications of academies and industrial bodies are called *Trudy. Uchenye Zapiski, Nauchnye Zapiski,* and *Nauchnyĭ Byulleten'* are used for university publications. The titles of trade journals are highly specific —*Ugol* (*Coal*), *Stal* (*Steel*), *Khimicheskaya Promyshlennost'* (*Chemical Industry*), *Spirtovaya Promyshlennost'* (*Alcohol Industry*), *Tsement* (*Cement*), *Steklo i Keramika* (*Glass and Ceramics*), and so on.

This, however, is not a hard and fast rule. There is also a *Zhurnal Mikrobiologii, Epidemiologii i Immunobiologii,* published by the Ministry of Health, and a *Vestnik Rentgenologii i Radiologii,* published by the same ministry. The Moscow and Leningrad universities publish a *Vestnik* each, while the USSR Academy publishes such specific titles as *Mikrobiologiya* and *Biokhimiya.*

Review Journals. The Scientific Information Branch of the Publishers of Foreign Literature, Upravlenie Nauchnoĭ Informatsii, Izdatel'stvo Inostrannoĭ Literatury, in Moscow, which evidently is connected with the Ministry of Culture, Ministerstvo Kul'tury SSSR, publishes a number of condensed translations of foreign scientific and technical literature. Each of these publications is devoted to some field of science or technology—e.g., *Khimiya i Khimicheskaya Tekhnologiya, Problemy Sovremennoĭ Fiziki* (*Problems of Contemporary Physics*), *Problemy Sovremennoĭ Metallurgii, Mekhanika* (*Engineering*), *Antibiotiki,* and so on. These contain condensed translations of foreign periodical literature. The same body also publishes a review of foreign scientific books, called *Novye Knigi za Rubezhem* (*New Books Abroad*).

Abstract Journals. The Institute of Scientific Information, Institut Nauchnoĭ Informatsii, of the USSR Academy started in 1953 a series of abstract journals in chemistry, physics, engineering, astronomy, and mathematics. At present the institute is publishing 16 abstract journals in astronomy and geodesy, biological chemistry, biology, electrical and power engineering, physics, geophysics, geography, geology, mining, chemistry, machine building, mathematics, mechanics, metallurgy, and transport. In addition, the institute publishes *Referativnyĭ Sbornik: Ekonomika Promyshlennosti,* which includes abstracts of selected material (domestic and foreign) on industrial organization, cooperation, productivity, cost, automation, standardization, financing, training of personnel (all levels), and related problems. The name of the entire series is *Referativnyĭ Zhurnal* and each series is identified by a specific designation—*Referativnyĭ Zhurnal, Khimiya, Referativnyĭ*

Zhurnal, Fizika, and so on. The format and the two-column arrangement resemble those of *Chemical Abstracts.* The abstracts are numbered consecutively, a practice followed by the *Bulletin analytique;* the arrangement of subject matter resembles that of *Chemisches Zentralblatt.*

The most voluminous series of the *Referativnyĭ Zhurnal* is that of chemistry, officially abbreviated as *RZhKhim.* It started appearing in October 1953 and continues in two issues a month. The material, both foreign and domestic, which is covered by the abstracts has been published since January 1, 1953. The names of non-Russian authors are given in Russian and in the original language; even Chinese characters are used where needed. Each issue contains an author index in Russian of all the names and a Latin alphabet index of foreign authors as well as a Chinese index. Foreign names in the Russian index present a problem. The Russian language transliterates phonetically. Thus, our Hildebrand and the German Hildebrandt do not appear in consecutive order. The "l" in the German name is labialized, calling for a soft sign in Russian transliteration. The soft sign is well toward the end of the Russian alphabet and therefore the German Hildebrandt is listed way below our Hildebrand.

Referativnyĭ Zhurnal, Khimiya published in its six issues of 1953 10,042 abstracts or an average of 1674 abstracts per issue. Extrapolating this figure for 24 issues, the annual output of *RZhKhim.* for its first year would be 40,176 abstracts. In 1955 the number of abstracts printed was 57,470 and in 1960 99,365. These figures do not give a complete picture. *Biologicheskaya Khimiya,* although issued separately, is a part of *Khimiya.* Adding the number of abstracts in *Biologicheskaya Khimiya* to the above figures would make it 75,474 in 1955 and 134,547 abstracts in 1960. Thus the number of abstracts published in *Referativnyĭ Zhurnal, Khimiya* more than tripled in seven years.

The abstracts are informative, the print is clear and legible, the paper is of good quality.

Occasionally, *Referativnyĭ Zhurnal, Khimiya* reprints abstracts from *Chemical Abstracts,* giving the latter credit.

Price of Publications. It is hard to arrive at a general rule as to how Soviet Union publications are priced in relation to number of pages or some other physical feature. There is, however, a clearly discernible price policy relating to the purpose of a publication. Publications of the popular kind in the field of hygiene, health, medicine, and agriculture are priced very low. Generally, publications of higher professional levels cost more. Some university publications are free. The price of a publication is printed at the top left corner of the back cover.

Colophon. Introduced at the beginning of printing and now almost universally abandoned, the colophon is still in use on Soviet publications. It is usually printed at the bottom of the last page or on the verso of the title page. It tells when the material was sent to the printer, when it was set in type, the format, the paper used, the number of printed copies, and similar information.

Distribution. The distribution of published material in the Soviet Union is handled by Soyuzpechat, which is an agency of the Ministry of Communication, Ministerstvo Syazi SSSR.

The Soyuzpechat maintains direct outlets and agencies throughout the Soviet Union and in countries outside it.

The academy has its own outlets, Akademkniga, in the major cities of the Soviet Union.

University publications, except those of the Moscow and Leningrad universities, are not generally distributed by Soyuzpechat.

Facts and Figures

When starting a literature search for published material in a particular field, one usually consults a library catalog for the call number, which indicates the location of the material on the library shelves. It is comparatively simple in the case of monographs but much more complicated in the case of periodical and similar material which is not easily classifiable within the frame of a subject catalog. Here, the searcher may have to know the specific title: *Iron Age, Pit and Quarry, Glückauf,* and so on. If he is trying to find the *Journal of the American Chemical Society, Transactions of the Faraday Society,* or *Trudy Vsesoyuznogo-Issledovatel'skogo Instituta Lubyanykh Volokon,* he had better start with a guide to the catalog, for these publications are not listed under the obvious titles.

Essential Background Information. The literature searcher will be greatly aided if he knows something of the literature which he is about to search. Not the subject—for this is a *conditio sine qua non*—but the background of the published body of information. This background comprises research institutes, universities and professional schools, sponsoring bodies, publishers, and some aspects of publishing technique. The results of his search will be directly proportional to the extent of the searcher's knowledge of this background. It is of special importance when searching the literature published in the Soviet Union, not only because of language difficulties, but also because Soviet scientific literature is not generally available and bibliographical guides to it are equally scarce. Furthermore, Soviet publishing and its distribution pattern differ widely from our own and from the ones with which we are familiar.

The first question which I expect to be asked is "Of what value is information about material which we do not have nor are able to obtain?" The implication of this question is correct on the face of it. If archeologists were to announce that they had proof of the existence of a papyrus which gave the composition of the writing dye used in ancient Egypt, but the papyrus itself was lost, the ink chemists, much as they would like to know the composition that had defied time, would dismiss the whole matter as immaterial and irrelevant. What the chemists want is information in the papyrus and not about the papyrus.

However, this analogy is only superficial. The scientific and technical literature of the Soviet Union is quite unlike the papyrus. This literature is not lost; it exists, and moreover, it is potentially available to us.

The degree to which we can convert the potentially available to direct use depends in large measure on what we want. If the search is to be effective and not a floundering in a nebulous world of unknown quantities, we must be able to look for a specific publication having a title, an issuing body, a publisher, and similar data defining published matter.

Not long ago a representative of one of our largest and best equipped libraries consulted me on how to obtain scientific and technical publications from the USSR. When asked what it was specifically that his library wanted, he was vague and assured me that they had ample funds to buy "everything" of a scientific and technical nature to satisfy the many and various demands of their readers. Not having a special selection officer, the library has placed orders for "everything," yet receipts are meager. I could not help wondering how it is possible to estimate receipts when you do not know what you are supposed to receive. Blanket orders for "everything published" may work, but only barely, in areas where the incentive of profit is operative. In the USSR, where private enterprise is nonexistent and the motive of financial profit absent, such orders are totally useless.

To obtain USSR publications you have to know what you want and know it well. This is one of the reasons for the present paper.

In 1948 I compiled a list of USSR publications of possible interest to chemists. The list contained approximately 500 titles. That list was amended in 1950 and again recently. If brought up to date, it would contain between 700 and 800 titles, possibly even more. The number of items would be vastly increased if it were to include other sciences and engineering.

The titles in the 1948 list were divided into three groups:

A. Publications devoted to chemistry, chemical engineering, and closely related fields: ceramics, ore dressing, and metallurgy.

B. Publications of primary interest to other sciences but in which chemistry is of great importance: geology, pedology, microbiology, bacteriology, and physiology.

C. Publications in fields unrelated to chemistry or chemical engineering but where chemical properties of materials or subjects of study are significant: mechanical engineering, electrical engineering, geophysics, astrophysics, medicine, veterinary science, public health, etc.

Of the titles entered on that list 18.53% fell in group A, 31.03% in group B, and 50.44% in group C. Thus, groups A and B accounted for 49.56% of the items.

Basic research in the USSR is carried on predominantly by the academies and universities, and the results are reported accordingly in academy and university publications. Industrial and applied research is carried on in industrial training and research institutes, usually called Nauchno-Issledovatel'skiĭ Institut, and in technological institutes, called Politekhnicheskiĭ Institut. Scientific research is also conducted in pedagogical institutes, Pedagogicheskiĭ Institut, and the publications of these institutes contain very good papers.

There are scores of these industrial training and research institutes in the USSR. Their fields range from training and research in confectionery and pastry, Institut Konditorskoĭ Promyshlennosti, and leather and footware, Institut Kozhevenno-Obuvnoĭ Promyshlennosti, to steel, Institut Stali, and chemical intermediates, Institut Khimicheskikh Poluproduktov. Many of the institutes provide for further academic training, analogous to our postgraduate work, leading to higher academic degrees. In this phase of their work the institutes are subject to regulations of the Ministry of Higher Education, Ministerstvo Vysshego Obrazovaniya.

The industrial training and research institutes carry on research for an entire field of industry—e.g., cement, steel, or glass—and not for one particular plant or industrial establishment which they call "kombinat" roughly comparable to our corporation. The results of research carried out in these institutes are usually published in full in their own serials. The material included in theses and submitted in partial fulfillment of requirements for academic degrees are published is condensed form and are usually referred to as "Avtoreferat dissertatsii."

Patent practices of the USSR are different from ours and those of other countries. A patent is granted for a discovery, an invention, or an improvement by the Patent Commission of the Council of Ministers. The inventor is compensated and the invention, if it has merits, is incorporated where it is applicable. The patent has no restrictive force.

Patent specifications are published in a form similar to ours and the abstracts are published in the *Bulletin of Inventions, Byullleten' Izobreteniĭ*, which is roughly comparable to the *Official Gazette, United States Patent Office* (2).

Individual plants (zavod, fabrika) or corporations (kombinat) usually have their own control and experimental laboratories. Papers written by members of these laboratories are usually published in the industrial journals.

Judging from our receipts and available information, the largest volume of printed matter appears to be issued by the Ministry of Agriculture, Ministerstvo Sel'skogo Khozyaĭstva SSSR, and the Ministry of Health, Ministerstvo Zdravookhraneniya SSSR.

The publications of the industrial institutes are serials rather than periodicals and they are not readily available. Some of the reasons for this will be discussed later.

The scientific and technical publications can be roughly divided into groups:

1. Those published by the academy, its subdivisions and institutes, and by the major universities, Moscow, Leningrad, Kiev, Kazan, and others. These publications report fundamental research in their respective fields.
2. Publications of the industrial training and research institutes. These report predominantly applied research.
3. Industrial publications reporting little research and dealing mainly with plant-laboratory tests of a practical nature.

There are no hard and fast rules, and the demarcation lines are easily crossed. For that matter, the very division between fundamental and applied science can hardly be very clear-cut.

The academies of the Federated Republics, with the exception of the Ukranian Academy, cannot afford as sharp a division between fundamental and applied research. Of necessity they have to deal with problems peculiar to their regions and this is reflected in the contents of their publications. For the same reason, the level and contents of their publications are uneven.

The same is true of the material published by the many provincial universities, which do not have as large teaching staffs and are not of as high caliber as the major universities.

Recently, 715 USSR scientific and technical periodical publications falling within the three above-mentioned groups—i.e., containing material of interest to chemists—were examined to ascertain their sponsoring bodies and fields of interest.

With reference to the sponsoring body, the publications are grouped as follows:

1. Academies and their subdivisions	215 or 30.0%
2. Universities, pedagogical institutes, schools of agriculture, of medicine, and other professional schools	196 or 27.4%
3. Industrial training and research institutes	141 or 19.9%
4. Miscellaneous	17 or 2.3%
5. Trade journals	146 or 20.4%

The "miscellaneous" group comprises publications of professional societies, such as the All-Union Engineering Society, All-Union Chemical Society, All-Union Mineralogical Society, Metallurgical Society, Society of Physiologists, Biochemists, and Pharmacologists, or the Society of Naturalists.

The bodies grouped in (2) and (3) are essentially schools and can therefore be grouped together; in this list they account for 337 publications or 47.3%. Some of the schools, notably the universities, and particularly the large ones, emphasize theoretical research, while the engineering, technology, and other professional schools stress applied research.

With reference to their subject fields, the 715 titles can be grouped as follows:

Field	Count	Field	Count
Agriculture	100 or 14.0%	Geology and geophysics	59 or 8.3%
Astronomy and mathematics	13 or 1.8%	Medicine	120 or 16.8%
Biology, botany, and zoology	51 or 7.1%	Mining and metallurgy	39 or 5.5%
Building, heavy industry, power	50 or 7.0%	Petroleum	13 or 1.8%
Chemistry	51 or 7.1%	Physics	14 or 1.9%
Engineering	23 or 3.2%	Process industries	38 or 5.3%
Food industry	22 or 3.2%	Miscellaneous	3 or 0.4%
General	119 or 16.6%		

This is a rather rough classification. Agriculture includes pedology, agronomy, animal husbandry, poultry, apiculture, veterinary medicine, etc. The "general" group includes publications which cover several subject fields—e.g., *Doklady, Vestnik,* and *Soobshcheniya* of the academies, the general publications of academy branches, and the general publications of universities. The publications of academies, universities, and institutes having specific subject fields are grouped in the respective fields. Geology and geophysics also include prospecting, engineering geology, geodesy, mineralogy, petrography, oceanography, hydrology, limnology, vulcanology, etc. Medicine includes surgery, pathology, physiology, pharmacology, nutrition, public health, hygiene, sanitation, immunology, etc. Process industries include textiles, leather, rubber, cement, etc. The "miscellaneous" group includes patents, standardization, and instrumentation.

This should leave no doubt that a large volume of scientific and technical literature is published in the Soviet Union and that a large portion of it is of interest to scientists, engineers, and bioscientists.

A good knowledge of the nature and quality of these publications, a knowledge extending horizontally and vertically, is indispensable for effective and efficient search of USSR scientific and technical literature. By horizontal and vertical distribution is here understood the distribution with respect to field of interest (steel, dyes, cement) and the professional level within the specific field (theoretical considerations, manufacturing practices, production, plant safety, etc.). Such knowledge is essential in searching the literature in any language, but since fewer of us know Russian than other major languages, because USSR literature is not generally available, and because few if any reliable guides to it are extant, this background knowledge is much more important.

To take a specific example: If you are interested in naval stores, it would be futile to search the publications of the Armenian Academy, or of the Crimean Branch of the USSR Academy, or of the Kishinev University. This particular search should concentrate on the publications of the Forest Technology Institute, *Sbornik Nauchno-Issledovatel'skikh Rabot, Lesotekhnicheskiĭ Institut,* those of the Forest Technology Academy, *Trudy, Lesotekhnicheskaya Akademiya,* of the Belorussian Forest-Technology Institute, *Sbornik Nauchnykh Trudov, Belorusskiĭ Lesotekhnicheskiĭ Institut,* the publications of the Siberian Branch of the USSR Academy, Sibirskiĭ Filial Academii Nauk SSSR, of the Ural Branch, Ural'skiĭ Filial Akademii Nauk SSR, of the several Siberian universities, or the pertinent publications of the Latvian and Lithuanian academies and universities, to mention the most important sources.

The same holds true for any of the innumerable problems a literature searcher is likely to face.

The background information is essential for the literature chemist, and it is paramount for library procurement officers and the science reference librarian.

Size of Editions. It is obvious that the size of an edition greatly affects the availability of a publication. One can argue that to satisfy the demand the publisher should increase the number of printed copies. This is a point I am in no position to answer. Still other factors which limit the distribution of USSR publications are discussed further on.

Ordinarily, the number of printed copies is of little interest to the chemist searching the literature. If a publication is needed but not available in the library, its purchase can be requested even if this means ordering it from abroad. In the worst case, a reprint of a particular paper or a photocopy can be obtained. This is not the case with USSR publications. Unless the publication is available at our national library (Library of Congress), you cannot obtain it.

This is one of the reasons why a knowledge of Soviet publishing practices is important to the searcher of Soviet scientific and technical literature. The size of editions is part of general publishing practices.

For the purpose of examining the size of editions—i.e., the number of printed copies as it varies with the character of the publication and over a period of time—100 titles currently received in this country were selected. These publications comprise predominantly periodicals—i.e., publications scheduled to appear at definite time intervals—and a few serials or publications appearing continuously but having no definite periodicity.

Of the selected titles 76 are published by bodies of the central government: the USSR Academy of Sciences publishes 24 and the ministries (since the reorganization of the central administration the GNTK, now replaced by the State Committee for Coordination of Research) publish 52 of this selection. Eleven other titles are the various series of *Referativnyĭ Zhurnal.* Ten others are published by the academies of the Federated Republics, and the rest by universities.

The 76 publications of the central government can be grouped with respect to their fields as follows:

1. Pure (predominantly) and applied chemistry	20
2. Agriculture	10
3. Food	8
4. Process industries	8
5. Heavy industries	8
6. Power	4
7. Mining	3
8. Nutrition, pharmacology, hygiene, health, and medicine	15

The professional level of the selected publications varies from those which are intended for technicians and industrial foremen to publications of purely theoretical interest.

No attempt was made to subdivide the publications of the Federated Republics. For the purpose of this essay they have certain characteristics in common and therefore are discussed as a group.

The main publication of a university, if it appears in one series, includes both humanities and sciences. Frequently, two series are published, one devoted to humanities and the other to natural and mathematical sciences. If a university publishes more than one serial, such as *Vestnik* and *Nauchnye* or *Uchenye Zapiski,* the *Zapiski* (usually a serial) may contain papers in more than one department of sciences or it may be devoted to chemistry in one issue, to physics, geology, or other fields in subsequent issues.

University publications, be they of Moscow, Petrozavodsk, or Tashkent, have certain points in common and are discussed together.

The period covered by this study extends from 1940 to 1960 and the comparative surveys were made at 5-year intervals. In 1940, or just before the war, the output of scientific and technical literature in the USSR was normal for that time. Immediately following the outbreak of the war, the number of publications and the size of editions dropped. Publications in related fields combined and others were suspended. The downward trend continued to about 1945, at which time it started upward again. In 1950 the recovery was completed. In 1954–55 new titles appeared in number and the size of editions increased greatly.

Of the publications examined, *Sovetskaya Meditsina* has the largest number of printed copies—58,000. This publication is sponsored by the Ministry of Health (Ministerstvo Zdravookhraneniya SSSR) and is published by Medgiz, the publishing arm of the same ministry. Among the publications issued by the Academy, the serial *Izvestiya Sektora Platiny i Drugikh Blagorodnykh Metallov* had the smallest number of copies—1500. It dealt with noble metals and their coordination compounds, the work being done by a subdivision of the Department of General and Inorganic Chemistry in the USSR Academy of Sciences. It was published by the Academy (*Izvestiya* ceased publication in 1956). The second and third largest editions, 55,000 and 43,000, respectively, are those of *Veterinariya* and *Energetik,* the former (*Veterinary Medicine*) sponsored by the Ministry of Agriculture (Ministerstvo Sel'skogo Khozyaĭstva SSSR) and published by Sel'khozgiz, and the latter (*Power Engineer*) sponsored by the Ministry of Power Generating Stations (Ministerstvo Elektrostantsii SSSR) (since the reorganization of the central administration by GNTK) and now by the State Committee for Coordination of Research and published by Gosenergizdat.

I do not know what determines the number of printed copies of a USSR publication nor the relation between cost and return from sales. It is justifiable to assume that the need of a publication—i.e., the number of readers—is largely responsible for the number of copies printed. Undoubtedly, the government can stimulate the demand by its pricing policies. The cheapest are popular publications in the field of public health and agriculture.

Of the academy publications examined, the largest editions were those of the *Vestnik Akademii Nauk SSSR* (the house organ of the academy), 7625 copies; *Uspekhi Khimii* (*Advances in Chemistry*), 6725 copies; and *Zhurnal Analiticheskoĭ Khimii* (*Analytical Chemistry*), 6625 copies. The smallest editions were those of *Izvestiya Sektora Platiny* and *Izvestiya Sektora Fiziko-Khimicheskogo Analiza,* 1500 copies each; *Trudy Pochvennogo Instituta* (*Soil Institute*) and *Trudy Instituta Fiziologii Rastenii* (*Plant Physiology*), around 2000 copies each; and *Kolloidnyĭ Zhurnal,* 3080 copies.

Periodical publications of the food industry, *Molochnaya Promyshlennost* (*Dairy Industry*) and *Rybnoe Khozyaĭstvo* (*Fishing Industry*) have 9800 copies each, while *Spirtovaya Promyshlennost* (*Alcohol Industry*), 3250, *Tabak* (*Tobacco*), and *Sakharnaya Promyshlennost* (*Sugar Industry*), 4000 copies each, have the lowest number.

In the process industries the size of editions varies from 8100 copies for *Legkaya Promyshlennost* (*Light Industry*) and *Tekstil'naya Promyshlennost* (*Textile Industry*) to 3650 copies for *Tsement* (*Cement*).

The size of editions for the three mining journals—*Gornyĭ Zhurnal* (*Mining Journal*), *Neftyanoe Khozyaĭstvo* (*Petroleum Industry*), and *Ugol'* (*Coal*)—is 8650, 6700, and 10,700 copies, respectively.

Power, machine, and metallurgical industries have large editions, with an average of over 10,000 copies. The sole exception is the recently reappearing

Ogneupory (*Refractories*) with 3450 copies. (In 1960 the edition rose to 4610.)

The increase in the number of copies printed in 1955 over that of 1940 or 1939 (whichever was available for examination) is very substantial, except in the case of one publication *Zavodskaya Laboratoriya* (*Industrial Laboratory*), where there was a decrease of 16.7%. (In 1960 the edition rose to 9800, which is appreciably larger than the 1940 figure of 7629.)

For academy publications, the increase ranges from 41% for *Pochvovedenie* (*Pedology*) and 43% for *Zhurnal Obshcheĭ Khimii* (*Journal of General Chemistry*) to 148% for *Izvestiya Akademii Nauk, Otdelenie Tekhnicheskikh Nauk* (*Division of Technological Sciences*) and 221% for *Zhurnal Analiticheskoĭ Khimii.* The average increase in the number of copies of periodicals printed in the field of heavy industry is 68.6% and ranges from 200% for *Vestnik Mashinostroeniya* (*Machine Construction*) to minus 16.7% for *Zavodskaya Laboratoriya.*

The increase in the size of editions in 1955 over that of 1940 or 1939 of periodical publications in the fields of mining, power, medicine, and agriculture is of the same order of magnitude. Periodicals of the Ukrainian Academy of Sciences appear in 1000 to 1200 copies, an exception being *Avtomaticheskaya Svarka* (*Automatic Welding*), 5000 copies. The Kazakh Academy of Sciences prints 1200 copies of its *Vestnik.* Most of the academies of the other Federated Republics print 700 to 750 copies of each of their periodicals.

The *Vestnik* of the Moscow and Leningrad universities appear in 1400 to 1600 copies, the *Nauchnye* and *Uchenye Zapiski* of most of the universities appear in 700 copies or less. Some of the provincial university publications, not included in this survey, appear in approximately 300 copies.

The *Referativnyĭ Zhurnal* series appears in 21,950 copies. Of these the largest edition is that of the *Khimiya* series (4850 copies) and the smallest is the *Biologicheskaya Khimiya* (1500 copies). The latter was split out from *Khimiya* and is actually a part of it; thus, the chemistry series appears in 6350 copies. The other series, *Fizika, Geologiya i Geografiya, Astronomiya i Geodeziya, Mekhanika,* and *Biologiya,* appear in approximately 3000 copies each.

In 1956–8, the time coinciding with the decentralization, major changes were wrought in the publication program. Important publications were suspended and new ones were started, so that by 1960 some of the important old publications which had become too bulky and expensive were split up. Among these was the *Izvestiya Akademii Nauk, Otdelenie Tekhnicheskikh Nauk* with an edition of 2250 in 1940 and 5650 in 1955, which was split in 1959 into three separate bimonthlies: *Mekhanika i Mashinostroenie, Energetika i Avtomatika,* and *Metallurgiya i Toplivo* with a total edition of 8760 in 1960. New journals were started, among which are *Zhurnal Neorganicheskoĭ Khimii* (*Inorganic Chemistry*), a monthly started in 1956; *Radiokhimiya* (*Radiochemistry*), a bimonthly started in 1959; *Geokhimiya* (*Geochemistry*), started in 1956 with eight issues per year; *Fizika Tverdogo Tela* (*Solid State Physics*), a bimonthly started in 1959; *Plasticheskie Massy* (*Plastics*), a monthly started in 1960; *Khimicheskie Volokna* (*Synthetic Fibers*), a bimonthly started in 1959; *Khimicheskoe Mashinostroenie* (*Chemical Equipment*), a bimonthly started in 1959; and *Lakokrasochnye Materialy i ikh Primenenie* (*Paints, Varnishes and Their Use*), a bimonthly started in 1960.

The size of the editions of many journals mentioned before has decreased somewhat. As new more specialized journals appeared, the size of the editions of the more general periodicals was cut back. Greater specialization also affected the *Referativnyĭ Zhurnal* series. In addition to the general volume, *Khimiya* now publishes nine separates. *Metallurgiya* issues nine separates in addition to the general volume, *Mashinostroenie* issues 20 separates; *Biologiya,* 12 separates, *Geologiya,* five separates; and *Geofizika,* four.

The knowledge of these facts will not by itself produce Soviet publications when needed, but it will aid materially in searching the literature, and in combination with other factors will be helpful in procuring USSR scientific literature.

Distribution

Numerous publications of interest to scientists appear in the Soviet Union. Many of these can be obtained readily by subscription; others, only by exchange with the issuing institutions. Recently, the Soviet Government promulgated regulations permitting corporate bodies to enter into direct exchange arrangement with foreign bodies. The next step is up to us.

The seemingly straightforward path with an examination should take becomes a winding maze when one attempts to unravel the interrelationship among the main administration of publishing houses, the printing industry, and the book trade (Glavizdat) which is a department of the Ministry of Culture (Ministerstvo Kul'tury SSSR), the very same publishing houses within the jurisdiction of the various ministries, and other central government bodies, and the book trade bodies of the Federated Republics, autonomous areas, and other administratively autonomous regions.

Here we are not greatly concerned with the organizational features of the book trade in the Soviet Union. However, an over-all picture of it will be very helpful in understanding why certain publications are readily obtainable here while others are not, how book exchange with the USSR operates, and similar questions.

Editing, publishing, and distributing printed matter are three distinct and separate activities in the Soviet Union.

Since 1953 the publishing, printing, and distributing of books, periodicals, posters, sheet music, etc., have been centered in Glavizdat (Glavnoe upravlenie izdatel'stv poligraficheskoĭ promyshlennosti i knizhnoĭ torgovli). The Glavizdat is within the Ministry of Culture (Ministerstvo Kul'tury SSSR). It administers the production and distribution of printed matter regardless of the jurisdiction to which a publishing house or a book trade organization belongs. Thus, the publishing house Metallurgizdat, for example, is under the jurisdiction of the Ministry of Ferrous and Nonferrous Metallurgy and the book trade organization Soyuzpechat is under the jurisdiction of the Ministry of Communication, yet the over-all administration of both is vested in the Glavizdat. The Glavizdat has three branches: Upravlenie izdatel'stv, Upravlenie poligraficheskoĭ promyshlennosti, and Upravlenie knizhnoĭ torgovli, of which the former two deal with publishing and printing, respectively, and the third, Soyuzknigtorg, directs the distribution of printed matter. The Soyuzknigtorg supplies books, periodicals, etc., to other booksellers and also maintains retail outlets (bookstores and bookstalls, kiosk). It sells books, etc., by mail and has traveling book vendors for rural and sparsely populated areas.

When a publishing house (Izdatel'stvo) plans to issue a book, monograph, journal, or other printed material, the Glavizdat provides it with information about the possible volume of sale derived either on the basis of a survey or past performance. The format, size of the edition, required paper, ink, and binding supplies are worked out, and time schedules are set for the delivery of the product by the publisher to the Glavizdat. The date of delivery, quality, packaging, etc., are embodied in a contract secured by penalty clauses. The Glavizdat supplies the publisher with paper, binding materials, etc., and production starts. When the finished product is received by the Glavizdat, it is then distributed to wholesalers and retailers.

Until recently, before the production of a book or periodical was started quotas were set for each outlet. Thus, the outlets received a definite number of previously assigned copies. If the demand exceeded the supply of the particular outlet, prospective buyers were turned down. The same applied to subscriptions to periodicals. Subscriptions were accepted to the limit of the quota for a given area and no more. Thus, if you lived in Minsk, for example, which had a quota of 100 copies of *Stal'* and because of a cold you came a day late, thus becoming the hundred-and-first subscriber, you were out of luck and your subscription was not accepted. Now the quotas for almost all scientific and technical publications are abolished and subscriptions are accepted without limitation.

Bookstores are emptied a day or two after a new shipment arrives and periodical subscriptions have to be placed four to five months in advance. Titles not available in one city can be readily bought in another. Occasionally, back issues become available a year, or two, or three after subscription to them was refused. The person whose task it is to procure Soviet Union publications should keep this in mind.

The largest book trading organization specializing in periodical literature is the Soyuzpechat', belonging to the Ministry of Communication. Its full name is Glavnoe upravlenie rasprostraneniya i ekspedirovaniya pechati Ministerstva Svyazi SSSR. The Soyuzpechat' maintains a large network of bookstores, bookstalls, carriers, etc., throughout the Soviet Union.

Other book trading organizations are Potrebitel'skaya Kooperatsiya (Consumers' Cooperative) distributing books, etc., in rural areas. Voenknigtorg maintains bookstores in military establishments. Transpechat supplies books, etc., to railroad workers and their families.

The above mentioned are all-union organizations—i.e., they sell publications put out by the central publishing houses throughout the Soviet Union. In addition, each Federated Republic and autonomous area has a publishing and bookselling organization of its own. The Glavizdat supplies the local book trading organizations with the output of the central publishing houses and purchases from them the output of the local publishing houses for distribution outside the local limits.

The publications of the Federated Republics and autonomous areas have a very limited distribution outside their own borders and it is difficult to subscribe to them or buy them.

Since the establishment of Glavizdat (1953) the publishing houses have been freed of the chore of selling their own output and the Glavizdat does it for them. The only exception is the Academy of Sciences, which maintains a bookselling unit for its publications, Akademkniga. The Akademkniga maintains outlets in the principal cities of the Soviet Union.

The book trade outside the Soviet Union is carried on by the Mezhdunarodnaya Kniga (International Book), an organization of the Ministry of External Trade (Ministerstvo Vneshneĭ Torgovli SSSR). This organization maintains outlets in most countries outside the USSR where Soviet books can be bought and through which periodical subscriptions may be placed. These outlets issue lists of periodicals available for subscription and will accept orders only for items listed. It is possible that a publication not available in New York can be subscribed to in Paris, London, or Stockholm.

Another organization within the Ministry of Culture is the Vsesoyuznaya Knizhnaya Palata (All-Union Book Palace) charged with maintaining the National Bibliography of the Soviet Union. The law provides that the Vsesoyuznaya Knizhnaya Palata receive one or more copies of each item printed anywhere in the Soviet Union. The material received by the Knizhnaya Palata is recorded in a series of bibliographies called *Letopis'* (*Record*) published by the Knizhnaya Palata. Of primary interest to the searcher of scientific and technical literature are the *Knizhnaya Letopis'* (*Book Record*) and the *Letopis' Zhurnal'nykh Stateĭ* (*Record of Periodical Articles*). There is also a record of newspaper articles, one for music, one for art, and so on. The *Record of Periodicals,* issued weekly, comprises a briefly annotated listing of articles published in the periodical literature arranged by subject. Each issue has an alphabetical index of periodicals reviewed in that particular issue.

The *Letopis' Zhurnal'nykh Stateĭ* is not a very efficient tool for subject searching. It is of primary importance as a title bibliography—i.e., a listing of what is being published.

Exchanges. Of paramount importance to the literature chemist are the two main libraries of the Soviet Union: the Lenin State Library (Gosudarstvennaya Biblioteka im. Lenina) in Moscow and the library of the Academy of Sciences (Biblioteka Akademii Nauk SSSR) in Leningrad. These two libraries are important not only because of their wealth but also because they are actively engaged in book exchange. Until recently, these were the only exchange agencies in the Soviet Union. No other body would enter into direct exchange agreements with foreign institutions. In 1951 *Chemical Abstracts* addressed exchange proposals to most of the republic academies, to a number of universities, and to some research institutes. Some of the letters were written in English and others in Russian. None were answered. In two cases the library of the Union Academy informed *Chemical Abstracts* that it was the agency through which exchanges with other academies and academy branches must be funneled. Furthermore, the letter informed us that the two academies in question agreed to the *CA* exchange proposal and that since these exchanges are already established the flow of material would be direct between these academies and *CA;* other administrative matters, such as complaints, addition of new titles to the exchange list, etc., should be taken up with the Union Academy Library.

Recently conditions have changed radically for the better. At present, all bodies within the Soviet Union which sponsor or issue publications are encouraged to enter into literature exchange agreements with foreign institutions. They no longer have to channel such agreements through the Lenin State Library or the Academy Library; they may act directly.

Procurement. The three largest recipients of Soviet publications in this country are the Government, the Library of Congress, and *Chemical Abstracts.* To supply the needs of the various departmental and agency libraries (Agriculture, Interior, Commerce, National Library of Medicine, Bureau of Standards, Bureau of Mines, etc.) the Department of State maintains a foreign publications branch which in turn has special personnel, so-called publication procurement officers, stationed in many of our embassies. The departmental and agency libraries submit lists of material which they wish to have along with necessary funds, to the Department of State. The latter instructs the publication officer (P.P.O.) to purchase or place subscriptions for the requisite material and ship it to the respective libraries. In rendering this help to agencies requiring Soviet publications, the Department of State performs a highly important service in a very efficient manner, often under most trying conditions. Since this project started about fifteen years ago, the Department of State has picked a succession of publication procurement officers of skill and devotion. To deal with the unpredictable and often arbitrary bookselling methods and officials in Moscow was—at least until recently—a very trying assignment. To apportion this material equitably among the subscribing agencies in cases when not all the requested copies could be secured, decisions had to be made as to who would get the few available copies, or sometimes the single available copy; this naturally added to the difficulties. All this notwithstanding, even during the period of the "coldest" war more USSR material was being received in this country than in any other outside the Soviet Union. The job done by the Department of State is highly gratifying and well deserves praise from us scientists.

The Library of Congress, acting for itself and cooperatively for several universities, receives by far the greatest volume of USSR publications (books, periodicals, newspapers, etc.). Naturally, only a fraction of this material is of interest to scientists, but this fraction is impressive. The Library of Congress acquires this material by every available means: through the Department of State, by exchange, subscription, and outright purchase wherever possible. As befits a national library, its acquisition program is enormous and very active. Newly acquired Soviet material is reported in the *Monthly Index of Russian Accessions*. Now that the procedure governing exchanges of publications has been relaxed by the USSR, the Library of Congress has started action to enlarge its exchanges materially.

Chemical Abstracts operates an extensive exchange program of its own with the USSR Academy of Sciences and the Lenin State Library, and is about to enlarge it. *Chemical Abstracts* also receives a goodly number of Soviet publications through the good offices of the Department of State and by direct subscription.

Domestic and foreign distribution of Soviet publications is cumbersome and anything but efficient. At least until recently, the difficulties were attributable in part to an inadequate distribution system rather than to ill will. To what extent the recently announced improvements will facilitate our receipts remains to be seen.

How to proceed to get USSR publications? To this end two ways are open: subscription and exchange. Subscriptions are best placed through the outlet of Mezhkniga. In this country it is the Four Continent Book Corp. in New York. Sometime in September this firm distributes a list of titles available for subscription for the coming year. Large subscribers should also examine the lists of titles of the Maison du Livre Étranger in Paris and of Collet's Holdings, Ltd., in London. This is advisable because the listings may vary somewhat and titles not available at one outlet can sometimes be obtained at another.

Not all the wanted publications will be found in the above-mentioned listings. Judging by past experiences, these catalogs will not list university publications except those of Moscow and Leningrad, nor publications of the academy branches, of the various national academies, or of the institutes (professional schools). If the newly announced regulations mean anything, these publications should become available by exchange.

Large scale exchanges are best entered into with the Biblioteka Akademii Nauk SSSR (Library of the Academy of Sciences) and with the Gosudarstvennaya Biblioteka im. Lenina (Lenin State Library). The former will provide only academy publications. The Lenin State Library operates on a much wider basis, but its exchangeable material does not include the above-mentioned categories

Russian Scientific Journals Abstracted in CA (from Original) That Are Also Available in English

Title	Translation Beginning	Frequency	Pages Per Year	Agency	Subscription Price Per Year
Antiobiotiki (Antibiotics)	Jan. 1959	Bimonthly		Consultants Bureau, Inc.	$25
Atomnaya Energiya (Atomic Energy)	1956 issues	Monthly	1200	Consultants Bureau, Inc.	$75
Avtomaticheskaya Svarka (Automatic Welding)	Jan. 1959	Monthly		British Welding Research Association (DSIR)[a]	£10.10s ($29.50)
Biofizika (Biophysics)	1957 issues	Bimonthly	750	Pergamon Press (NIH)[b,e]	$60
Biokhimiya (Biochemistry)	1956 volume	Bimonthly	1100	Consultants Bureau, Inc. (NIH)	$20
Byulleten' Izobreteniĭ (Bulletin of Inventions)	Jan. 1959	Monthly	1800	Pergamon Press	$100
	May 1959			Research Information Service	$120
	1959			Derwent Information Service	
	1959			Technical Information Co.	
Derevoobrabatyvayushchaya Promyshlennost' (Wood Processing Industry)	July 1959 issue	Monthly		Timber Development Association (DSIR)	£5.5s
Doklady Akademii Nauk SSSR (Proceedings of the Academy of Sciences, USSR)					
Agrochemistry papers	1956–58 only	Bimonthly		Consultants Bureau, Inc.	$15
Applied physics papers	1956–58 only	Bimonthly	600	Consultants Bureau, Inc.	$200
Biochemistry papers	1956	Bimonthly	500	American Institute of Biological Sciences (NSF)[c]	$15; $10 to libraries of academic institutions
Biological sciences papers	1957	Bimonthly	900	American Institute of Biological Sciences (NSF)	$20
Chemical technology papers	1956	Bimonthly	100	Consultants Bureau, Inc.	$15
Chemistry papers	1956	Bimonthly	800	Consultants Bureau, Inc.	$110
Geochemistry papers	1956–58	Bimonthly	110	Consultants Bureau, Inc.	$15

Title	*Translation Beginning*	*Frequency*	*Pages per Year*	*Agency*	*Subscription Price per Year*
Doklady Akademii Nauk (continued)					
Geological sciences papers	1957	Bimonthly	750	American Geological Institute (NSF)	$40; $15 to libraries of academic institutions
Physical chemistry papers	1957	Bimonthly	500	Consultants Bureau, Inc.	$160
Farmakologiya i Toksikologiya (*Pharmacology and Toxicology*)	Jan. 1957	Monthly	1000	Consultants Bureau, Inc.	$25
Fizika Metallov i Metallovedenie (*Physics of Metals and Metallography*)	Jan.-Feb. 1957	Bimonthly	1162	*Acta Metallurgica* (NSF)	$40, $20 to libraries of academic institutions
Fizika Tverdogo Tela (*Solid State Physics*)	Jan. 1959	Monthly	2200	American Inst. of Physics (NSF)	$55, $25 to libraries of academic institutions
Fiziologicheskiĭ Zhurnal SSSR im. I. M. Sechenova (*I.M. Sechenov Physiological Journal*)	1957 issues	Monthly	1400	Pergamon Press (NIH)•	$60
Fiziologiya Rasteniĭ (*Plant Physiology*)	1957	Bimonthly	700	Am. Inst. Biological Sciences (NSF)	$15
Geokhimiya (*Geochemistry*)	1956 issues	8 issues per year	800	Geochemical Society (NSF)	$20, $10 to libraries of academic institutions
Geologiya Nefti i Gaza (*Petroleum Geology*)	1958	Semimonthly	1080	Review of Russian Geology	$18
Izvestia Akademii Nauk SSSR (*Bulletin of Academy of Sciences, USSR*)					
Otdelenie Khimicheskikh Nauk (*Division of Chemical Sciences*)	1952	Monthly	1500	Consultants Bureau, Inc.	$80; $30 to libraries of academic institutions
Seriya Fizicheskaya (*Physical Series*)	1954	Monthly	1600	Columbia Technical Translations	$215
Seriya Geofizicheskaya (*Geophysics Series*)	1957	Monthly	1200	American Geophysical Union	$25; $10 to libraries of academic institutions
Seriya Geologicheskaya (*Geological Series*)	1958	Monthly	1500	National Academy of Sciences (NSF)	$45; $27 to libraries of academic institutions
Izvestiya Vysschikh Uchebnykh Zavedeniĭ: Tekhnologiya Tekstil'noĭ Promyshlennosti (*Technology of Textile Industry*)		Bimonthly		Planned (DSIR)	

Title	*Translation Beginning*	*Frequency*	*Pages per Year*	*Agency*	*Subscription Price per Year*
Kauchuk i Rezina (Crude and Finished Rubber)	May 1959	Monthly		Research Assoc. of British Rubber Mfrs, (DSIR)	£5.5s
Kinetika i Kataliz (Kinetics and Catalysis)	May-June 1960	Bimonthly	1050	Consultants Bureau, Inc.	$150
Koks i Khimiya (Coke and Chemistry)	1959	Monthly		Coal Research Assoc. (DSIR)	$24, $12 to academic libraries
Kolloidnyĭ Zhurnal (Colloid Journal)	1952 issues	Bimonthly	600	Consultants Bureau, Inc.	$80
Kristallografiya (Crystallography)	1957	Bimonthly	1000	American Inst. of Physics (NSF)	$25, $10 to libraries of academic institutions
Liteĭnoe Proizvodstvo (Foundry Production)				Planned (DSIR)	
Metallovedenie i Termicheskaya Obrabotka Metallov (Metallography and Heat Treating)	Jan. 1958	Monthly	420	*Acta Metallurgica* (NSF)	$24, $18 to members
Metallurg (Metallurgist)	1956 issues	Monthly	540	*Acta Metallurgica* (NSF)	$25, $12.50 to members
Mikrobiologiya (Microbiology)	1957	Bimonthly	900	American Institute of Biological Sciences (NSF)	$20
Optika i Spektroskopiya (Optics and Spectroscopy)	Jan. 1959	Monthly	1000	Optical Society of America (NSF)	$15 to non-members; $7.50 to OSA members; $11 to OIS club scheme members
Plasticheskie Massy (Plastics)				Planned (DSIR)	
Pochvovedenie (Soil Science)	Jan. 1958 issue	Monthly	1600	American Institute of Biological Sciences (NSF)	$40, $20 to libraries of academic institutions
Referativnyi Zhurnal, Metallurgiya (Abstract Journal, Metallurgy)	Jan. 1957	Monthly	1300	*Acta Metallurgica* (NSF)	$50, $25 to libraries of academic institutions
Stal' (Steel)	June 1959	Monthly		Iron & Steel Institute (DSIR)	$50 to individuals, $58 to libraries

Title	Translation Beginning	Frequency	Pages Per Year	Agency	Subscription Price Per Year
Steklo i Keramika (Glass and Ceramics)	1956 issues	Monthly	540	American Ceramic Soc., Inc. (NSF)	$80
Svarochnoe Proizvodstvo (Welding Industry)	April 1959	Monthly		British Welding Research Association (DSIR)	£5.5s
Tsment (Cement)	1956 & 57 only	Bimonthly		Consultants Bureau, Inc.	$60
Tsvetnye Metally (Nonferrous Metals)	Jan. 1960	Monthly		Primary Sources	$95
Uspekhi Fizicheskikh Nauk (Advances in Physical Sciences)	1958	Bimonthly	500	American Inst. of Physics (NSF)	$45, $20 to libraries of academic institutions
Uspekhi Khimii (Advances in Chemistry)	Jan. 1960 issue	Monthly		Cleaver-Hume Press, Ltd. (DSIR)	£15
Uspekhi Sovremennoĭ Biologii (Advances in Modern Biology)	July-Aug. 1959 issues	Bimonthly		Oliver & Boyd, Ltd. (DSIR)	£6.10s
Voprosy Virusologii (Problems of Virology)	Jan. 1957	Bimonthly	384	Pergamon Press (NIH)[d]	$30
Vysokomolekulyarnye Soedineniya (Polymer Science)	Sept. 1960	Quarterly	900	Pergamon Press, Ltd.	$60
Zavodskaya Laboratoriya (Industrial Laboratory)	Jan. 1958	Monthly	1500	Instrument Soc. of America (NSF)	$35, $17.50 to libraries of academic institutions
Zhurnal Analiticheskoĭ Khimii (Journal of Analytical Chemistry)	1952 issues	Bimonthly	800	Consultants Bureau, Inc.	$80
Zhurnal Eksperimental'noĭ i Teoreticheskoĭ Fiziki (Journal of Experimental and Theoretical Physics)	1955	Monthly	3700	American Inst. of Physics (NSF)	$75, $35 to libraries of academic institutions
Zhurnal Fizicheskoĭ Khimii (Journal of Physical Chemistry)	July-Aug. 1959 issue	Monthly		Cleaver-Hume Press, Ltd. (DSIR)	£30
Zhurnal Mikrobiologii, Epidemiologii i Immunobiologii (Journal of Microbiology, Epidemiology and Immunobiology)	Jan. 1957	Monthly	2000	Pergamon Press (NIH)[d]	$60

Title	Translation Beginning	Frequency	Pages Per Year	Agency	Subscription Price Per Year
Zhurnal Neorganicheskoĭ Khimii (Journal of Inorganic Chemistry)	June 1959	Monthly		Cleaver-Hume Press, Ltd. (DSIR)	£30
Zhurnal Obshcheĭ Khimii (Journal of General Chemistry)	1949	Monthly	3600	Consultants Bureau, Inc. (NSF)	$120, $50 to libraries of academic institutions
Zhurnal Prikladnoi Khimii (Journal of Applied Chemistry)	1950	Monthly	1900	Consultants Bureau, Inc. (NSF)	$95, $35 to libraries of academic institutions
Zhurnal Strukturnoĭ Khimii (Journal of Structural Chemistry)	May-June 1960	Bimonthly	750	Consultants Bureau, Inc.	$80
Zhurnal Tekhnicheskoĭ Fiziki (Journal of Technical Physics)	1956	Monthly	2000	American Inst. of Physics (NSF)	$55, $25 to libraries of academic institutions

Sponsors

[a] Department of Scientific & Industrial Research (Great Britain).
[b] National Institutes of Health.
[c] National Science Foundation.
[d] Consultants Bureau has NIH contract for 1961 translations.
[e] Royer and Rogers have NIH contract for 1961 translations.

Translators

Acta Metallurgica
Subscriptions handled by:
Pergamon Press
122 East 55th St.
New York 22, N. Y.

American Ceramic Soc., Inc.
Subscriptions handled by:
Consultants Bureau, Inc.
227 West 17th St.
New York 11, N. Y.

American Geological Institute
2101 Constitution Ave., N.W.
Washington 25, D. C.

American Geophysical Union
1530 P St., N. W.
Washington 5, D. C.

American Institute of Biological Sciences
2000 P St., N. W.
Washington 6, D. C.

American Institute of Physics
335 East 45th St.
New York 17, N. Y.

British Welding Research Association
29 Park Crescent
London, W.1., England

Cleaver-Hume Press, Ltd.
31 Wright's Lane
London, W.8., England

The Coal Research Association
Oxford Road
Gomersal, near Leeds, England

Columbia Technical Translations
5 Vermont Ave.
White Plains, N. Y.

Consultants Bureau Enterprises, Inc.
227 West 17th St.
New York 22, N. Y.

Derwent Information Service
Theobalds Rd.
London, W.C.1, England

The Geochemical Society
Dr. John W. Winchester
Department of Geology
Massachusetts Institute of Technology
Cambridge 39, Mass.

Instrument Soc. of America
313 Sixth Ave.
Pittsburgh 22, Pa.

Iron and Steel Institute
Grosvenor Gardens
London, S.W.1., England

National Academy of Sciences
2101 Constitution Ave., N.W.
Washington 25, D. C.

Oliver & Boyd, Ltd.
Tweeddale Court
Edinburgh, Scotland

Optical Society of America
1155–16th St., N. W.
Washington, D. C.

Pergamon Press
122 East 55th St.
New York 22, N. Y.

Primary Sources
11 Bleecker St.
New York 12, N. Y.

Research Assoc. of British Rubber Mfrs.,
Shawbury, Shrewsbury,
Shropshire, England

Research Information Service
40 East 23rd St.
New York 10, N. Y.

Review of Russian Geology
212 So. Pitt St.
Alexandria, Va.

Royer and Rogers
41 East 28th St.
New York 16, N. Y.

Technical Information Co.
Chancery Lane
London, W.C.2, England

Timber Development Association
21 College Hill
London, E.C.4., England

Table courtesy of Consultants Bureau and the National Science Foundation, which calls attention to two main translation depositories in the United States: (1) the Special Libraries Association Translation Center located at the John Crerar Library in Chicago and (2) the Office of Technical Services, Technical Information Division, in the Department of Commerce, Washington, D. C.

(provincial universities and institutes, engineering schools, industrial research institutes, etc.). Consequently, publications of universities other than Moscow and Leningrad, those of the many Nauchno-Issledovatel'skie Instituty, of the Pedagogicheskie Instituty, of the national (republic) academies, and of some of the USSR Academy branches and stations are best obtained by direct exchange with these institutions.

If you wish to enter into an exchange arrangement with some institution in the Soviet Union you should: (1) prepare a list of exact and full titles of the publications wanted, (2) obtain as much information as possible about the periodicity and price of these publications, (3) have the full name and correct addresses of the institutions sponsoring the desired publications, (4) prepare a list of publications which you are ready to offer in exchange, including the periodicity and price of these publications, and (5) keep in mind that the publications of the universities (except the big ones), of institutes, museums, and similar bodies appear in one to three, seldom more, issues per year, and that these publications carrying often the same general title may appear in more than one series, with one issue devoted to chemistry, another to geology, and the next to agriculture. Let us say that you saw a reference to or perhaps the original of a publication of the Tomsk Polytechnic Institute. It contained papers on various topics of chemistry in which you are interested. Well, you wrote to the institute offering an exchange for the *Izvestiya Tomskogo Politekhnicheskogo Instituta*. They informed you that the *Izvestiya* appears, for example, in two issues a year. The exchange was arranged. The first copy which you received was compiled by the department of pedology and is devoted to soils, the second was compiled by the department of geology, and you begin to wonder what has happened to chemistry; actually, it is possible that in this particular year it will not be issued. But let us continue: After satisfying the above five points, write to the institution in question. Then arm yourself with a great deal of patience and go on an extended vacation. By the time you return, and tell about all the ones that got away, and then catch up with piled-up work you can begin a patient wait for a reply—it just possibly may come. This at least was the usual case before the "new look" was announced. In my opinion these difficulties were not necessarily the outcome of ill will. The strangeness of communication with the outside world, the uncertainty of what the official policy might be, the necessity of going "through channels," and last but by no means least, the hesitancy about one's own product contributed heavily to the reluctance to enter into negotiations with foreign institutions.

If your perseverance held fast and you received an agreement to your proposal, you are not yet in the clear. When the long awaited publication arrives in this country it has to pass our censor at the port of entry. He is charged with the interception of political propaganda. And if the title of your publication starts, for example, with *Izvestiya*—and *Izvestiya,* the newspaper, as we all know, is red hot propaganda—the censor who may not know the difference between the newspaper *Izvestiya* and the *Izvestiya* of some university, will stop your publication and save the day. Such things are known to have happened.

Are these publications of provincial universities, professional schools (institutes), and republic academies of enough importance to warrant so much trouble? We can readily enough obtain the "most important" publications, such as those of the USSR Academy, most trade publications (those sponsored by the ministries), and possibly the publications of most, if not all, of the republic academies. Hence, is it worth the effort to obtain university and institute publications? It seems to me so. Some of my reasons are:

The academy publications are reserved primarily for members of the academy and the research staff of its numerous research institutes. The chances of a paper originating in a university being published in one of the "big" publications are not very great. Thus, the bulk of university research is reported in university publications.

Most, if not all, of the research in applied science and in specific narrow fields is done in the professional training institutes, and the results of this research will be found almost exclusively in institute publications.

The combined volume of university, institute, and similar publications is very impressive. Even though the percentage of important contributions can be small, its very volume is likely to be significant. Furthermore, abstract services, libraries, and information services should be wary of evaluating the importance of information. This is better reserved for the specialist.

Searching the Literature

Except for a brief period from 1938 to 1941 during which *Khimicheskiĭ Referativnyĭ Zhurnal* appeared, abstracting of chemical literature in the Soviet Union did not start until 1953. Therefore, any search of that material has to start with *Chemical Abstracts.*

In 1953 the various series of *Referativnyĭ Zhurnal* started appearing. The coverage also started with that year—i.e., material published prior to that does not enter the *Referativnyĭ Zhurnal. Chemical Abstracts* has an understanding with *Referativnyĭ Zhurnal* that abstracts appearing in either may be translated and published in the other, giving credit to the source.

Beside the *Referativnyĭ Zhurnal,* which appears in 16 series—astronomy and geodesy, biological chemistry, biology, electrical and power engineering, physics, geophysics, geography, geology, mining, chemistry, machine building, mathematics, mechanics, metallurgy, transport, and industrial economics—there appears also *Sovetskoe Meditsinskoe Referativenoe Obozrenie* (SMRO), an abstract journal for medical literature. This publication appears in 15 series dealing with the various branches of medicine and has an author and subject index.

Three Soviet publications, *Uspekhi Khimii, Uspekhi Fizicheskikh Nauk,* and *Uspekhi Sovermennoĭ Biologii,* are largely devoted to reviews. These publications should be noted by the searcher because of extensive bibliographies appended to the review articles. Pertinent, extensive bibliographies are to be found in *Trudy Instituta Geologicheskikh Nauk AN SSSR.* Review articles on specific topics are likely to appear in other publications and they are worth perusing for their bibliographies.

The publications just mentioned are periodicals. In addition, there are *Uspekhi* (*Advances*) appearing as serials—e.g., *Uspekhi Biologicheskoĭ Khimii,* published by the Academy, *Uspekhi Khimii i Teknologii Polimerov* (*Advances in Chemistry and Technology of Polymers*) sponsored by the All-Union Chemical Society, and others. These publications too carry extensive bibliographies.

Soviet periodicals are rather prompt in publishing indexes at the end of the year. The subject indexes of specific publications should be examined when searching for specific topics.

Finally, two publications already mentioned, *Letopis' Zhurnal'nykh Stateĭ* and *Knizhnaya Letopis'*, even though they are of less use in subject searching, are paramount in importance when searching for book and periodical titles. *Knizhnaya Letopis'* also indexes dissertations for advanced degrees.

Literature Cited

(1) Hoseh, M., *J. Chem. Educ.* **33**, 397 (1956); **34**, 182, 235 (1957).
(2) Hoseh, M., *J. Research Educ.* **4**, 220–32 (1960).

BASED on four papers presented before the Division of Chemical Literature at the 126th, 128th, and 130th meetings, ACS, 1954 through 1956, and published in the *Journal of Chemical Education* (*1*); revised 1961 with permission of the editor of that journal.

Chemical Trade-Marks

HARRY BENNETT and M. A. GREENFIELD

Cheminform Institute, Coliseum Tower, New York 19, N. Y.

In searching for the composition, manufacturer, or use of a trade-marked chemical, books, directories, trade papers, and available lists are consulted. Service organizations make legal searches of trade-mark availability and one organization also performs technical searches for the composition and use of chemical and allied trade-marks. Lists of trade-mark applications filed but not yet acted upon are also available. An extensive listing of reference sources for trade-mark information and a classified breakdown are presented.

Manufacturers' names and trade-marks have been used for hundreds of years on all kinds of products, although the modern system of trade-marks was introduced in the United States about 1865. Trade-marks are of value not only to the seller but also to the buyer, who, for example, can more easily remember PEG than polyoxyethylene monostearate. The seller of a trade-marked product finds it to his advantage to furnish a product of uniform and satisfactory quality; the buyer can depend upon getting uniform quality with each purchase.

A trade-mark refers to the source of a commercial product usually designated by a coined or fanciful name, which is rarely its true designation. A trade name (often confused with a trade-mark) is defined by law as referring to the name of the firm or house that produces or sells the product. Thus, "Glycopon" is a trade-mark covering a chemical product; "Glyco Products Co." is a trade name.

The naming of a new product is not as simple as it may appear at first glance. The name must be unique in the field in which it is to be used. Because of the many thousands of names now registered, it is not too easy to find a name that is suitable for the product and yet does not bear too close a resemblance to a trade-mark already in use. Generally, a preliminary list of names is drawn up and is then weeded out until only a very few names are left. Even these names, however, may have to be discarded because conscious or subconscious analogies are drawn from existing names.

There are four general types of trade-marks:

1. The name of a company, its abbreviation, or modification. Dowicide, Goodrich, Esso.

2. A synthetic or coined word or words indirectly descriptive. Acrawax, Duriron, Fiberglas.
3. Nondescriptive word or words. Acme, Crown, Supreme.
4. Synthetic nondescriptive words. Abopon, Daisite, Gamal.

Under chemical trade-marks it is proper to consider not only chemicals but mixtures of chemicals, plastics, coatings, detergents, insecticides, textile specialties, pharmaceuticals, and diverse other chemical specialties used in industry.

While many trade-marks are registered in the U. S. Patent Office and in the patent offices of foreign countries, a good number are not registered. Those that are registered are listed in the weekly issues of the *Official Gazette of the United States Patent Office* and in corresponding publications of foreign countries. Trade journals covering the various industries usually list trade-marks granted in their fields. Thus *Drug and Cosmetic Industry* (a monthly) lists trade-marks granted during the previous month for cosmetics, drugs, perfumes, and soaps. Many journals and trade papers—*Chemical and Engineering News, Chemical Industries,* etc.—have notes on new products, some of which are marketed under trade-marks. Some trade papers have an annual directory or yearbook in which are listed trade-marks with the name of the owner. In some cases the chemical composition is partially or fully disclosed.

In starting a search for the composition, manufacturer, or use of a trade-mark chemical or allied product, books, directories, trade papers, or lists on one's premises are used first. If these are not sufficient, recourse is made to the larger industrial, college, or public libraries.

When checking on the availability of a proposed trade-mark one must also check its phonetic analogs. A number of commercial service organizations perform searches for trade-mark availability.

Lists of cosmetic trade-marks filed but not acted upon are available from the Toilet Goods Association, New York, N. Y.

Often one tries to derive from the name a clue to the chemical composition, properties, or uses of a trade-mark chemical. Sometimes this is possible; more often it is not.

Aldo (glyceryl monostearate) gives no true indication of its composition.
Alacet (aluminum acetate) is somewhat descriptive.
Bubene (butylbenzene) is somewhat less easy to figure out.
Cadaloy (cadmium-mercury-zinc alloy) is indicative of a cadmium alloy, but gives no clue as to the other components.
Caranol (sodium lorol sulfate) is not an alcohol, as the terminal "ol" would seem to indicate.
Pyridose (pyridyl mercuric acetate) is not a sugar, as the terminal "ose" would seem to indicate.

The uses of trade-mark chemicals are frequently discernible.

Hydratite indicates waterproofing.
Mersize suggests a sizing compound.
Moldol is a mold inhibitor.
Opax is an opacifier for glass.
Tanak is a tanning agent.

Some trade-mark chemicals offer a clue to their progenitors.

Gastex is made from natural gas.
Kelgin is made from kelp.
Spermafol is made from sperm oil.
Tallex is made from tall oil.

Part of a company name in a trade-mark often identifies the manufacturer or seller.

Cibanet, a product of Ciba Co.
Dowicide, a product of Dow Chemical Co.
Glycowax, a product of Glyco Products Co.
Hercolyn, a product of Hercules Powder Co.
Santomerse, a product of Monsanto Chemical Co.

Many individuals who wish to coin and search their own trade-marks use the following method. Recourse can be first made to a book such as "Trade Marks" (*67*) which gives an extensive list of chemical trade-marks, their compositions, uses, and suppliers, the entire U. S. and British trade-mark laws, methods of coining new trade-marks, and trade-marks classified by industries. Another excellent guide to the selection of new trade-marks is "Trade Mark Management," published by the U.S. Trade-Mark Association, New York, N. Y.

In searching proposed trade-marks, the appended classified reference sources should be consulted and a search made of those sources listed under pertinent classifications. Because new trade-marks appear daily, auxiliary current sources must be used, such as the *Official Gazette of the United States Patent Office,* and new products notes in relevant technical journals. Some of the publications in the appended reference sources are annual publications and each issue contains new listings. These are next examined. When these courses do not provide the desired information, requests may be made of the librarians in some of our larger industrial concerns, who keep running files of trade-mark chemicals. Foreign trade-marks are traced through the journals of the patent offices of the leading countries. Foreign directories, yearbooks, etc., as listed are also consulted. The above methods are at best temporary measures and before a new trade-mark is adopted by a company, it is extremely important to have it cleared by one or more of the commercial search services (*16, 65, 68*). Adoption of a trade-mark that has not been properly cleared can result in law suits and consequent expensive court settlements, loss of money already spent on advertising, labels, etc.

For the convenience of the reader, the following list has been broken down into two parts. The first consists of proved sources of technical and legal listings of trade-marks; the second indicates specifically where to look for information in different fields.

I. Technical and Legal Reference Sources

(1) American Association of Textile Chemists and Colorists, Lowell, Mass., "Annual Yearbook."
(2) "American Drug Index."
(3) American Druggist, New York, N. Y., "Blue Book."
(4) Association of British Chemical Manufacturers, London, England, "British Chemicals."
(5) "Austria Codex," Österreichischer Apotheker-Verlag, Vienna, Austria.
(6) "British Plastics Yearbook," Iliffe & Sons, Ltd., London, England.
(7) "Chemical Trade Names and Commercial Synonyms," Williams Haynes, Van Nostrand, New York.
(8) *Chemical Week,* "Buyers Guide," McGraw-Hill, New York.
(9) The Chemist and Druggist, London, England, "Year Book."
(10) "Chemical Engineering Catalog," Reinhold, New York.
(11) "Chemical Formulary," H. Bennett, Chemical Pub. Co., New York.
(12) "Chemical Industries Directory," Kelley's Directories, Ltd., London, England.
(13) "Chemical Materials Catalog," Reinhold, New York.
(14) "Chemical Synonyms and Tradenames, Gardner's," Van Nostrand, New York.

(15) "Chemie Lexicon," Römpp, Germany.
(16) Cheminorm Institute, 10 Columbus Circle, New York (service organization, technical and legal searching).
(17) "Clinical Toxicology of Commercial Products" (and supplements), Williams & Wilkins, Baltimore, Md.
(18) "Colour Index," London, England.
(19) "Commercial Waxes," H. Bennett, Chemical Pub. Co., New York.
(20) "Concise Chemical and Technical Dictionary," H. Bennett, Chemical Pub. Co., New York.
(21) "Condensed Chemical Dictionary," Reinhold, New York.
(22) "Diccionario Español de Especialidades Farmaceuticas" (and supplements), San Sebastian, Spain.
(23) "Dictionary of Color Names," National Bureau of Standards, Washington, D. C.
(24) "Dictionary of Textiles," Fairchild Pub. Inc., New York.
(25) Drug Merchandising, Canada, "Drug Index."
(26) Drug Topics, "Red Book," Topics Pub. Co., New York.
(27) "Enciclopedia Annuaro de Materie Plastiche," Italy.
(28) "Encyclopedia of Chemical Technology," Kirk-Othmer, Interscience, New York.
(29) The Engineer, London, England, "Buyer's Guide."
(30) "Entoma Directory of Insect and Plant Pest Control."
(31) "Firmenhandbuch Chemische Industrie," Econ-Verlag, Düsseldorf, Germany.
(32) "Fraser's Canadian Textile, Apparel and Fur Trade Directory."
(33) "Gehes Codex" (and supplements), Schwarzeck-Verlag, Munich, Germany.
(34) "Handbook of Chemistry," N. A. Lange, ed., Handbook Pub., Inc., Sandusky, Ohio.
(35) "Handbook of Chemistry & Physics," Chemical Rubber Pub. Co., Cleveland, Ohio.
(36) "Handbook of Material Trade Names" (and supplements), Zimmerman & Levine, Industrial Research Service, Inc., Dover, N. H.
(37) International Encyclopedia of Cosmetic Trade Names," de Navarre, Moore Pub. Co., New York.
(38) *Iron Age,* New York, "Directory of Tool, Die Steels and Sintered Carbides."
(39) "Le Livre Blanc," Editions Henri Perrier, Paris, France.
(40) "Manual de Especialidades Medicinales," Buenos Aires, Argentina.
(41) "Materials Handbook," Brady, McGraw-Hill, New York.
(42) "Merck Index," 7th ed., Merck & Co., Inc., Rahway, N. J.
(43) "Metal Industries Catalog," Reinhold, New York.
(44) "Minerva Medica," Specialità Farmaceutiche, Turin, Italy.
(45) "Modern Drug Encyclopedia and Therapeutic Index," Gutman.
(46) Modern Plastics, New York, "Encyclopedia Issue."
(47) National Fire Protection Association, Boston, Mass., "Flash Point Index of Trade Name Liquids."
(48) National Paint, Varnish & Lacquer Association, Washington, D. C., "Trade Mark Directory."
(49) "New and Nonofficial Drugs."
(50) "Pesticide Handbook," D. E. H. Frear, State College, Pa.
(51) "Physicians' Desk Reference to Pharmaceutical Specialties and Biologicals," Medical Economics, Inc., Oradell, N. J.
(52) Pharmaceutical Manufacturers Association, Washington, D. C., "Bulletin."
(53) "Plastics Year Book," Plastics Press, Ltd., London, England.
(54) "Practical Emulsions (Surface Active Agents)," H. Bennett, Chemical Pub. Co., New York.
(55) Proprietary Association, Washington, D. C., "Bulletin."
(56) "Register of Brand Names and Trade Marks of the Thread Industry."
(57) "Répertoire Alphabétique des Marques Internationales," Metz and Geiger, Zurich, Switzerland.
(58) "Rubber Index," Rubber Age, London, England.
(59) "Rubber Red Book," Rubber Age, New York.
(60) "Rubber Trade Directory of Great Britain."
(61) "Surface Coating Resin Index," The British Plastics Federation, England.

(62) "Swiss Chemical Industry," Ver. Wirtschaftsliteratur, Zurich, Switzerland.
(63) "Synthetic Detergents," McCutcheon.
(64) "Thomas Register of American Manufacturers," Vol. 4, New York.
(65) Thomson and Thomson, 80 Federal St., Boston 10, Mass. (service organization, legal searching).
(66) Toilet Goods Association, "Trade Mark Record," Beauty Fashion, Drug and Cosmetic Industry, New York.
(67) "Trade Marks," H. Bennett, Chemical Pub. Co., New York.
(68) Trade Mark Service Corp., 233 Broadway, New York (service organization, legal searching).
(69) United States Dispensatory, Osol-Farrar, Lippincott, Philadelphia, Pa.
(70) "Veterinary Drug Encyclopedia & Therapeutic Index," Drug Pub. Inc., New York.
(71) "World Chemical Directory," Atlas Pub. Co., New York.

II. Classified Reference Sources

Agricultural specialties	*(17, 28, 30, 36, 50, 64)*
Alloys	*(28, 34, 36, 38, 43, 64)*
Ceramics, technical	*(10, 12, 13, 28, 34, 36, 64)*
Chemicals	*(4, 7, 8, 10, 12, 14, 15, 20, 21, 28, 31, 34–36, 62, 64, 71)*
Coatings	*(17, 28, 36, 48, 61, 64)*
Coining trade-marks (commercial services)	*(16)*
Construction and refractory materials	*(13, 28, 29, 36, 41, 64)*
Cosmetics	*(3, 9, 17, 25, 26, 37, 52, 55, 64, 66)*
Detergents	*(1, 17, 28, 36, 48, 54, 63, 64, 66)*
Dyes and pigments	*(1, 18, 23, 28, 34, 35, 48, 64)*
Legal only, all fields	*(57)*
Legal searching (commercial services)	*(16, 65, 68)*
Lubricants, oils, fuels	*(17, 28, 36, 48, 64)*
Miscellaneous	*(4, 7, 8, 10–12, 14, 15, 17, 20, 21, 28, 29, 31, 34–36, 41, 47, 54, 62, 64, 67, 71)*
Pharmaceuticals	*(2, 3, 5, 9, 17, 22, 25, 26, 33, 39, 40, 42, 44, 45, 49, 51, 52, 64, 65, 69)*
Plastics	*(6, 27, 28, 46, 53, 64)*
Rubber and rubber chemicals	*(28, 34, 58–60, 64)*
Service organizations (commercial)	*(16, 65, 68)*
Technical searching (commercial services)	*(1, 24, 28, 32, 54, 56, 64)*
Textiles and textile specialties	*(16)*
Waxes	*(17, 19, 28, 48, 64)*

BASED on paper presented before Division of Chemical Literature, Symposium on Searching the Chemical Literature, 117th Meeting, ACS, Detroit, Mich., April 1950. Revised 1960.

Searching United States Government Documents

BARBARA A. GALLAGHER
ACS Applied Publications, Washington, D.C.

Approximately 25% of government agencies report their work in scientific and technical journals solely, while the remaining 75% usually combine their own information-reporting systems with the journals. Some agencies act as sales outlets or clearinghouses, such as Government Printing Office and Office of Technical Services. The majority of them also participate in the depository library system, besides maintaining their own individual libraries. The latter are most helpful in regard to interlibrary loan or reference questions. The depository libraries are particularly helpful for locating out of print documents, as well as having a current collection of reports. Therefore, there is usually more than one way to find out what is available and from whom.

One of the most serious and costly problems facing research today is that of potential duplication of effort. This results from the fact that tens of thousands of reports, articles, books, and other means of disseminating information are published each year, making it increasingly difficult to locate any specific document.

One of the large producers of information is the Federal Government. Many government agencies conduct or sponsor scientific research; others collect, sort, and make information available. Some agencies have their own media for disseminating their information; some use the scientific and technical press. No one agency is the key to this vast storehouse of information, so in many cases it is necessary to look in a number of places. This is why each agency that handles information of interest to the chemical profession is discussed individually.

One system for location of out-of-print documents which is not discussed under each agency but is used by most is the depository library. A description of the method used to distribute reports to depository libraries has been included under Government Printing Office. Aside from the nearly 600 GPO depository libraries, some agencies have selected additional libraries to receive their publications. Therefore, requests for lists of depository libraries should be directed to the individual agency in question.

Almost all the agencies considered here also have individual libraries and these provide additional aids in locating materials. They not only provide reference services, but in some cases photoduplication service. Also, most participate in the interlibrary loan system and are open to the public for reference work. Requests for information on any of these individual libraries should also be addressed to the agency in question.

Publications of U.S. Government agencies are announced in:

A. *Monthly Catalog of U.S. Government Publications*
B. *U.S. Government Research Reports*
C. *Technical Translations*
D. *Technical Abstract Bulletin*
E. *Business Service Checklist*

as indicated by key letters opposite the name of each agency.

A dagger (†) following the name of an agency or a publication indicates coverage by *Chemical Abstracts* for new chemical information.

United States Government Printing Office (GPO)

Since the main responsibility of the United States Government Printing Office is the executing or monitoring of printing for the federal agencies and selling and distributing government publications, it issues several guides to the availability of these documents. The classification numbers assigned to government publications serve as catalog numbers which should be used when ordering publications. A publication entitled "An Explanation of the Superintendent of Documents Classification System" is available at no cost from that office. The following publications of GPO are used to announce the availability of government literature.

Monthly Catalog of United States Government Publications. This is the official record of all publications originating in the various federal departments, bureaus, and agencies, including Congress, bearing the government imprint. About 60% of the publications listed are available through GPO, while the other 40%, even though listed by GPO, are available from other sources. It is an alphabetical listing by name of originating agency, by title and under the title of each series, by number. Also, it includes an index by subject, originating agency, and title in every issue with a cumulative index covering a calendar year in the December issue. The catalog is available from the Superintendent of Documents, Government Printing Office, Washington 25, D.C. (hereafter referred to as GPO) at 25 cents per copy or $3 per year (including index) domestic, $4.50 per year foreign.

"The Decennial Cumulative Index to the Monthly Catalog of the U.S. Government Publications, 1941–50." $25 a copy.

Selected U.S. Government Publications. This guide announces selected publications that are maintained in GPO stock and available directly from the Superintendent of Documents. Issued biweekly, it appears in leaflet form with annotations and prices. It is available free from GPO.

Selected Lists. An annotated listing of significant publications on special subjects of seasonal or current interest. Issued occasionally, these lists contain only publications which are available for sale directly by GPO. The lists are available free.

Checklist. This volume contains brief descriptions of all documents issued by the U.S. Government from 1789 to 1909, listed by classification number. The Checklist can be consulted at most libraries, but is available in reprint from J. W. Edwards, Publisher, Inc., Ann Arbor, Mich.

GPO Price Lists. Lists on broad subjects, arranged by subtopic and including prices and titles of available publications in particular fields. They are available free on request to GPO.

Catalog of Public Documents. This is a dictionary catalog including all government publications issued between March 3, 1893, and December 31, 1940. Although discontinued because of its tremendous cost and limited use, the Documents Catalog can be consulted at most libraries.

In addition, government publications are also made accessible to the public at depository libraries which are entitled to receive a free copy of every publication made available to the Superintendent of Documents. The libraries may select which of these they desire. A list of depository libraries is included in each September issue of the *Monthly Catalog of U.S. Government Publications.*

Business and Defense Services Administration (BDSA), U.S. Department of Commerce (A, E)

The BDSA conducts industrial economic studies, on a world-wide basis, of the production, uses, trends, and outlook for the major commodities and products. Some of the publications which are used to make this information available to the public are: *Chemical and Rubber Industry Report; Copper Industry Report; Pulp, Paper, and Board Industry Report;* Industry Trend Series; and the Outlook Studies. Copies of the latest list of BDSA publications may be obtained from any Department of Commerce field office or from the Publications Officer, BDSA, U.S. Department of Commerce, Washington 25, D.C.

Reports considered to be of general interest to industry or the general public are initially announced through press releases sent to the trade journals and trade associations as well as the press. In addition, all BDSA reports are announced in supplements to "United States Department of Commerce Publications (1790–1950)."

Office of Technical Services, U.S. Department of Commerce (OTS)

The Office of Technical Services is one of four program offices in the Business and Defense Services Administration. As one of its principal functions, OTS collects and distributes research and development information generated by other federal agencies. Although OTS does not act as a clearinghouse on current research in progress, it does receive periodic research and development task summary and progress reports from the Army Research Office, Naval Research Laboratories, and other agencies. These reports are announced in U.S. Government Research Reports (USGRR), which is discussed below.

Under working arrangements with many of the federal agencies, OTS automatically receives multiple copies of each agency's reports. For those reports which are received in a single-copy reproducible form, the OTS Trust Fund Committee determines their potential value and whether they will be made available in full-size printed form or only in photocopy or microfilm. Specialized reports, and reports of limited interest, which constitute approximately 96% of the OTS collection, are not reproduced in volume. These are deposited at the Library of Congress Annex and may be examined in the Science Reading Room. Microfilm or photocopy reproductions may be obtained from the Photoduplication Service, Library of Congress, Washington 25, D.C.

The more than 200,000 technical reports which OTS has collected since 1945 are in three collections.

1. Publication Board (PB) Reports. This collection originally contained captured German and Japanese scientific reports and German patents which were acquired between 1946 and 1949. The collection now includes unclassified technical reports of the Army, Navy, Air Force, and their contractors, National Bureau of Standards, Maritime Administration, Federal Aviation Agency, Bureau of Mines, Department of Health, Education, and Welfare, and the National Aeronautics and Space Administration.

As the reports are received, OTS assigns an accession number (PB number) and prepares catalog cards. These cards provide for retrieval by source, personal author, title, subject, series, and contract number. All PB reports are announced in USGRR.

2. AEC Reports. These reports are received by OTS on automatic distribution, and since 1950 OTS has been the chief sales outlet for unclassified AEC reports. AEC reports are identified by their original AEC series numbers and are not assigned new identification numbers by OTS. All AEC reports supplied to OTS, including those available in photostat or microfilm are listed in USGRR. (For further information on AEC reports see the description of Atomic Energy Commission.)

3. Translations. This collection contains abstracts and complete translations of Russian and other foreign technical publications as well as weekly reviews of various areas of Soviet science. Among the translation series available through the Office of Technical Services on a subscription basis are: *Current Review of the Soviet Technical Press* (weekly) and *English Abstracts of Selected Articles from Soviet Bloc and Mainland China Technical Journals.* Translations are assigned an identification number which consists of the year of the translation followed by the accession number. All translations received by OTS or the John Crerar Library in Chicago are announced in *Technical Translations,* which is discussed below.

The reports and papers in the OTS collection are announced to the public through one or more of the following publications.

U.S. Government Research Report (USGRR). This is a monthly bibliographic and abstract journal which lists titles of unclassified AEC reports and abstracts or annotations of PB reports. It also gives complete information on subscription procedures, prices, and availability of publications in the OTS collection. Each issue of USGRR, beginning with Volume 31, January 1959, contains indexes to PB reports by source, subject, and PB number. In addition a cumulative index is published every six months as an integral part of USGRR. The first issue of USGRR appeared as Volume 22, No. 4, October 1954. Its former titles were *Bibliography of Scientific and Industrial Reports,* Vol. 1–11, January 1946–June 1949, and *Bibliography of Technical Reports,* Vol. 12–22, No. 3, July 1949–September 1954. Lists of numerical and subject indexes to the above reference volumes, as well as information regarding the availability of individual issues of the bibliographies, are available from OTS on request. The subscription price to USGRR is $9 annually and may be purchased from GPO. Coverage of USGRR by *Chemical Abstracts* started January 1, 1960.

Technical Reports Newsletter. In each monthly issue, the *Newsletter* reviews eight to ten research reports of special interest to small and medium-sized business firms. It also furnishes information on new products and commercial applications. The *Newsletter* is sold on subscription by GPO at $1 a year.

Technical Translations. Prepared in cooperation with the Special Libraries Association Translation Center, John Crerar Library, Chicago, Ill., this publication serves as a principal guide to translated material available to American science and industry, as well as translations in preparation. It lists and abstracts all translated technical articles, books, and periodicals which are available from OTS, Library of Congress, Special Libraries Association (SLA), cooperating foreign governments, commercial translators, publishers, universities and other sources. Author, subject, journal, and translation number indexes are included in each issue, and a cumulative index is published every six months. Issued twice a month, *Technical Translations* is available on annual subscription of $12 from GPO.

OTS Selective Bibliographies. Approximately 150 Selective Bibliographies have been prepared for areas considered to be of special interest, such as plastics, welding, and transistors. The cost is usually 10 cents per copy and a free list of these bibliographies may be obtained from OTS.

Literature searches are also available from OTS on a fee basis. These are performed to meet special needs which are not covered by a currently available OTS Selective Bibliography. Under this service OTS will compile lists of relevant publications in its collection of government research reports, unclassified and declassified AEC reports, technical translations, and OTS files of government-owned patents. The fee for this service is $8 per hour, and the customer may limit the time to be spent on a search. Additional information on these searches may be obtained by writing to the Technical Information Division, Office of Technical Services, Washington 25, D.C.

OTS has no definite policy for announcing declassified reports. However, when a large block of material is declassified, OTS usually makes a statement to this effect in *U.S. Government Research Reports* and in press releases. Many times these reports do not become a part of the OTS collection because they are more military than scientific in nature. When the public learns of the existence of certain reports through the technical press, they may request them from OTS. If the report is not already in its collection, OTS will request it from the originating agency or the agency which is declassifying it, and it will then become a part of the PB collection.

Also, on July 1, 1961, the Office of Technical Services began to incorporate the unclassified, unlimited distribution section of ASTIA's *Technical Announcement Bulletin* with its own *U.S. Government Research Reports.* ASTIA will continue to announce reports available to the Department of Defense and their contractors but OTS will also be announcing ASTIA documents which are available through OTS. This offers a more timely announcement service and increases the number of reports available.

National Bureau of Standards (A, B, E)
***U.S. Department of Commerce*†**

The scientific activities of NBS are conducted through 21 scientific divisions which roughly correspond to the major branches of physical science and engineering. Each of these divisions is also divided into sections which are responsible for technical areas within that branch. Of these divisions 15 are located in Washington, D.C., and six in Boulder, Colo. The bureau's Office of Technical Information is responsible for issuing the results of NBS activities. In addition, OTI produces motion pictures of bureau activities, conducts a speaker's bureau, maintains an up-to-date slide and photo file, and operates an inquiry service on the bureau's technical activities.

There is no complete list of current projects of the bureau; however, its annual report, "Research Highlights of the National Bureau of Standards," gives summaries of the more significant projects conducted during the previous year. Other publications used to report NBS research results are *The Journal of Research of the National Bureau of Standards* and *Technical News Bulletin. The Journal* is published in four separate sections which are available by subscription from GPO:

A. Physics and Chemistry. $4 per year (75 cents additional for foreign mailing) or 70 cents per single copy.
B. Mathematics and Mathematical Physics. $2.25 per year (50 cents additional for foreign mailing) or 75 cents per single copy.
C. Engineering and Instrumentation. $2.25 per year (50 cents additional for foreign mailing) or 70 cents per single copy.
D. Radio Propagation. $4 per year (75 cents additional for foreign mailing) or 70 cents per single copy.

Technical News Bulletin summarizes and reports the more important bureau research results. In addition, each issue lists the articles by NBS staff published during the previous month, and four times a year patents granted on NBS inventions are listed. The price of the *Technical News Bulletin* is $1.50 per year (75 cents additional for foreign mailing) or 15 cents per single copy. The bureau also has several nonperiodical series which are used to disseminate results of investigations.

In addition to these publications, NBS announces its publications in GPO Price Lists 64 and 82, and "U.S. Department of Commerce Publications," all of which are available from GPO. Another publication of NBS is its bibliography entitled "Publications of the National Bureau of Standards, 1901 to June 30, 1947" and its supplement, "Supplementary List of Publications of the National Bureau of Standards, July 1, 1947, to June 30, 1957." A second supplement extends this list through June 1960. This bibliography, as well as its supplements, may be purchased from GPO. The cost of the basic publication is $1.25; the first supplement, $1.50; and the second supplement, $2.25.

Bureaus of the Census, U.S. Department of Commerce (A)

In addition to its population censuses, the Bureau of the Census also conducts periodic censuses of agriculture, business, foreign trade, and manufacturing and mineral industries. In order to provide up-to-date information on many of these subjects, the bureau collects current data at monthly, quarterly, or annual intervals.

As its reports are issued, the Census Bureau publishes leaflets, containing order coupons, which describe each report series—for example, Current Industrial Reports, Current Business Reports, Construction Statistics, etc. Such announcements also are issued as each series of reports resulting from the full scale censuses is inaugurated. Persons desiring to be placed on the mailing list for announcements of census publications should write to the Public Information Office, Bureau of the Census, Washington 25, D.C., specifying the subject in which they are interested.

The Bureau of the Census employs the following means to announce its reports and publications.

Catalog of United States Census Publications. Issued quarterly, this catalog contains detailed descriptions of the contents of the reports issued during the period covered, as well as a geographic and a subject index. Monthly supplements and an annual cumulative supplement are also issued. The catalog is available from GPO on annual subscription of $1.25 domestic and 75 cents additional for foreign mailing.

Business Service Checklist. The Checklist is a weekly annotated list containing information on the price and availability of all publications, including selected press releases and speeches, released by the various bureaus of the Department of Commerce during the past week. It is available from GPO at the annual subscription rate of $1.50 ($2 additional for foreign mailing).

"U.S. Department of Commerce Publications, 1790–1950." This is a catalog and index of all Department of Commerce publications, including those of the Bureau of the Census. Annual supplements from 1951 to date are available and are essentially cumulations of the Business Service Checklist. Both the basic volume and the supplements are available from the Superintendent of Documents. The cost of the basic volume is $2.75, and the supplements range in price from 20 cents to $1.75.

GPO Price List 70: Census Publications. This lists Census publications according to subject.

Bureau of Public Roads, U.S. Department of Commerce (A, E)

Some of the research activities of the Bureau of Public Roads include physical and chemical testing of paving mixtures, road materials, and soil materials; the design and characteristics of nonrigid pavements and concrete pavements; and related topics.

All of the major publications of the bureau are announced in its list entitled "Publications of the Bureau of Public Roads," which is available on request from the Bureau of Public Roads, Washington 25, D.C. In addition, all bureau publications are listed in U. S. Department of Commerce Publications, and GPO Price List 25: Transportation, Highways, and Roads. These announcement publications are available from GPO and have been described elsewhere in this paper. The Bureau of Public Roads also publishes a bimonthly journal titled *Public Roads, A Journal of Highway Research*, which contains two or three research papers per issue. It is available from GPO at $1 per year (50 cents additional for foreign mailing) or 20 cents per single issue. A classified subject list of the more important articles that have appeared in *Public Roads* may be obtained upon request from the Bureau of Public Roads, Washington 25, D.C.

Bureau of Foreign Commerce (BFC), U.S. Department of Commerce (A, E)

The Bureau of Foreign Commerce publishes information relating to the foreign trade of the United States and other nations. Some of the fields include industrial developments; total exports and imports; exports and imports of specific commodities; and information dealing with specific foreign businesses.

The two most important publications of the BFC are *Foreign Commerce Weekly* and the *World Trade Information Service*. Together they form the core of BFC's business information service. Annual subscription to *Foreign Commerce Weekly* is $6 ($3.25 additional for foreign mailing) and $14.50 for domestic airmailing or 15 cents per single copy. An annual subscription to each of three parts of World Trade Information Service is $6 (additional for foreign mailing: part 1,

$3.75; part 2, $5; part 3, $2.50). WTIS single copy: part 1, 15 cents; part 2, 10 cents; part 3, 20 cents. Both publications are available from GPO.

These, as well as all other BFC publications, are announced in United States Department of Commerce Publications, and GPO Price List 62: Commerce. The Checklist of BFC Publications, published semiannually, is available free on request from the Bureau of Foreign Commerce, U.S. Department of Commerce, Washington 25, D.C.

Office of Business Economics (OBE), U.S. Department of Commerce (A, E)

The OBE collects and generates information on the gross national product and income accounts, balance of international payments, business expenditures for new plants and equipment, manufacturers' and distributors' sales, manufacturing and trade inventories, as well as several other subjects. The means used to disseminate this information is mainly the *Survey of Current Business* and the various supplements thereto.

The *Survey of Current Business* is a monthly periodical with weekly *Business Statistics Supplements,* and all other OBE publications are either expansions or detailed refinements of information appearing in this journal. In addition to subjects previously mentioned, the journal provides business data showing indicators of economic activity for a variety of subjects, including: chemicals and allied products; electric power and gas; foodstuffs and tobacco; leather and products; lumber and manufacturers; petroleum, coal, and products; pulp, paper, and printing; rubber and rubber products; stone, clay, and glass products; and textile products. This periodical is available from GPO at $4 per year ($3.50 additional for foreign mailing), single copies 30 cents each.

OBE announces its publications in GPO Price List; Finance (PL 28), and United States Department of Commerce Publications (PL 62). These are available from GPO.

Patent Office, U.S. Department of Commerce

Although the Patent Office has several publications available, they are not discussed here, since this office has been considered in detail in other parts of this book.

U.S. Tariff Commission [†] (A)

One of the Tariff Commission's reports which is very valuable to chemists is "Synthetic Organic Chemicals, U.S. Production and Sales." It is an annual volume which comprises three major sections: chemical raw materials, cyclic intermediates, and finished synthetic organic chemical products. The most recent report (Report 206, Second Series) may be purchased from GPO for $1.

However, in order to release the material in the annual volume at an early date, preliminary reports are issued in 14 separate sections. Some of these are: Crude products from petroleum and natural gas for chemical conversion; Medicinals; Plastics and resin materials; Rubber-processing chemicals; and Pesticides and other organic agricultural chemicals. Requests to be placed on mailing lists for any of the 14 sections should be addressed to the U.S. Tariff Commission, Washington 25, D.C.

Library of Congress, Science and Technology Division (A)

Bibliographies† are one of the chief means used by the Science and Technology Division of the Library of Congress to fulfill its primary function of providing a general and advanced scientific reference service. Since World War II this division has prepared several large-scale bibliographies on funds transferred from the Department of Defense. A list of these bibliographies, as well as their availability, may be obtained from the Science and Technology Division, Library of Congress, Washington 25, D.C.

The library also issues lists to announce its accessions in certain fields, including science and technology. These include *New Serial Titles,*† which is available from the Card Division, Library of Congress, Washington 25, D.C., at $55 a year for monthly issues and a cumulative annual volume; *Monthly Index of Russian Accessions,* which is available from GPO at $12 per year; and *East European Accession Index,* which is also available from GPO at $10 a year.

Announcement of all the library's publications is made in Library of Congress Publications in Print (free, Office of the Secretary, Library of Congress, Washington 25, D.C.) and the Annual Report of the Library of Congress.

Literature searches are also available from the Science and Technology Division on a fee basis. They will cite pertinent references from examination of the general collections of the library and of appropriate index and abstract publications at a cost of $8 per hour. This is a cooperative arrangement with OTS.

In addition, the Air Information Division of the library prepares several translation series. Among these are *Current Review of the Soviet Technical Press* (weekly) and *English Abstracts of Selected Articles from Soviet Bloc and Mainland China Technical Journals* (bimonthly). Other services of this group are its complete book reports (mainly of Russian books) and extensive bibliographies of Soviet references on specific subjects. All of these are available through the Office of Technical Services and are announced in the OTS publication, *Technical Translations.*

The Atomic Energy Commission (AEC), Office of Technical Information (A, B, C)

The Office of Technical Information (OTI) was established and charged with the responsibility for developing organizing, and operating the information programs of AEC. The basic functions of these programs are to record, reproduce, and distribute the data developed in the commission's research and development programs, to acquire and organize a comprehensive collection of publications on nuclear energy, and to organize this body of literature bibliographically.

The AEC reports are sent to OTS for sale to the public. Some of these are available in full-size copy and others are available in photostat or microfilm from the Library of Congress. These reports are also available on Microcard from Microcard Editions, Inc., Washington, D.C.

AEC disseminates, as widely as possible, the results of research and development activities in nuclear science through one or more of the following publications.

Nuclear Science Abstracts (*NSA*).† This semimonthly AEC publication announces and brings under bibliographic control the literature of the world on nuclear science and engineering. Within the field of nuclear science, NSA covers the unclassified and declassified technical reports of the AEC and its contractors, of U.S. and foreign government agencies and their contractors, and of industrial and research organizations. It also covers monographs, serial publications, theses of universities and learned societies, patents, books, and journal articles published both in the U.S. and abroad. Currently, each issue of the journal includes the following indexes: corporate author, personal author, subject, and report number (which includes the availability of reports). These indexes are cumulated at the end of the first quarter, semiannually, at the end of the third quarter, annually, and at five year intervals. NSA is available from GPO at an annual subscription of $18 domestic; $22.50 foreign. Single copy prices are $1.25 domestic, 25 cents extra for foreign mailing.

Cumulative index issues of NSA may also be purchased separately. Annual subscription rates for these are $15 domestic and $17.50 foreign. Single copy prices vary according to the number of pages. These are also available from GPO.

"Public Availability of Reports Abstracted in Nuclear Science Abstracts." This publication lists in one alpha-numerical sequence all of the reports abstracted in NSA and its predecessor, *Abstracts of Declassified Reports* (1947–1948). In addition to providing a reference to the volume and abstract number for each report, the publication gives the public source and price (if known) for the reports. The latest edition (TID-4000, 5th edition) is available from OTS for $5.

Proceedings of Technical Meetings. These are reports of meetings in which the commission or its contractors were sponsors, cosponsors, or major participants. Although these proceedings are abstracted in NSA, the commission has issued this catalog of them also. Copies can be obtained without charge from the Office of Technical Information Extension, P. O. Box 62, Oak Ridge, Tenn.

Bibliographies of Interest to the Atomic Energy Program. To facilitate identification of the large number of unclassified bibliographies that have been prepared on nuclear science and related fields, OTI has compiled this special bibliography. The basic volume (TID-3043, Rev.1) includes bibliographies received by OTI prior to March 15, 1958, and is available from OTS for $3. TID-3043 (Rev.1, Supp.1) covers the literature for March 1958 to October 1959 and is available from OTS for $2.25. Annual supplements are planned.

To provide this information more currently OTI issues *Informal Listing of Bibliographies of Atomic Energy Literature* on a bimonthly basis. In addition to listing available bibliographies, this publication lists those "in preparation." Those interested can be placed on the distribution list at no charge. The back issues covering the period since October 1959 also can be obtained free.

Translations List. This list, which is issued monthly, announces both completed translations and translations "in process." Each issue contains an author index, and cumulative indexes are issued at frequent intervals. Contributors include the AEC and its contractors and the British, Canadian, and French atomic energy agencies. AEC translations have deposited at the Special Library Association Translation Center of John Crerar Library, Chicago, Ill., since the center was established. Since January 1959, the translations have been sold by OTS.

"Technical Books Sponsored by the United States Atomic Energy Commission." The commission has sponsored many books to provide concise, comprehensive coverage of pertinent topics. Although these books are prepared under the direction of the commission and its contractors, they are sold by commercial publishers. This booklet, which lists both books in print and in preparation, is available without charge, from OTI Extension.

"Atomic Energy Commission Reports." This is a semiannual price list of unclassified AEC reports that have not been published in technical and professional journals, which have been placed on sale by OTS. This may be obtained free upon request to OTS. The OTS collection of AEC reports is described in the section on the Office of Technical Services.

Atomic Energy and Civil Defense Price List. GPO puts out this list of a small number of special AEC unclassified reports which are available upon request.

In addition to the above-mentioned publications, in 1957 AEC started publishing quarterly "Technical Progress Reviews." Their purpose is to keep abreast of important developments reported in the atomic energy literature. The reviews, which are prepared under contract by recognized authorities, digest and evaluate significant developments in selected areas of nuclear science and technology. Four reviews issued quarterly are: *Power Reactor Technology, Reactor Fuel Processing, Reactor Core Materials* and *Nuclear Safety.* All are available from GPO at 55 cents per single issue; $2 per year domestic, and $2.50 per year foreign subscription.

The AEC also disseminates information to ensure that most useful engineering materials are made available. OTI Extension publishes "Engineering Materials List" to identify, describe, index, and announce the availability of engineering materials (drawings, specifications, etc.). TID-4100 (1st rev.) and its supplements can be obtained from OTI Extension and are distributed without charge to AEC contractors, organizations, and individuals who have a need for them.

Literature searches are also available from OTI on a fee basis. The searches are less formal than the bibliographies mentioned previously and usually consist of only a title listing. Literature searches are limited to report literature. The standard rate for this service is $6.60 per hour, and all requests should be submitted to OTI Extension, Oak Ridge, Tenn.

Department of Defense (A, B, D)

The research interests of the Army, Navy, and Air Force are justifiably broad; some general subject fields of scientific reports include earth sciences, material sciences, chemistry, physical sciences, mathematical sciences, and biological sciences. These reports are published extensively in scientific and technical journals. In addition, the Army and Navy also issue periodicals which briefly cover certain highlights of technical progress in research by their laboratories and contractors. Both publications, *Army Research and Development* and *Naval Research Reviews,* are issued monthly and are available from GPO. The cost of *Army Research and Development* is $2.25 per year (75 cents additional for foreign mailing) or 20 cents per single copy and of *Naval Research Reviews* is $1.50 a year (50 cents additional for foreign mailing) or 15 cents per single copy.

Armed Services Technical Information Agency (ASTIA)

ASTIA does not serve the general public, since this group is served in the field of science and technology by the Office of Technical Services. ASTIA serves more than 1600 military activities of the Department of Defense, including research and development test and evaluation elements of the Army, Navy, Air Force, and Marines. It also serves an equal number of their civilian contractors and subcontractors, potential contractors, and grantees. In addition, ASTIA serves, within its resources, other agencies of the Executive Branch of the Federal Government and provides unclassified reports which have no release limitations to NATO, SEATO, and other allied nations. Organizations that may require ASTIA services in support of military or government projects and contracts may obtain a Registration Packet on request from the Armed Services Technical Information Agency, Arlington Hall Station, Arlington 12, Va. Civilian organizations must have written military approval before service can be furnished.

As new reports are received they are screened for suitability, AD (ASTIA Document) numbers are assigned, and the reports are cataloged and analyzed. To announce new reports, ASTIA publishes *The Technical Abstract Bulletin* (TAB). This is a semimonthly publication, arranged by subject fields of interest. TAB lists both classified and unclassified reports but is itself unclassified and also has a numerical index of all reports announced in it. In addition, it includes a "Notice of Changes in Classifications or Limitations" in the status of documents which were previously announced. As a further reference aid, ASTIA publishes quarterly and annual indexes which list reports by descriptors and by sources.

Scientific and technical reports, secret, confidential, and unclassified, are furnished, on individual request, in full size or microfilm copies from a collection in excess of 600,000 titles, which is increasing at the rate of about 25,000 annually.

Bibliographies are another service of ASTIA. These include not only general catalog and index information but abstracts where appropriate. Currently these are furnished in the form of catalog cards except in a few areas where demand has been so great that compilations have been printed in bound volumes. Bibliographies pertaining to all fields of science and technology applicable to any project are available to ASTIA customers on request. ASTIA is prefunded by the Department of Defense and does not charge for any of its services.

National Aeronautics and Space Administration (A, B, C)

Currently, NASA has four series of technical publications. These include NASA Technical Reports, which are unclassified presentations of a body of information which is considered to be complete and important; NASA Technical Notes, which supplement but do not overlap the Technical Reports; NASA Technical Memorandums, which are principally classified documents to be reissued as reports or notes if they are considered to be of general interest at the time they are declassified; and NASA Technical Translations, which present information which has been published in a foreign language. NASA reports and publications are announced in *Technical Publications Announcements.* This is a biweekly abstract list of all published NASA documents. It is supplemented by the annually published Index of NASA Technical Publications. Both are available from the NASA Office of Technical Information and Educational Programs, Code ETD, Washington 25, D.C.

United States Department of Agriculture (USDA) (A)

USDA publications in their Department Series contain principally reports on original USDA scientific research. These include Technical Bulletins, Production Research Reports, Utilization Research Reports, and Miscellaneous Publications.

USDA Monthly List of Publications and Motion Pictures. A list which indicates which reports are available free or for sale. The list is free on request from Office of Information, USDA, Washington 25, D.C.

Bibliography of Agriculture.† A monthly index to the world's literature on agriculture and the related sciences, as received in the USDA library. Each issue contains an author index, and the final issue of each volume consists of a cumulative author and subject index. It is available from GPO at $10 per year.

"List of Available Publications of the USDA" (List 11). Revised every few years, this list also indicates which reports are free and which are for sale. Single copies are available free from the Office of Information, USDA, Washington 25, D.C. Multiple copies, at 35 cents each, should be ordered from GPO.

The USDA does not deposit copies of its technical reports with the Office of Technical Services for announcement.

USDA Technical Reports are generally furnished on request from the issuing office, with the exception of the more expensively produced publications which are available only by purchase from GPO.

***U.S. Bureau of Mines, U.S. Department of the Interior*†** (A)

The Bureau of Mines publishes a wide range of reports reflecting its national research in: beneficiating and refining ores; chemical and physical properties of mineral raw materials; explosibility and other characteristics of liquids, gases, and dusts; petroleum engineering and refining; safety practices and equipment; composition and utilization of fossil fuels; air pollution; mining methods; and composition and application of commercial explosives. It likewise conducts economic studies, domestic and foreign, regarding certain minerals and provides statistical coverage for all key mineral commodities in the United States and territories.

Reports of the Bureau of Mines are generally published in the bureau's own series of publications. However, to disseminate information more quickly, the bureau frequently relies upon scientific, technical, and trade journals, convention proceedings, books, and other outside publications. Annual and five-year indexed catalogs of published articles and books by bureau scientists and engineers are also issued.

At the present time, the Bureau of Mines has available a book entitled "List of Publications Issued by the Bureau of Mines from July 1, 1910, to Jan. 1, 1960." It describes the many thousands of technical publications of the bureau and is complete with subject and author indexes, prices, and availability of all publications listed. It is available from GPO for $4.25.

Another recent publication, "List of Journal Articles by Bureau of Mines Authors Published July 1, 1910, to Jan. 1, 1960," mentions 9000 articles. It is complete with a subject and author index and is available from GPO for $1.75. "Mineral Facts and Problems," an encyclopedia of U.S. minerals, is issued every five years. Latest edition (1960) sells for $6 (cloth) at GPO.

The Bureau of Mines likewise issues the Minerals Yearbooks (in 3 volumes) which contain official government statistics on production and distribution of metals, minerals, and mineral fuels. They also include factual accounts of economic and technologic developments and trends. Entire yearbooks and separate chapters of the latest volumes can be obtained from GPO at prices indicated in the List of Publications mentioned above.

Geological Survey, (A)
U.S. Department of the Interior†

The U.S. Geological Survey collects, interprets, publishes, and distributes data about the physical and geologic features, minerals, mineral fuels, and water resources of the United States, its territories, and possessions. Survey reports are of two main types: book reports (professional papers, bulletins, water-supply papers, and circulars), and maps.

Since its organization in 1879, the survey has published more than 5000 reports and 22,000 different topographic maps. In addition, thousands of reports and papers have been published in scientific and engineering journals.

The Geological Survey puts out "Publications of the Geological Survey," which is revised every five years, and is kept up to date with monthly and annual announcements of new items. This publication, and the periodic supplements, are available free on request from Geological Survey, U.S. Department of Interior, Washington 25, D.C.

In 1960, the survey issued a new type of publication, titled "Geological Survey Research 1960." Consisting of two main parts and published as Professional Paper 400, the report is intended to summarize the results of the recent work of the Geologic Division of the survey, and to make these results available to the public as soon as possible. Chapter A, "Synopsis of Geologic Results," includes a summary of new findings either published or yet unpublished for the year ending June 30, 1960. It also contains a list of investigations in progress during that period, along with the names and headquarters of those in charge of each, and a list of reports published. Chapter B, "Short Papers," consisting of reports of generally less than 1000 words, announces new discoveries or observations on problems of limited scope, or conclusions drawn from extensive investigations that have been in progress for some time. Both chapters of USGS Professional Paper 400 are available from the GPO, Chapter A at $1, Chapter B at $4.25.

Bureau of Reclamation, (A)
U.S. Department of the Interior†

In the development of our most important single natural resource, water, the Bureau of Reclamation, at its Division of Engineering Laboratories, carries on research activities in nine areas: concrete and concrete making materials; hydraulics; earth materials; petrography; protective coatings; analytical chemistry; bituminous materials; saline water demineralization; and special investigations, such as aquatic weed controls, cathodic protection, corrosion, and evaporation reduction.

The bureau publishes two brochures which list the publications that are free or for sale. The bureau also issues laboratory reports primarily for its own use. Some of these, however, are available to the public as long as the supply lasts. They may be obtained by writing to U.S. Department of Interior, Bureau of Reclamation, Attention Code 841, Building 53, Denver Federal Center, Denver 25, Colo.

National Institutes of Health,
U.S. Department of Health, Education and Welfare

The seven institutes that make up NIH conduct research on cancer, heart disease, arthritis, neurological disorders, mental illness, allergies, and oral diseases. The only medium of publication for the reports generated by these studies is the scientific and technical press.

In addition to technical reports, the National Institutes of Health issue several other publications. One of these is the *Journal of the National Cancer Institute* which publishes not only a large part of the work done at the National Cancer Institute but also research in many other institutions in the U.S. and other countries. It is available from GPO at $20 a year for 12 issues. Another publication is the *Psychopharmacology Service Center Bulletin* which is distributed at irregular intervals by the Psychopharmocology Service Center, National Institute of Mental Health, Bethesda 14, Md. It is issued for information purposes to investigators interested in psychopharmacology. Two other publications of NIH are *Cancer Chemotherapy Reports* and *Cancer Chemotherapy Abstracts* which may be obtained from National Cancer Institute, Publication Office, Room 213 Robin Building, Bethesda 14, Md.

Other publications of NIH include selected bibliographies which have been prepared by the Psychopharmacology Service Center, Scientific Information Unit, and are distributed by this group on request. Also, a complete listing of all journals currently received by the library is available on request to the National Institutes of Health Library, Bethesda 14, Md.

National Library of Medicine,
U.S. Department of Health, Education and Welfare

The aim of the National Library of Medicine is to make its resources available to all workers who have need of them, and in fulfilling this aim, the National Library of Medicine considers that its main role should be to supplement the resources of local and regional libraries.

All printed material in the library's collection is available for interlibrary loan to libraries, not to individuals, with the exception of ordinary current, in-trade publications where there is widespread accessibility elsewhere. Individuals may use the resources on the library premises.

Material in the library will be loaned in the original form or in photoduplicates, and the library reserves the right to determine in which form the loan will be made. If photocopies are sent instead of original material, they are sent free of charge by the National Library of Medicine and may be retained permanently by the borrowing library.

Bibliographic searches on specific subjects will be undertaken as the library's facilities permit. These searches may be requested by libraries or by individuals who have exhausted the resources of their local libraries. A list of available bibliographies prepared by the National Library of Medicine is available upon request to the library.

The National Library of Medicine publishes several services:

Index Medicus† and **Cumulated Index Medicus.** *Index Medicus* beginning with January 1960 is a monthly publication and is available from GOP at $20 a year.

"Cumulated Index Medicus" (a three-volume set) is sold by the American

Medical Association, 535 North Dearborn St., Chicago 10, Ill., at $32 per year domestic and $35 per year foreign.

Occasional bibliographies and other publications on subjects of current interest are issued and distributed free or at a nominal cost. Publications which are sold should be ordered from GPO, and free publications should be requested from the National Library of Medicine, Washington 25, D.C. A complete listing of the library's publications is available on request from the library.

National Science Foundation (*NSF*) (A)

The National Science Foundation is responsible for promoting and encouraging scientific progress in the United States. It is organized into seven major components: the Division of Biological and Medical Sciences; the Division of Mathematical, Physical, and Engineering Sciences; the Division of Social Sciences; the Division of Scientific Personnel and Education; the Office of Science Information Service; the Office of Special International Programs; and the Office of Special Studies. These groups encompass four areas of activity: promotion of basic research in the sciences, promotion of education and training in the sciences, appraisal of national research and development efforts and resources, and promotion of effective dissemination of scientific information.

The results of NSF-sponsored research activities are reported mainly in the journals of the professional societies. Additional information is disseminated through NSF's own series of reports: *Manpower and Education Reports, Research and Development Reports, Science Administration Reports, Science Information Exchange Reports,* and *Annual Reports.*

NSF reports are announced in "Selected United States Government Publications," which is available from GPO. Also, a free list entitled "Publications of the National Science Foundation" may be obtained from the Printing and Publication Section, National Science Foundation, Washington 25, D.C.

Tennessee Valley Authority (*TVA*) (A)

TVA is an independent federal agency responsible for development of the resources of the Tennessee River Valley and adjoining territory. Therefore, it carries on a scientific research and development program, which includes both basic and applied research. Some of TVA's fields of interest are: soil chemistry, stream pollution control, air pollution control, medicine, chemistry, engineering, mathematics, and economics.

The findings of these studies are reported in scientific journals or in literature prepared by TVA or its contractors. The types of publications prepared by TVA include technical reports, technical monographs, chemical engineering bulletins, weekly news letters, and annual reports.

Information regarding price and availability of all TVA publications may be obtained from the announcement bulletins which list them. These publications include: Selected U.S. Government Publications, and GPO Price Lists 42 and 46. All of these are available from GPO.

The TVA supplements these services through some other publications, one of which is the "Analytical Index of Chemical Engineering Publications, Patents and Reports." This index catalogs by subject publications covering a large part of TVA's chemical engineering activities between 1933 and 1954. No information is given regarding price or availability of publications cited. The Analytical Index may be purchased from GPO for 55 cents. Also the Technical Library of TVA prepares two bibliographies titled "Indexed Bibliography of TVA" and "A Bibliography for the TVA Program." The first consists of a basic volume for the period 1933 through 1936, and annual supplements. The basic volume is out of print; however, the supplements may be obtained free from the TVA Director of Information, Knoxville, Tenn. The "Bibliography for the TVA Program" is a list of selected titles of books, articles, reports, and government publications relating to TVA. It is not comprehensive and is revised only at irregular intervals. These revisions may also be obtained free of charge from the TVA Director of Information.

National Academy of Sciences–National Research Council†

The National Academy of Sciences–National Research Council is a privately supported organization closely linked to the Federal Government. It is composed of eight divisions which operate through boards and institutes, committees, subcommittees, panels, and groups for special projects. The divisions are: Anthropology and Psychology, Biology and Agriculture, Chemistry and Chemical Technology, Earth Sciences, Engineering and Industrial Research, Mathematics, Medical Sciences, and Physical Science.

Some of the subgroups which are of special interest are: the Office of Scientific Personnel; the Office of Documentation; the Nuclear Data Project; which publishes Nuclear Data Tables, Nuclear Reaction Graphs, and Nuclear Theory Cards; Office of Critical Tables, which publishes the Directory of Continuing Numerical Data Projects; and the Prevention of Deterioration Center which publishes *Prevention of Deterioration Abstracts, Environmental Effects on Materials and Equipment Abstracts,* and *PDC Newsletter.* The Cardiovascular Literature Project which recently left NAS-NRC is now operating as the Washington office of the Institute for Advancement of Medical Communications.

Other publications of the divisions include proceedings, bulletins, periodicals, bibliographies, and special reports. The publications which are issued each year are listed in the list of publications which appears each spring. It is available from the National Academy of Sciences–National Research Council, Printing and Publication Office, 2101 Constitution Ave., Washington 25, D. C.

Smithsonian Institution† (A)

Information on new facts and specimens gathered from all over the world is disseminated through the Editorial and Publications Division of the Smithsonian Institution. Technical papers are published as appendixes to the annual report, as bulletins, and in the *Proceedings of the U.S. National Museum.* Price lists for publications which are available in the field of chemistry may be obtained by writing to Publications Distribution Section, Editorial and Publication Division, Smithsonian Institution, Washington 25, D.C.

Bibliography

Andrews, D. D., "Progress Report on U. S. Patent Office Mechanized Searching," "Abstracts of Papers," 133rd Meeting, ACS, April 1958, p. 5G.

Andrews, D. D., "Technical Problems in the Reclassification of Chemical Patents," "Abstracts of Papers," 129th Meeting, ACS, April 1956, p. 15G.

Andrews, E. O., Rienstra, H. S., Cox, E. W., "Operations and Services of the Liquid

Propellant Information Agency," "Abstracts of Papers," 137th Meeting, ACS, April 1960, p. 11G.

Barden, W. A., *Am. Documentation* **7,** 108–200 (July 1956). Armed Services Technical Information Agency.

Barden, W. A., Hammond, W., Heald, J. H., "Automation of ASTIA: A Preliminary Report," Office of Technical Service, Washington, 1960.

Berry, S. G., "Are Unpublished Reports of the Office of Technical Services Printed Under Sec. 102 of the Patent Act?", "Abstracts of Papers," 132nd Meeting, ACS, September 1957, p. 20G.

Brownson, H. L., "Support of Publication by the National Science Foundation," "Abstracts of Papers," 128th Meeting, ACS, September 1955, p. 18G.

Caprio, A. F., "U. S. Patents as a Source of Technical Information," "Abstracts of Papers," 132nd Meeting, ACS, September 1957, p. 19G.

Clapp, V. W., *J. Chem. Educ.* **24,** 75–8 (1947). Present-day problems in obtaining foreign scientific publications.

Cohn, E. M., Perry, Harry, *Ibid.,* **33,** 331–3 (1956). Activities and publications of the Bureau of Mines.

Day, M. S., Lebow, Irving, *Am. Documentation* **11,** 120–7 (April 1960). New indexing pattern for *Nuclear Science Abstracts.*

DeWitt, J. B., "Information of Chemical Interest That Can Be Obtained from the U. S. Fish and Wildlife Service," "Abstracts of Papers," 125th Meeting, ACS, March 1954, p. 6G.

Donnelly, M. V., ADVANCES IN CHEM. SER., No. **10,** 3–9 (1954). Government production statistics as source for chemical planning.

Dunlop, W. W., "The Armed Services Technical Information Agency: Its Purposes, Problems, and Progress," "Abstracts of Papers," 137th Meeting, ACS, April 1960, p. 11G.

Fahey, J. J., "Chemical Publications of the United States Geological Survey," "Abstracts of Papers," 134th Meeting, ACS, September 1958, p. 11G.

Fishbein, E. P., Wescott, E. C., *Spec. Libraries* **48,** 96–9 (March 1957). Brief introduction of research tools for AEC and government scientific reports.

Fishenden, R. M., *ASLIB Proc.* **9,** 229–33 (August 1957). Availability of atomic energy information.

Fleischer, Michael, *Advances in Documentation and Library Sci.* **1,** 105–11 (1957). Experiences with a notched card file of geochemical data.

Gamble, D. F., "Chemical Activities and Publications of the Public Health Services," "Abstracts of Papers," 122nd Meeting, ACS, April 1958, p. 6G.

Gamble, D. F., "Coordinate Index of Organic Compounds," "Abstracts of Papers," 127th Meeting, ACS, April 1955, p. 7G.

Gilbert, W. C., ADVANCES IN CHEM. SER., No. **10,** 107–13 (1954). Congressional committee hearings.

Glockler, George, "Department of Defense Regulations and Technical Information," "Abstracts of Papers," 129th Meeting, ACS, April 1956, p. 12G.

Gray, D. E., "Centralized Abstracting in the Department of Defense," "Abstracts of Papers," 119th Meeting, ACS, April 1951, p. 13E.

Gray, D. E., *College & Research Libraries* **18,** No. 1, 23–7 (1957). Scientists and government research information.

Gray, D. E., "Government Research Reports for Scientists," "Abstracts of Papers," 131st Meeting, ACS, April 1957, p. 9G.

Gray, D. E., *Phys. Today* **4,** No. 1, 28–9 (1951). Library of Congress Science Division.

Ibid., **4,** No. 3, 8–9 (1951). Experiment in standardization (of documentation).

Ibid., **4,** No. 9, 17–19 (1951). Basic research in the Office of Naval Research.

Ibid., **5,** No. 1, 20–3 (1952). National Academy of Sciences and the National Research Council.

Green, J. C., *Chem. Eng. News* **25,** 1335–6 (1947). OTS translation clearing house.

Green, J. C., "Publication Board and Its Function in Disseminating Scientific Information from Government-Sponsored Research and Enemy Sources," "Abstracts of Papers," 109th Meeting, ACS, April 1946, p. 3D.

Greer, P. S., Kanegis, James, "Government Reports on Rubber," Symposium on Literature of Rubber, Papers Presented at 130th ACS Meeting, September 1956, ACS Division of Rubber Chemistry (1956); PB Report **131096** (75 cents at GPO).

Gull, D. D., "The Preparation of the *Cumulative Catalog* at the Library of Congress," "Abstracts of Papers," 112th Meeting, ACS, September 1947, p. 14E.

Harris, L. E., "Interest of the Chemical Corps in Chemical-Biological Coordination," "Abstracts of Papers," 121st Meeting, ACS, April 1952, p. 4F.

Heald, J. H., *Spec. Libraries* **51,** 115–21 (March 1960). Project Mars.

Heald, J. H., *Spec. Libraries Assoc. Sci.-Tech. News,* **14,** 6–7 (Spring 1960). User effects of ASTIA automation.

Heumann, K. F., Dale, Estaleta, "Statistical Survey of Chemical Structure," Progress re-

port in chemical literature retrieval, p. 201, Interscience Publishers, New York, 1957.
Hoffheins, F. M., Colten, O. A., ADVANCES IN CHEM. SER., No. **10**, 10–13 (1954). Chemical statistics and Commerce's Chemical Division.
Hooker, Marjorie, "The Literature of Rock and Mineral Analyses," "Abstracts of Papers," 128th Meeting, ACS, September 1955, p. 16G.
Hylander, C. J., Amoss, A. M., "Dissemination of Technical Information at the Chemical Warfare Laboratories," "Abstracts of Papers," 130th Meeting, ACS, September 1956, p. 4G.
Jackson, E. B., *Spec. Libraries* **51**, 115–21 (March 1960). Aeronautical documentation practices in Europe and America.
Johnson, R. K., "Higher American Military Educational Institutions and Their Libraries" (Aspects of Librarianship No. 10), Kent State University, Kent, Ohio, 1956.
Kamran, G. S., "Information and Publication Activities of the U. S. Department of Agriculture," "Abstracts of Papers," 129th Meeting, ACS, 1956, p. 13G.
Kanegis, James, ADVANCES IN CHEM. SER., No. **10**, 151–9 (1954). Plastics literature in government reports.
Kanegis, James, *J. Chem. Documentation* **1**, 7–10 (1960). Technical literature of OTS and its related services.
Kirner, W. R., "Organization, Objectives, and Progress of the Chemical-Biological Coordination Center," National Research Council–National Academy of Science, Washington, D. C., Pub. **206**, 125–6.
Lanham, B. E., "The Use of the U.S. Patent Office Classification in Chemical Searches," "Abstracts of Papers," 119th Meeting, ACS, April 1951, p. 7F.
Lederman, Lorna, Green, John, Graf, Dorothy, ADVANCES IN CHEM. SER., No. **10**, 477–87 (1954). Searching the PB collection for chemical information.
Leiter, Joseph, Scheiderman, Marvin, Miller, Eugene, "Data Processing Program of the Cancer Chemotherapy National Service Center," "Abstracts of Papers," 136th Meeting, ACS, September 1959, p. 5G.
Lindenmeyer, H. F., *J. Patent Office Soc.* **36**, 463–81 (1954). What does the Patent Office scientific library have to offer the chemist?
Lowry, W. K., *Spec. Libraries* **47**, 70–73 (February 1956). Aeronautical documentation in the United States.
McMurray, G. S., "Operation and Services of the Solid Propellant Information Agency," "Abstracts of Papers," 137th Meeting, ACS, April 1960, p. 11G.
Maizell, R. E., *Phys. Today* **12**, 42–44 (December 1959). Locating unclassified government-sponsored research reports.
Mohat, Halador, ADVANCES IN CHEM. SER., No. **10**, 114–20 (1954). Information on the chemical industry developed by antitrust cases.
National Bureau of Standards, U.S. Department of Commerce, Part III, *Scientific Information Activities of Federal Agencies,* No. 8 (1960) (NSF 60-59).
National Science Foundation Report "Organization of the Federal Government for Scientific Activities," 1956 (NSF 56-17), ($1.75, GPO).
National Science Foundation, *Scientific Information Activities of Federal Agencies,* No. 6 (1960) (NSF 60-56).
Newman, E. I., Copeland, L. D., "Analytical Index of Chemical Engineering Publications, Patents, and Reports," U.S. Government Printing Office, Washington, 1954.
North, J. B., *Spec. Libraries Assoc. Sci.-Tech. News* **13**, 10 (fall 1959). Trouble with ASTIA.
Oatfield, Harold, Lowe, D. J., ADVANCES IN CHEM. SER., No. **10**, **455–76** (1954). Domestic sources of foreign information on trade, statistics, and scientific activities.
Ockert, K. F., McMurray, G. S., "The Solid Propellant Information Agency," Am. Rocket Soc. Reprint **976-59** (1959).
Office of Naval Research, *Scientific Information Activities of Federal Agencies,* No. **2** (1959) (NSF 59–19).
Orne, Jerrold, *Spec. Libraries* **47**, 373–7 (October 1956). Librarian looks at military literature.
Parks, A. F., *Anal. Chem.* **27**, No. 6, 13A (1955). Technical information of the U. S. Customs Service.
Peterson, I. H., "Government Sources (Executive Conference on Organizing and Managing Information; Proceedings)," University of Chicago, Chicago, 1958.
Postell, P. E., Pflueger, M. L., *Spec. Libraries* **48**, 91–6 (March 1957). Recent technical information activities of the U. S. Atomic Energy Commission.
Potter, E. P., "Development of the Chemical Literature Classification in the Dewey Decimal Classification," "Abstracts of Papers," 116th Meeting, ACS, September 1949, p. 12F.
Premo, J. G., *J. Chem. Educ.* **35**, 353 (1958). Simplified procedure for searching United States chemical patents.
Prickett, C. S., "Activities and Publications of the Food and Drug Administration," "Abstracts of Papers," 132nd Meeting, ACS, September 1957, p. 14G.

Read, W. T., "Utilizing the National Roster of Scientific and Specialized Personnel," "Abstracts of Papers," 110th Meeting, ACS, September 1946, p. 12D.
Rossini, F. D., "Technical and Scientific Services of the National Bureau of Standards for the Petroleum Industry," "Abstracts of Papers," 111th Meeting, ACS, April 1947, p. 9D.
"Science Information Service Established by the National Science Foundation," *Am. Documentation* **10**, 165–6 (April 1959).
Scott, E. W., "Communication of U.S. Government Technical Information," "Abstracts of Papers," 120th Meeting, ACS, September 1951, p. 5F.
Scott, E. W., *Science* **114**, 653–651 (1951). Technical information activities of the Department of Defense.
Scott, E. W., Ball, T., "Scientific Information Problems of the National Military Establishment," "Abstracts of Papers," 114th Meeting, ACS, September 1948, p. 16E.
Shepard, H. H., "Economic and Marketing Information on Pesticides," "Abstracts of Papers," 127th Meeting, ACS, April 1955, p. 3G.
Smith, J. F., Ware, R. P., "Technical Information Facilities of the District of Columbia," "Abstract of Papers," 118th Meeting, ACS, September 1950, p. 3F.
Sternberg, Virginia, *Spec. Libraries* **47**, 417–21 (1956). Atomic Energy business services.
Taube, Mortimer, Thompson, A. F., "The Abstracting of Government Reports," "Abstracts of Papers," 119th Meeting, ACS, April 1951, p. 12F.
Tennessee Valley Authority, *Scientific Information Activities of Federal Agencies,* No. **5** (1960) (NSF 60-44).
Thompson, A. F., Taube, Mortimer, "The Purpose and Performance of Nuclear Science Abstracts," "Abstracts of Papers," 119th Meeting, ACS, April 1951, p. 13F.
U.S. Department of Agriculture, *Scientific Information Activities of Federal Agencies,* No. **1** (1958) (NSF 58-27).
U.S. Department of Commerce, Part I, *Scientific Information Activities of Federal Agencies,* No. **3** (1959) (NSF 59-58).
Ibid., Part II, **7** (1960) (NSF 60-58).
U.S. 85th Congress, 2nd Session, Senate, Science and Technology Act 1958, Availability of Technical Information from Federal Departments and Agencies (Hearings before a D.C., 1959.
U.S. Government Printing Office, *Scientific Information Activities of Federal Agencies,* No. **4** (1960) (NSF 60-9).
Wagner, F. S., Jr., *Texas Chapter SLA Bulletin* **12**, No. 4, 26–29 (1961). Studies on improved literature survey methods. I. Literature surveys using reviews.
Wagner, F. S., Jr., "Study of Patents Documentation," "Abstracts of Papers," 133rd Meeting, ACS, April 1958, p. 8G.
Warbeit, I. A., *Spec. Libraries Assoc. Sci.-Tech. News* **13**, 3–5 (Spring 1959). Geneva conference on utilization of atomic energy scientific and technical information.
Welt, I. D., "Aspects of the CBCC Biology Code of Interest to Chemists," "Abstracts of Papers," 138th Meeting, ACS, September 1960, p. 10G; *J. Chem. Documentation* **1**, 19–21 (1961).
Welt, I. D., *Bull. Med. Library Assoc.* **46**, 367–80 (1958). Detailed indexing of biological effects of chemical substances.
White, B. J., "Literature Dealing with Forensic Chemistry," "Abstracts of Papers," 137th Meeting, ACS, April 1960, p. 10G.
Wilcox, J. K., "Bibliography of New Guides and Aides to Public Documents Use, 1953–1956" (SLA Bibliography No. 2), Spec. Libraries Assoc., New York, 1957.
Wood, G. C. [Geer, H. A., Dale, Esteleta, Williams, A. S., Thurlow, J. F.], "Types of Questions Answered by the Chemical-Biological Coordination Center," National Academy of Sciences–National Research Council, Washington, D.C., 1955.

THIS paper replaces and expands on one by the same title in ADVANCES No. 4 by Norman T. Ball and Cedric R. Flagg. As nucleus for the bibliography, Mr. Flagg also supplied a list compiled by the late Spencer C. Stanford.

Exploring United States Chemical Patent Literature

JOSEPH FLEISCHER

Olin Mathieson Chemical Corp., New Haven, Conn.

"The issue of patents for new discoveries has given a spring to invention beyond my conception."—Thomas Jefferson. "The patent system added the fuel of interest to the fire of genius."—Abraham Lincoln. "The American patent system has promoted countless applications of the arts and sciences to the needs and well-being of our people."—Franklin D. Roosevelt.

The publication of printed patents has been an important factor in the development of science and industry. Published patents have stimulated technological advances directly; and indirectly by revealing information that might otherwise have disappeared. Classified sets of patents are often unique collections of knowledge and may be the only existing good source showing the evolution of important fields of industrial activity.

In the United States, this as well as other features of our patent system can be credited primarily to the wisdom of the founding fathers in laying the basis for the fostering of inventive genius by means of the well-known constitutional provision for patents. We are also the beneficiaries of the far-seeing statesmen and conscientious office holders who implemented this provision by enacting the basic patent laws and by formulating and administering the essential rules. We are no less indebted to their able successors who improved the laws and rules when they considered it necessary to "promote the progress of science and useful arts."

Our first Commissioner of Patents under the Act of 1836 deserves special mention because his capable administration gave a good start to the patent system now in force in our country, and also because he has been so grossly misrepresented in recent years.

Henry L. Ellsworth, son of Oliver Ellsworth, a Chief Justice of the U. S. Supreme Court, was born in 1791 at Windsor, Conn. He was in charge of the Patent Office from 1835 to 1845. His annual reports on Patent Office activities are excellent summaries which were not limited to problems of the Patent Office, but included statistics and discussions of our industrial, agricultural, and economic progress.

One paragraph, in his annual report for 1843 (*4*), has been so distorted from the context in which it was presented as to lead to false rumors that he had prophesied the near arrival of an era of no more inventions, and the end of the usefulness of the Patent Office. In truth, it is clear from this report as well as from others he wrote, that his views were quite the opposite. The paragraph.

> The advancement of the arts from year to year taxes our credulity, and seems to presage the arrival of that period when human improvement must end.

appeared as part of his plea to Congress to approve funds for the publication of patent claims and other information about patents and to increase the salaries of Patent Office personnel. Said he, "If there is any bureau where are needed scientific attainments of a high order, it is in the Patent Office."

His 1843 report also includes (page B33) the following passage from the pen of one of the examiners:

> The great mass of inventions are of a character to make us alike proud of the genius of our countrymen, and the Government which fosters and protects it. Man's wants increase with his progress in knowledge; and hence the paradoxical truth, that the growing number of inventions instead of filling the measure, increases its capacity. The offspring of each distinct and notable invention may be hundreds, or even thousands; and each of these may claim its host of descendants. In an incalculable ratio will inventions increase, till space will hardly be found to preserve their representations. No other conclusion can be reached by the deep thinker upon this subject; no truth to him more forcible than that so happily expressed by Sir Humphrey Davy: "the greater the circle of light, the greater the boundary of darkness which surrounds it."—Charles G. Page.

In his letter of resignation, dated April 1, 1845, Commissioner Ellsworth could well say, "I now leave the bureau in a prosperous condition." This letter also states (*8*):

> During my superintendency, a reorganization has taken place and I have been grateful to witness the expediency of the changes I so strongly recommended. In common with many others I have found the discharge of public duties incompatible with a due attention to private concerns. Nor will I omit to acknowledge the existence of an honest jealousy against the monopoly of emoluments. I wish to express a willingness that others may share public favors and have an opportunity to make greater improvements.

It is hoped that these brief quotations will evoke in the reader due feelings of gratitude and respect toward the architects and builders of our patent system.

Any doubts concerning the significance of patents as sources of chemical information will be dispelled on perusal of recent annual reports on *Chemical Abstracts,* which during 1949 listed 11,390 patents, distributed among 29 of the 32 sections (*3*). The bibliography section of recent books and review articles in various chemical fields generally carries a goodly proportion of patent numbers.

The proportion of chemical patents in the United States has risen from a figure which may have been as low as one chemical patent per 30 patents issued in 1907 to about one in five during the past three decades. The detailed statistics are given in Table I and are shown graphically in Figure 1. The totals are based on the United States patents listed in the "Patent Index to *Chemical Abstracts* 1907–1936" (*12*) and later issues of the "Numerical Patent Index to *Chemical Abstracts.*" The percentages of chemical patents for the early years may be somewhat lower than the true figure, because of incomplete coverage of chemical patents at that time. However, there can be no doubt that a significant increase in this percentage occurred during the period 1907 to 1937.

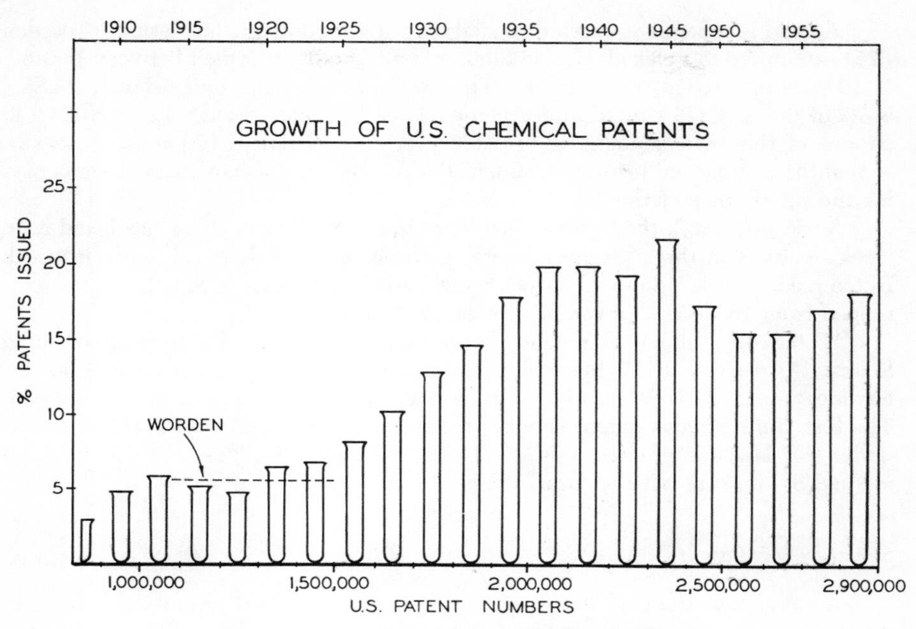

Figure 1. Statistics on United States patents

Table I. U. S. Chemical Patents[a] Issued between July 3, 1906, and August 18, 1959

Patent No. Range	*Date*	*Total Chemical Patents*	*% Chemical Patents*
825,000	July 1906	...	...
900,000	Sept. 1908	2,240	3.0
1,000,000	Aug. 1911	4,870	4.9
1,100,000	June 1914	5,950	6.0
1,200,000	Oct. 1916	5,320	5.3
1,300,000	April 1919	4,860	4.9
1,400,000	Dec. 1921	6,740	6.7
1,500,000	July 1924	7,000	7.0
1,600,000	Sept. 1926	8,360	8.4
1,700,000	January 1929	10,400	10.4
1,800,000	April 1931	12,980	13.0
1,900,000	March 1933	14,780	14.8
2,000,000	April 1935	18,030	18.0
2,100,000	Nov. 1937	19,970	20.0
2,200,000	May 1940	20,050	20.1
2,300,000	Oct. 1942	19,410	19.4
2,400,000	May 1946	21,770	21.8
2,500,000	March 1950	17,522	17.5
2,600,000	June 1952	15,693	15.7
2,700,000	January 1955	15,679	15.7
2,800,000	July 1957	17,146	17.2
2,900,000	August 1959	18,373	18.4
Worden 1,123,212 to 1,521,589, inclusive		22,882 (*15*)	5.7
C. A. (Jan. 1, 1915–Dec. 31, 1924)		24,140	6.1

[a] Abstracted in *Chemical Abstracts*, not counting reissues.

A good independent check is available for the middle of this period. Worden (*15*) attempted to index all United States chemical patents issued between January 1, 1915, and December 31, 1924. The number of patents indexed was 22,882, 5.7% of the 398,378 United States patents issued in that period. Close to 24,140 patents of this span, amounting to 6.1%, were abstracted in *Chemical Abstracts*, so that the comparison inspires confidence in the extent of its coverage while verifying the significance of the data in Table I.

Since July 1952, the *Official Gazette of the U. S. Patent Office* has listed each week's patents in three groups—general and mechanical, chemical, and electrical. In ten recent weeks (September to November 1960) patents in the chemical group ranged from 18 to 26% of the total, averaging 20%.

Historically, chemical patents have always been important in the United States. As early as 1641, Massachusetts granted a patent, the first issued on this continent, to Samuel Winslow, for a 10-year term, on a method of making salt. The first United States patent law was the Act of April 10, 1790. The first patent under this law was granted July 31, 1790, to Samuel Hopkins of Vermont for a method of "making pot and pearl ashes."

Structure of Patents

An understanding of the general structure of modern patents will lead to greater efficiency in reading and understanding them.

Many modern chemical patents are well-written documents which have much in common with scientific papers on the same subject. An obvious reason for this happy circumstance is that essential portions of the specifications in these cases are written by the chemists who did the work or reported it. During the past two decades, many chemists have become engaged in patent work, so that what might be termed the legalistic part of a considerable proportion of chemical patents has also been written by chemically trained personnel.

The patent specification corresponds to the body portion of a scientific paper. It generally starts out with a brief statement of the field of the subject matter. Usually, one then finds a listing of the objects of the invention, followed or preceded by a discussion of earlier efforts in the same or related fields, often with special emphasis on their deficiencies.

The setting has now been indicated both as to field and the existing difficulties which were to be overcome. The solution to the problem is then revealed by a general statement of the invention.

The patent then proceeds to describe specific examples or embodiments of the invention. This is the section of chemical patents which is frequently taken directly from or largely based upon reports written by chemists.

The specification usually ends with a broad restatement of the invention and its most important advantages and applications.

These patent components are similar to corresponding sections of scientific papers. The section devoted to the description of specific examples or embodiments can very well be identical for the two types of publication.

The greater differences are apt to occur in the discussion of earlier work (prior art), in the listing of objectives (sometimes characterized by what Chaucer would have called "superfluitee abomynable"), and particularly in the general statement of the invention. It sometimes involves more art than science for an inventor to recognize his own brain child, luxuriously bedecked in polysyllabic raiment in the patent application. Fortunately, there seems to be a decreasing tendency toward the use in patents of what a judge once called (7) "those erosive and mind-grooving processes of unyielding reiteration of concept and ready prestidigitation of words."

Mark Twain had some words for this sort of thing, when in 1870 he promised "to strip the nutritious facts bare of that effulgence of imagination and sublimity of diction which too often mar the excellence of these great works," in connection with his purpose to write condensations of the annual Patent Office Reports (6).

It is noteworthy, however, that Mark Twain, despite serious financial losses in the backing of inventions of others, had Sir Boss say, in his "Connecticut Yankee," that "a country without a patent office and good patent laws is just a crab and can't travel any way but sideways and backways."

The summary, which is generally found at the end of scientific papers, differs from the claim section which concludes patents. A summary should emphasize what is new in the paper. But the applicant for a patent must, according to the patent laws, "particularly point out and distinctly claim the part, improvement, or combination which he claims as his invention or discovery." The claims thus constitute the section of the patent which defines the new technological area in which exclusive rights are granted to the patentee or his assignee during the life of the patent. The drafting of proper claims is the most difficult and essential task in obtaining good patents and is the phase which makes greatest demands on the unusual combination of insight, literary skill, and thorough knowledge of the art as well as of patent law, which characterizes most successful patent solicitors.

It may happen that patent claims constitute good summaries of the new subject matter in the patent specification. But the legalistic form and expressions will often be found a hindrance to the utility of claims as summaries. It is not unusual to find that the disclosure in a patent is much more extensive than indicated by the claims.

Drawings are required in patents "whenever the nature of the case admits of it" (Rule 81, Rules of Practice of the United States Patent Office in patent cases). "The drawing must show every feature of the invention specified in the claims" (Rule 83). Similarly, scientific papers include drawings illustrating new relationships, or novel components or arrangements of apparatus.

Patents and papers both carry titles, which should be informative but all too often are not, especially in patents. Too frequently, one finds modern patents with unjustifiably broad titles such as "Process of extracting metals from ores," "Chemical process," "Chemical composition," or "Controlling chemical reactions." As a patent title, "Chemical testing device" will indicate a new and improved test tube only to the uninitiated.

Scientific papers usually carry a bibliography at the end. There used to be no corresponding section in United States patents, except for the occasional mention of earlier publications in the specification. However, United States patents now end with a list of all references which were cited during the prosecution of the application in the Patent Office. This worthy addition was introduced in 1947 during the tenure of Casper W. Ooms, appointed Commissioner of Patents in 1945. Among other advances made by Commissioner Ooms before his retirement from the office in 1947 was the adoption of the single signature form for patent applications, so that one inventor's signature now does the work of three formerly required.

It will be evident from the foregoing analysis of the usual structure and contents of patents that particular emphasis should be concentrated for the purposes of literature surveys or abstracts on the section describing specific examples.

Attention should also be given to the general statements of the invention which usually precede and sometimes follow the description of the specific embodiments.

The patent claims are, of course, of primary interest when the patent is being studied for scope or validity in connection with determining a question of infringement. However, it is more the exception than the rule for patent claims to be helpful in a literature survey.

The above generalization may fortunately be going out of style, in that more and more chemical patents carry specific titles and have claims that are informative even to amateur patent attorneys. An excellent example is the patent on streptomycin and process of preparation, which was assigned to the nonprofit Rutgers Research and Endowment Foundation (*14*). The specification scarcely differs from a scientific paper and the process claims constitute easily understandable summaries of essential steps in the manufacturing procedure. Claim 13, a product claim, cannot be surpassed for conciseness: "13. Streptomycin."

An unusual ending appears in a patent issued to L. B. Swan in 1847 (*13*) and entitled "Improvement in Galvanic Batteries for Telegraphs":

> In the foregoing specification and claim I have, as it will be seen, limited my claim to the use of my solution in batteries used for telegraphic purposes, and this I have done that I may not be supposed in any way to interfere with experiments having for their object the advancement of science.

Locating Patents

Over 2,900,000 United States patents have been issued since 1836, over 200,000 of which contain information of chemical interest. Clearly, an efficient classification of patents is essential for the proper functioning of the patent system and for making the information available.

The first classification in 1830 grouped the total 6170 United States patents in 16 classes. At present, there are over 300 main classes, each further divided into subclasses. Nearly every patent has its niche in one of the 45,000 or so subclasses, and may also be cross-referenced in other related subclasses.

The classified list of 1830 was accompanied by a statement by the superintendent of patents, John D. Craig, from which the following is quoted (*1*):

> The difficulty of classifying natural objects is well known, the gradual and imperceptible shades of difference rendering it impossible to determine exactly where one class should end and another begin. In the productions of art this difficulty is not diminished. Hence, in compiling the list of patents a doubt frequently arose concerning the class to which some of the patents did properly belong. For instance, whether the partial rotting of hemp and flax should be classed under agriculture or chemistry, dry docks under navigation or land works, etc. Besides, many of the machines patented are applicable to purposes widely different, and consequently could not be included exclusively in any one class; while the titles of others are so indefinite as to render it impossible to determine either their genera or species. In such cases, no specific disposition being practicable, when the subject or patent sought is not found where it was expected it will be discovered under some other title, to which the nature of the subject will generally refer.

This appraisal and advice, issued in 1830 with respect to some 6000 patents classified in only 16 groups, can well be kept in mind 130 years and almost 3,000,000 patents later.

The chemical class was entitled, "Chemical compositions: Tanning, patent medicines, cements, dyes, etc."

In 1836, six classes were added, class 4 having the following definition:

"Chemical processes, manufactures, and compounds, including medicine, dyeing, color making, distilling, soap and candle making, mortars, cements, etc."

The classification was further expanded in 1868 (36 classes) and again in 1872 (145 classes). Subclasses appeared in the classification in 1880 (164 main classes).

The classification system has continued its growth with the years, a separate Classification Division being established in the Patent Office in 1898 for the administration of the work and problems pertaining to this field. The revisions and amplifications of the system have, of course, had to be accompanied by the movement of patents to their newly assigned locations.

The "bible" of this system is the "Manual of Classification of Patents," published by the Patent Office. Supplementing the manual are the class and subclass definitions contained in the Classification Bulletins, also obtainable from the Patent Office.

The manual comprises a listing of each class showing its subclass titles, and a lengthy (325 pages) subject index which gives the proper class and subclass for each item listed. A brief description of the use of the manual is included. There is also a list of the classes as assigned to the Patent Office Examining Divisions. A further interesting feature is a grouping of the classes under five main headings:

I. Chemical and Related Arts
II. Communications, Radiant Energy, and Electrical Arts
III. Mechanical Manufacturing and Machine Elements Arts
IV. Transportation, Material Handling and Treating, Motor and Pump, and Weapon Arts
V. Instruments of Precision, Body Treatment and Care, Heating and Cooling, Static Arts, Designs, Miscellaneous

Of the 75 examining divisions of the Patent Office, at least 30 deal with chemical patents. Eleven of these divisions handle chemical patents principally.

Table II lists the classes listed in the manual under Group I. The classes are arranged in numerical order and the titles have in some cases been abbreviated.

Some features of the United States classification system which it is important to keep in mind are:

The class numbers are arbitrary, serving merely to identify the individual classes. Generally, the basis of classification is essential function or effect. The order of the subclasses in a class is that of proceeding from the complex to the simple. When a patent is classified, it is placed in the most complex subclass suitable for it and it is cross-referenced in any appropriate subsequent (more elemental) subclass.

A patent is classified primarily on the basis of its claimed subject matter.

Various paths can be followed in conducting a patent search, just as in searching the nonpatent literature.

A thorough search of United States chemical patents since 1907 can be made in any good library by the use of *Chemical Abstracts.* The tables and Figure 1 inspire confidence in such a search. But it is a laborious and tedious method, especially since one must order and wait for the pertinent patent copies in order to complete the study.

The spacious, though usually crowded, Search Room at the Patent Office is the only place in this country where a thorough patent search can be made expeditiously. The term "expeditiously" is here used in a comparative sense, because the search in a complex field may require several days or weeks of concentrated effort even at the Patent Office, but would require much more work and time elsewhere.

Table II. Chemical and Related Arts

Class No.	*Class Title*
8	Bleaching and Dyeing
18	Plastics
21	Preserving, Disinfecting, Sterilizing
22	Metal Founding
23	Chemistry (Inorganic, Testing, Apparatus)
25	Plastic Block and Earthenware Apparatus
41	Ornamentation
44	Fuel, Igniting Devices
48	Gas, Heating and Illuminating
49	Glass
52	Explosive, Pyrotechnic, Match
71	Fertilizers
75	Metallurgy, Processes and Alloys
91	Apparatus
99	Foods, Beverages
106	Plastic, Coating
107	Bread, Pastry, and Confection Making
117	Coating, Processes and Miscellaneous Products
127	Sugar, Starch, Carbohydrates
130	Threshing
148	Metal Treating Processes
154	Laminated Fabrics
162	Paper
167	Medicines, Poisons, Cosmetics
183	Gas Separation
195	Fermentation
196	Mineral Oils
202	Distillation
204	Electrical and Wave Energy Chemistry
209	Classifying Solids
210	Liquid Separation or Purification
233	Centrifugal Separators
252	Compositions
259	Agitating
260	Chemistry, Carbon Compounds
261	Gas and Liquid Contact
266	Apparatus

A number of classes could well be added:

Class No.	*Class Title*
47	Plant Husbandry
51	Abrading
95	Photography
134	Cleaning
136	Batteries
250	Radiant Energy

The extensive collections of source material available in the Patent Office Search Room and Scientific Library have been summarized superbly by Lindenmeyer (*11*).

Patent Office Search Room

The Search Room is located on the first floor of the E Street end of the Commerce Building. Row after row of search desks, provided with racks arranged for convenient "flipping and scanning" of patent subclasses and each having its convenient fluorescent light, extend across the room. During working hours, there is a continuous hum of activity, searchers constantly emerging from the adjoining stack room loaded down with subclasses, or entering for more armsful, assistants collecting the discarded subclasses from the tops of the reading desks, here and there an animated discussion and above all the whirr of the patents as they are expertly flipped and perused for that 50-year-old anticipation of some fond inventor's "million-dollar-invention."

It is awe-inspiring to enter the stack room, crammed as it is with rows and columns of stacks, with one or more subclasses or a portion of a subclass housed in each rack opening. Here is the Patent Office set of classified patents, starting with the designs classes at the 14th Street side and then progressing numerically from Class 1, Nailing and Stapling, to Class 346, Recorders, toward the 15th Street side.

A complete numerical set of United States patents is housed conveniently along the walls of the Search Room and extends into the 15th Street end of the stack room. Annual indexes, Commissioner's Reports, and Commissioner's Decisions are also available.

A number of sets of the Classification Manual are located at a desk near the 14th Street entrance. There is also a complete set of class definitions in loose-leaf binders, arranged in numerical order at the start and close of each business day. Nearby is an important card file, listing the class and subclass of every United States patent (the entries are in pencil).

Midway along the front wall, one finds a useful patentee and assignee card index arranged in alphabetical order, listing for each patent issued since 1931 name of the inventor(s) and assignee, if any, patent and application numbers, date of issue of the patent, and the title of the invention.

At the other end of the room (15th Street end), file histories of issued patents can be obtained for study at the nearby desks, which are conveniently arranged for this purpose.

A thorough search requires the study of all the subclasses pertinent to the subject. It is therefore necessary to compile a list of such subclasses.

This can be done in a number of ways. According to what might be called the fundamental way, the first step is to find subclass numbers by looking up the subject and related terms in the index to the Manual of Classification. But occasionally no relevant term can be located in this index. It is then necessary to scan the class titles under the appropriate one of the five main groups of classes and then the subclass titles under any class that seems promising.

Then, by looking up the detailed explanation of each of the preliminary list of subclass numbers in the book of class definitions, one obtains an expanded list by adding such further subclasses as are cross-referenced there.

Subclass numbers may also be obtained during the course of perusing the patents in a classified set by noting patents that are cross-referenced. Recent patents carry the subclass number on page 1, immediately below the patent heading. The classification of earlier patents can be found in the card file, mentioned above.

The patents relevant to the subject are themselves a source of additional pertinent subclass numbers. One finds the classification of the patents which were cited during the Patent Office prosecution, again by use of the classification card file. The cited patents are listed on recent United States patents and, in the case of earlier patents, can be obtained from the file histories.

A useful list of subclass numbers can likewise be compiled, with the use of the classification card index, by means of a list of pertinent patent numbers found in *Chemical Abstracts,* books, or review articles.

These procedures can lead to an enormous list of subclass numbers, even though one starts with only a single or a few patent numbers. However, many such subclasses can be eliminated from the scope of the particular search on mere inspection of the titles.

Generally, it will save time to locate subclasses through patent numbers obtained from *Chemical Abstracts,* rather than via the index to the manual and the class definitions. This is in part due to the complexity of many of the definitions, which tend to be more confusing than clarifying until one has become thoroughly familiar with the method and style of presentation.

The index, although characterized by some disadvantages, such as type which is difficult to read, is an amazing guide, ranging in subject from Abacus (Class 35, subclass 33; Education–teaching–mathematics–abacus) to Zwieback (Class 99, subclass 86; Foods and Beverages–processes and products–cereals–baked products), or speaking chemically, from Abietic Acid (260/97; Chemistry, Carbon Compounds–natural resins and reaction products) to Zirconium (23/15; Chemistry–compounds–rare element compound recovery). Indeed, items neighboring those sought frequently will catch the eye and distract the reader's attention from the immediate objective. However, in a thorough search, the use of the Manual of Classification and the class definitions is usually advisable, at least as a check.

Having secured the list of subclasses needed, the searcher proceeds to gather them from the racks in the stack room. Each rackful consists of a flat pile of unbound "hard" copies of patents (each sheet laminated for stiffness) between two thick cover sheets, the upper one being imprinted with the class, subclass, and rack number.

The rack at the search desk conveniently holds such a group, which at the start is placed against the inclined back rest. The reader examines the topmost patents (lowest numbers) first, flipping them in turn against the front rest. With an experienced searcher, this flipping and perusing process is accomplished at a surprising speed, especially when drawings can be relied upon for the location of the information being sought. Chemical patent searching is more difficult and time-consuming, and is generally more accurately characterized as a process of "flip, read, turn the page, read, etc."

The Search Room is smoothly and efficiently run by a group of conscientious employees, whose first concern is to see that operations proceed so that information in the patents becomes readily available to the public. They are courteous and helpful in answering questions, and the answers are reliable and likely to save the searcher much time and effort. But, in view of their duties and responsibilities to the public, they cannot be expected to spend undue time and effort in solving all the problems peculiar to an individual search.

After several days of conscientious looking, reading, and note-taking, the searcher's spirits rise, as he flips feverishly through the last ten patents of his last subclass. The next to the last patent is a cross reference, in a subclass he hasn't yet searched. The manual and the definition indicate it should not be overlooked. "Oh well, just one more subclass," says he, as he strides confidently toward the proper stack. But all too often, it is one of those subclasses that extend from the top to the bottom of the stack and into the next row—which can well be expected to evoke the well-known comment from those skilled in the art, "There must exist some substantially more facile means for deriving adequate sustenance."

The happy solution to such unhappy situations is already available in certain fields, such as steroids, through mechanized searching. The expansion of the fields in which rapid and efficient searches can be accomplished by machine is ever more essential (*2, 9, 10*).

It seems appropriate to close this account with an apt quotation from one who helped build our patent system while fully realizing that he was not just earning a living, nor merely erecting masonry, but was participating in the construction of a cathedral. In Commissioner Ellsworth's Annual Report for 1844 (5), Charles G. Page, examiner of patents, wrote:

> The increase of man's wants is commensurate with the enlargement of the field of knowledge—not such actual want or privation as is characterized in the aphorism, "Necessity is the mother of invention," but something far happier, and more ennobling—the want or desire of those means which shall gratify his thirst for knowledge, and place him in a higher sphere. It is true we might, in running over the annals of invention, reverse, in many cases, the adage, and pronounce invention to be rather the mother of necessity, and tell of the unmerited fate of many a poor inventor; but, still, with all our sympathy for him, there is yet this encouragement to offer to others—that, in a large number of cases, genius meets with its true reward; and to it mankind will be ever indebted, though they may sometimes forget or withhold remuneration.

Literature Cited

(1) Bailey, M. F., *J. Patent Office Soc.* **28,** 466 (1946).
(2) Bailey, M. F., Lanham, B. E., Leibowitz, J., *Ibid.,* **35,** 566–87 (1953).
(3) Crane, E. J., *Chem. Eng. News* **28,** 585–6 (1950).
(4) Ellsworth, H. L., Report of Commissioner of Patents, 28th Congress, 1st Session, Doc. No. 177, p. 5, 1843.
(5) *Ibid.,* 2nd Session, Senate Rept. 75, p. 518, 1844.
(6) Federico, P. J., *J. Patent Office Soc.* **21,** 223 (1939).
(7) Gardner *v.* Buxton, 66 United States Patents Quarterly 11.
(8) Jeffery, E., *J. Patent Office Soc.* **22,** 479–81 (1940).
(9) Lanham, B. E., Leibowitz, J., *Ibid.,* **40,** 86–109 (1958).
(10) Lanham, B. E., Leibowitz, J., Koller, H. R., *Ibid.,* **38,** 820–38 (1956).
(11) Lindenmeyer, H. F., *Ibid.,* **36,** 463 (1954).
(12) Special Libraries Assoc., Science-Technology Group, "Patent Index to *Chemical Abstracts,* 1907–36," J. W. Edwards, Ann Arbor, Mich., 1944.
(13) Swan, L. B., U. S. Patent **5400** (Dec. 18, 1847).
(14) Waksman, S. A., Schatz, A., *Ibid.,* **2,449,866** (1948).
(15) Worden, E. C., "Chemical Patents Index," Chemical Catalog Co., New York, 1927.

Based on paper presented before Division of Chemical Literature, Symposium on Searching the Chemical Literature, 117th Meeting, ACS, Detroit, Mich., April 1950. Revised 1960.

Exploring Foreign Chemical Patent Literature

JOSEPH FLEISCHER
Olin Mathieson Chemical Corp., New Haven, Conn.

"Science knows no country because knowledge belongs to humanity, and is the light that illuminates the world."—Louis Pasteur. "In so far as we may at all claim that slavery has been abolished today, we owe its abolition to the practical consequences of science."—Albert Einstein.

Many of the patent publications in the Scientific Library of the Patent Office are to be found in no other library in the United States"—so starts the preface to the invaluable "Manual of Foreign Patents" (*263*).

Actually, there is no other library in this country where it is practical to attempt a thorough search of foreign patents. And no publication other than the manual is known to the writer which contains a concise, yet comprehensive, account of the patent publications of foreign countries, together with an indication of those obtainable at the Patent Office.

The manual also includes, as its introduction, a unique article on "Searching Foreign Patents," by Worischek (*19*). This is a survey of the broad subject which presents an interesting combination of the highlights and many unusual, but valuable, details garnered through years of experience.

It was possible in 1921 for a sole author, Frank E. Barrows (*3*), to write a series of articles having practically the scope of the present symposium for that time. The trend toward specialization in chemical fields now evidently extends into the area of the literature.

Patent Office Library

As indicated by the name, the Scientific Library of the Patent Office comprises far more than its vast collection of foreign patents. It is also an excellent library of science, both for the examining divisions of the Patent Office and for the public. The start was made in 1836, when Congress appropriated $1500 for the purchase of a library of scientific works and periodicals. Its predecessor in earlier years is stated to have been Thomas Jefferson's own collection of books. Increased appropriations would enable the filling of gaps and expansion of this valuable collection, and would constitute a wise investment.

A person entering the Department of Commerce Building through the doors on E Street near 15th, walking straight ahead through the short corridor (though invariably pausing at the glass cases exhibiting the intricate models of some nineteenth century inventions), and finally proceeding through the next doorway, finds himself in the reference section of the library. To the right are a number of offices. To the left, bookcases extend across the room and along the walls, except at the center. The shelves house the reference volumes, mainly customary and unusual abstract and index publications, foreign trade-mark compendia, and sets of patent source volumes for certain foreign countries. Study desks are available between bookcases. The complete set of *Chemical Abstracts* could well be supplemented by additional chemical reference works.

The library's extensive card catalog and the librarians' desks are located in the central area to the left. Behind these is the entrance to the two-floor stack room. This adjoins the stack room which houses the classified set of United States patents, and there is a connecting door between the two. Most of the several million foreign patents are housed in the many rows of tall bookcases extending across the ground floor of the stack room and along its left and rear walls. Reading desks or tables are provided at intervals between the bookcases, as are staircases leading to the upper floor. One side of the second floor houses an extensive collection of technical books, sets of journals, and volumes of government publications, practically all the well known ones and many that are rare. These are arranged according to subject. A "Table of Chemical Periodicals" (*51*) lists 38 chemical journals, their Patent Office Scientific Library call numbers, and the volume numbers for the years 1880 to 1948.

The opposite (E Street) side contains the Patent Office sets of Indian, Japanese, and Russian patents, and provides temporary storage space for unbound patents of other countries. The intermediate space has study tables. A tremendous variety of current technical periodicals is available at the 15th Street end of the upper floor.

The maintenance of this vast collection in proper order is the responsibility of a surprisingly small number of Patent Office employees. They perform their duties well, conscientiously, and swiftly. It is also fitting to acknowledge the courtesy and cooperation with which these fine workers respond to requests for information.

Foreign patents are in general similar to United States patents in form and content. They present the field of the invention, the difficulties overcome thereby, a general statement of the invention, and the specific examples, and conclude with one or more claims, as generally found in United States patents. However, the foreign patents are likely to be more concise, to avoid unnecessary repetition—for example, in the recitation of objects of the invention—and to be limited to one or a few claims. In some countries the inventor's name does not have to appear on the patent, while, in contrast, the United States law requires that the application for patent be made in the inventor's name. Swiss patents are outstanding for the legibility of their printed matter and Austrian patents for the clarity of their drawings.

The Patent Office collection of foreign patents is in the form of numbered bound volumes. Generally, two sets of each country's patents are available, one a numerical set and the other a set classified according to subject. However, the Belgian, Canadian, Hungarian, Indian, Irish, Japanese, Philippine, Polish, and Russian patents are available in only the numerically arranged set. When two sets are available, the arrangement of the patents is in accordance with the classification system in use by the issuing country at the time the patents were issued.

Each country has had its own classification system or systems, each of which differs from all other systems, except that some countries—for example, Austria, Czechoslovakia, Denmark, Finland, Holland, Hungary, Norway, Poland and Sweden—adopted systems based on and similar to the German classification. The British collection does not include a set of classified patents, but has instead bound sets of "Abridgements" in classified groups or classes.

Searching aids of various types supplement the collections of foreign patents; these are similar to, and in some cases more extensive than those provided in the search room for facilitating the location of pertinent United States patents. The manuals of classification and alphabetical indexes thereto are available, and usually in the form of English translations. Annual indexes listing in alphabetical order the names of patent applicants or the subjects of invention are frequently consulted. Cumulative indexes covering a span of years are great timesavers when they are available. The patent journals or gazettes of some countries present patent number lists of various kinds—for example, in accordance with subject classification, which can be utilized to good advantage in searches. Detailed information on the patent indexes and publications of each country can be found in Severance's "Manual of Foreign Patents" (*263*).

More up-to-date information, particularly about German and other European patents, has been presented admirably by Lindenmeyer (*254*).

An important step forward has been the recent introduction of an international classification system for patents (*184*). Each British, German, and Australian patent now carries the class and subclass under this system as well as that under the national classification. As discussed below, under "French Patents," this system has been adopted and is now used in France.

Data have been reported (*215*) showing the percentages of patents of chemical interest issued in the United States, Great Britain, and Germany in the three or four decades following 1907.

At present, the Patent Office is receiving patents currently issued by

Australia
Austria
Belgium
Canada
Denmark
Egypt
Finland
France
Germany
Great Britain
India
Ireland
Italy
Japan
Netherlands
Norway
Pakistan
Poland
Rumania
Sweden
Switzerland
U.S.S.R.

It seems best, within the scope of the present article, to limit the discussion to patents of a few of the countries, to the highlights of their chemical classifications, and to specific features which might be of general interest or importance.

British Patents

The historical development of British patents is of special interest to us, because the foundation of our own patent system depended considerably on traditions which originated in England and were retained in original or modified form by our early colonists. Modern patents got their start in 1623 with the enactment in England of the Statute of Monopolies. This statute forbade the grant of monopolies by the crown, the field of inventions or new manufactures excepted, as follows:

> Provided also, and be it enacted that any declaration before mentioned shall not extend to any letters patents, and grants of privilege for the term of 14 years or under hereafter to be made of the sole working or making of any manner of new manufacture within this realm to the true and first inventor and inventors of such manufacturers which others at the time of making such letters patents and grants shall not use so as also they be not contrary to the law nor mischievous to the State by raising prices of commodities at home or hurt of trade, or generally inconvenient . . . .

Earlier, monopolies had been granted on the manufacture of commodities—for example, salt, soap, and others—as well as on inventions. On July 1, 1617, John Casper Wolfen and John Miller obtained Letters Patent for 21 years for the sole making of "a certain oyle to keep armor and armes from rust and kanker," paying "into his Mats Exchequer yearlie XLS."

In connection with Letters Patent No. 5, dated Jan. 11, 1618, to Thomas Murraye for "a newe invention for the sole making of sword blades, faulchions, skeynes, and rapier blades," authority was given to the patentee and his agents, with a constable, to enter and search places where they had cause to suspect the invention was being put in practice.

A similar provision in Letters Patent No. 44, dated July 13, 1628, to Arnold Rotsipen provides "that the offenders therein may receive condigne punishment for the same," mention being made of such punishment, fine, and imprisonment as thought fitting by the Court. The same patentee received Letters Patent No. 71, dated June 24, 1635, for a term of 14 years "if he live soe long."

John Wilkinson was granted Patent No. 1063, dated January 27, 1774, on "a new method of casting and boring iron guns or cannon." A parenthetical note to the abridgment states, "The boring machine of the patentee, an ironmaster of Brosley, was the first machine capable of boring cylinders with sufficient truth to enable Watt to use them for his steam engine." Thus, we have an eighteenth century example of a conversion of "swords to ploughshares." Further details are given by Green (7).

Changes in the classification of British patents can be illustrated by the disposition of chemical patents. The abridgments covering the earliest patents, issued between 1588 and 1883, are divided into 103 classes. Volume 40 of this series, "Acids, Alkalies, Oxides, and Salts," contains abstracts dealing with the manufacture of salt, saltpeter, alum, and vitriol, and the separation of silver from lead, among other subjects.

Letters Patent No. 52, dated October 2, 1632, to Copley, Sharpey, and Hobart concerns "a peculiar newe way, mystery, arte, or meanes for making white salt and bay salt with sea water and brine without any such pannes or furnaces or other meanes as are now in use."

For the years 1855 to 1908, inclusive, illustrated abridgments were issued in 146 classes. Chemical patents appear in Class 1, "Acids, alkalies, oxides, and salts, inorganic," and in Class 2, "Acids and salts, organic, and other carbon compounds (including dyes)." Chemical patents will also be found in classes dealing with other subjects; Table I gives the classes under which the listed subject was classified.

These volumes of illustrated abridgments constitute convenient sources of information in searches. They contain abstracts of each patent (not merely a copy of a patent claim or claims), a part of the patent drawings considered most representative, and indexes both of the patent applicants and of subject matter.

Some indication of the importance of British chemical patents at that period is given by the comment of the United States Patent Office examiner in that field,

Charles G. Page, when he stated in 1844 ("Report of the Commissioner of Patents for the year 1843," 28th Congress, 1st session, Doc. No. 177, page 314):

> The progress of this branch, so far as may be inferred from the records of the Office, has been slower than might have been expected, considering the rapid progress of chemistry within a few years past. The proverbial ingenuity of our countrymen, their readiness and tact in availing themselves of scientific discoveries, in turning directly to practical account the investigations of philosophers, have failed to sustain their reputation in chemical science, when viewed in comparison with numerous improvements made abroad, more especially in England.

Page then mentioned, as a single exception, the development here by Draper of marked improvements in photography.

For the period 1909 to 1930, inclusive, the abridgments were divided among the same 146 main classes, but some of these were further subdivided, to bring the total number of classes to 271—for example, Class 1 (Inorganic) was subdivided as follows:

1 (I). Chemical processes and apparatus
1 (II). Inorganic compounds other than metallic oxides, hydrates, oxyacids, and salts (including alkali manufacture and cyanogen compounds)
1 (III). Oxides, hydrates, oxyacids, and salts, metallic (other than alkali manufacture and cyanogen compounds)

Class 2 (Organic) was subdivided as follows:

2 (I). Acetylene
2 (II). Cellulose, nonfibrous, and cellulose derivatives (including artificial filaments, sheets and the like containing same)
2 (III). Dyes and hydrocarbons and heterocyclic compounds and their substitution derivatives

The abridgment classes were next reshuffled into 40 groups, and British patents are now classified into these broader groups commencing with those whose specifications were published in 1931 (patent numbers higher than 340,000). Patents which previously would have appeared in classes 1 (I-III), 32, 90, 91, and 95 are now classified in Group III, "Chemistry, Inorganic. Distillation. Oils. Paints."

Present Group IV, "Acetylene. Cellulose. Chemistry, Organic. Dyes and Dyeing," includes the patents which would formerly have fallen in Classes 2 (I–III) and 15 (I–II). Similarly, the current Group V, "Cements. Indiarubber. Moulding, Nonmetallic. Starch," represents a consolidation of previous Classes 22, 70, 87 (II), and 121.

In some cases, the regrouping has brought together some strange companions. Group XXI, for example, is entitled "Excavating and mining. Fires, fighting. Lifesaving. Subaqueous buildings. Warfare," representing a consolidation of Classes 9 (I and II), 47 (1 and II), 68 (I and II), 77, 85, 92 (I and II), and 119. Group XXXVIII is designated "Music. Phonographs. Signals and Alarms." One almost expects to read next *Exeunt omnia* as part of this definition.

The older British patents have been thoroughly indexed in a number of publications of the British Patent Office. The 50-year subject index (1861) to 1910) is especially valuable, a separate index having been provided for each class; the patents in each subdivision are in chronological order (*182*).

The British classified abridgments provide a considerable aid to searches, because the abstracts and illustrative drawings can be scanned more rapidly than complete patents. However, there is a possibility that essential portions of patents escape mention in the abstracts published in the abridgments. The chore aspect

Table I. Classification of British Patents

Class	*Subject*	*Class*	*Subject*
9	Explosives	87	Molding plastic substances
15	Bleaching	90	Nonmetallic elements
22	Cements	91	Oils, fats, and soaps
32	Distilling and concentrating	95	Paints, colors, and varnishes
53	Batteries	96	Paper
56	Glass	98	Photography
70	India rubber and gutta-percha	121	Starch and adhesives
76	Leather	127	Sugar
82	Metals and alloys	140	Waterproof fabrics

of searches has been magnified by the broader groups introduced in 1931.

French Patents

The problem of searching French patents has been concisely and accurately summarized by Worischek (*19*):

Research in the French patents is a tedious matter. The classification is excessively broad and the patents are frequently erroneously placed; many errors in class numbers appear on the printed copies. Some of the classes have more than one hundred volumes. The "addition" patents must also be covered.

The difficulties of searching are greatly increased in some cases because of the absence from the Patent Office files of a numerical set from 1876 to 1902. Many French patents were not printed in the period from 1897 to 1902; manuscript copies of such patents can be obtained from France.

The Patent Office has available at the Scientific Library typewritten copies of a manual of classification of the French Patent Office (*191*). In this manual, Class XIV, "Chemical arts," has the following subclasses:

1. Chemical products
2. Coloring materials, dyes, varnishes, paints, and other coatings and inks
3. Powders and explosives, pyrotechnics
4. Fats, candles, soaps, and perfumery
5. Petroleum distillates, resins, waxes, rubber, and celluloid
6. Distillation, filtration, purification of liquids and gases
7. Hides and skins, glues and gelatin
8. Processes and products not otherwise specified

The itemized content of these subclass headings requires five typewritten pages in the translated manual (*191,* sheets 147 to 151).

The intricacies of classification when compounded with language difficulties are illustrated by the note under subclass 6 (purification of gases and liquids), "Not to be confounded with removal of dust for cleaning purposes: XIV–6 (The French word 'poussière' means both powder and dust)."

Extensive sets of subject and patentee indexes are available at the Patent Office, but the frequent need for consulting the copy of the patent itself prolongs the agony. Most of the time, the choice lies between the "devil" of consulting the indexes and finding the patents, and "the deep blue sea" of scanning through page after page of volume after volume of the broad subclass. A shining light in this area is the collective subject index in English, prepared by the United States Patent Office, of French patents granted between 1791 and 1876, inclusive (*200*).

The international classification system (*184*) was substituted entirely for the above in the classification of French patents October 1, 1959 (*185*), after several years, starting January 1, 1955, during which both were used.

In this system, patents are classified under the appropriate subclass of eight main classes:

A. Nécessités humaines	(Human necessities)
B. Opérations diverses	(Various processes)
C. Chimie et Métallurgie	(Chemistry and metallurgy)
D. Textiles et Papier	(Textiles and paper)
E. Constructions fixes	(Stationary structures)
F. Mécanique, Éclairage et Chauffage	(Mechanisms, illumination, and heating)
G. Physique	(Physics)
H. Électricité	(Electricity)

Chemical patents are classified under the following subclasses:

C01	Inorganic chemistry
C02	Water treatment[a]
C03	Glass[a]
C04	Cements[a]
C05	Manufacture of fertilizers
C06	Explosives and matches
C07	Organic chemistry
C08	Macromolecular compounds[a]
C09	Dyes[a]
C10	Fuels; lubricants; bitumens
C11	Animal and vegetable oils; greases, fatty and waxy substances, and their fatty acids; detergents; candles
C12	Fermentation industries; beer; spirits; wines; vinegar; yeast
C13	Sugars, starches, and similar carbohydrates
C14	Hides, furs, and leathers

[a] Titles shortened in translating.

The metallurgical subclasses completing Class C are:

C21	Metallurgy of iron
C22	Metallurgy (nonferrous metals) and alloys, including ferrous alloys
C23	Working and treatment of metals by nonmechanical processes

German Patents

In general, a search of a given subject can be conducted most easily and quickly in the German patents. One reason for this is that the Patent Office has provided a very compact and easily legible translation of the "Manual of Classification of the German Patent Office" and its companion volume, the subject index. The class, subclass, and group titles (*190, 192*) are generally clear-cut, and cross references, if any, appear after the titles, so that there is no need of consulting a separate book of definitions. The classes were set up logically and the subject indexing of the classification was thoroughly done. One rarely has to search more than several subclasses even in a thorough search and often a single subclass will provide the desired information.

There are also inconveniences in research in the German patents. Some of the publications and annual indexes are printed in the terrible Germanic type. One is haunted by the specter of artfully concealed disclosures or of deliberately misleading information, in accordance with charges that seem to be made more frequently concerning German patents than about others. Incompleteness of the Patent Office classified set, particularly with respect to the earlier patents, is a nuisance, because it is necessary to "pull" the missing patents from the numerical set. Further pulling is made necessary because of the revised classification of 1933.

The classification manual, which was translated by Lovett of the United States

Patent Office (*192*), is the second edition (1910) of the "Gruppeneinteilung der Patentklassen" (*188*). The companion subject index (key-word title index), which was translated by Kuhlmann of the United States Patent Office (*190*), is the 1914 edition of the "Stichwörterverzeichnis, alphabetische Zusammenstellung" (*196*). The bulky United States classification manual (*199*) and its index are wallflowers in comparison with these handy, attractive guides. The present discussion is based mainly on the 1910 (*192*) edition, because most of the classified set at the Patent Office is bound in accordance with it.

There are 89 main classes which are divided into alphabetically designated subclasses, further subdivided into numerical groups. The total number of groups is about 8000.

Class 12 is entitled "Chemical Processes and Apparatus, so far as not included in special classes." The alphabetical subclasses of this class are listed below; the cross references are omitted and the titles in some cases are abbreviated.

12*a*. Boiling and digesting processes and vessels
b. Calcining and fusing
c. Dissolving, lixiviating, crystallizing, solidifying, fluids
d. Clarifying, separating, filtering, including filters and filter presses
e. Absorption and purification of gases and vapors. Mixing
f. Siphons, containers, and closures for acids and condensed gases. Charging apparatus. Regulators for inflow and outflow
g. Purely chemical processes in general and related apparatus
h. General electrochemical processes and apparatus
i. Metalloids and their compounds
k. Ammonia, cyanogen, and their compounds
l. Compounds of the alkali metals
m. Compounds of the earth metals and alkaline earth metals
n. Compounds of the heavy metals
o. Hydrocarbons. Alcohols. Aldehydes. Ketones. Organic sulfur compounds. Hydrated compounds. Carbon acids. Carbon acid amides, urea, and other compounds
p. Nitrogen rings and nitrogenous compounds of unknown constitution
q. Amines, phenols, naphthols, aminophenols, aminonaphthols
r. Distillation of tar, extraction of wood vinegar, etc.

To illustrate the numerical subdivision of the alphabetical subclasses and the cross references, we may consider the following detailed listing of subclass 12*n* as given in the manual:

12*n*. Compounds of the heavy metals (metallurgical processes, 40*a*, 40*c*)
1. Metal oxides and salts in general. Colloidal metals and metal compounds; purely chemical preparation of metals and metal powders
2. Iron compounds in general (cf. 30*h*, 8)
3. Manganese compounds, including manganese peroxide
4. Nickel and cobalt compounds
5. Copper compounds
6. Zinc compounds
7. Lead compounds, including lead peroxide
8. Mercury, silver, and gold compounds
9. Tin compounds
10. Tungsten compounds

Many other classes and subclasses are of chemical interest (Table II).

In the 1933 revision (fifth edition) (*188*) the number of groups was increased to over 19,000, the general effect being to narrow the subject matter coverage of the individual groups.

While revising the manual, the German Patent Office also reclassified all

German patents and published the revised list of patent numbers belonging to each class, group, and subclass. This is the 1934 (fourth) edition of the "Gruppenliste der deutschen Patentschriften mit Angabe der zu jeder Klasse, Unterklasse und Gruppe gehörenden Nummern" (*189*). A companion volume, "Nummernliste," was also issued in 1934 and contains a numerical list of the patent numbers with the classification of each (*193*).

In making a thorough search in the Patent Office collection of German patents, one starts by searching the proper volumes of the classified set, checking the patent numbers against the list shown by the "Gruppenliste" (4th ed.) for the given class and group. The unchecked patents must then be pulled from the numerical set.

The German publication corresponding to the United States Patent Gazette is the "Auszüge" section of the weekly *Patentblatt*. The latter contains various lists relating to patent applications and patents. The "Auszüge" presents the patent information in the order of the subject classification.

The thorough annual indexes (Verzeichnis) contain a number of sections enabling the searcher to obtain complete data fairly readily starting from a knowledge of only the patent number, or the patent application number, or the applicant's name, or the classification. "The Manual of Foreign Patents" (*263*) contains an especially clear presentation concerning the German patent publications.

The Austrian, Czechoslovakian, Danish, Dutch, Finnish, Hungarian, Norwegian, Polish, and Swedish classifications are based on the German. Generally, the main classes are identical, but the subdivision of the classes is not so extensive. The Swedish Patent Office in December 1948 published a revised classification manual (*197*). The Patent Office sets of the patents of these countries are also supplemented by useful yearly indexes.

Lindenmeyer (*254*) has presented a concise summary of source material on later German patents and applications, particularly those of the war and postwar years.

Since January 1, 1956, printed copies of West German patent applications published for opposition have become available, involving less delay and eyestrain than the photostatic copies of typed pages obtained previously.

Table II. Various German Patent Classes

Subject	*Class*	*Subject*	*Class*
Alloys	40*b*, 40*c*	Medicines	30
Batteries	21*b*	Mercerizing	8*a*, 8*k*
Beer	6	Metal coating	48*b*
Bleaching	8	Metallurgy	40
Cement	80	Mixers	50*f*
Disinfecting	30*i*	Mortar	80
Dyes	22	Oils and fats	23
Electroplating	48*a*	Paints	22
Explosives	78	Paper making	55
Fertilizers	16	Photography	57
Fiber and fabric treatment	8, 29, 76*b*	Plastics	39
Filters	12*d*	Preserving foods	53
Glass	32	Rubber	39
Glue	22*i*	Soaps	23*e*, 23*f*
Inks	22*g*	Sugar and starch	89
Laundry	8*d*, 8*i*	Tanning	28
Leather	28	Textile fibers	29
Linoleum, etc.	8*h*, 81	Thermometers	42*i*
Matches	78*a*	Water purification	85

Russian Patents

The Patent Office collection of Russian patents is limited to a numerical set of those available. The collection of patents of Czarist Russia includes numbers 1 to 29,800, issued during the period 1897 to 1917.

Worischek (*19*) has outlined two methods of conducting a search at the Patent Office when only a numerical set is available: (1) assembling a list of patent publications of the particular country and pulling the patents from the numerical set, and (2) paging through the numerical set and noting the patents of interest. These methods are applicable to searching Russian, Hungarian, Japanese, Italian, Czechoslovakian, and Polish patents. The comment was added, "U. S. patents on oil refining have already been held invalid in view of Russian art, in costly litigation, and the Japanese art is replete with patents on alloys, magnetic testing, and the like which are not readily available to searchers in this country."

The United States Patent Office has a numerical set of Soviet patents numbered 1 to 3500 (1924 to 1927) and starting again with 116,000 (1958). The first two patents were chemical in nature, the first on a furnace for the continuous preparation of sodium sulfide and the second on water purification [*Chem. Abstracts,* 27, 3787, 3763 (1933)]. The patents issued since 1927 have not been available; information concerning some of the chemical patents has been published in *Chemical Abstracts* based on abstracts given in the Russian Patent Office periodical. The latter is a monthly publication containing abridgments of issued patents, lists of applications, utility models, information on trade-marks, Patent Office notices, and reviews of current technical literature. A superb summary of the patent law, its administration, and the availability of abstracts was presented recently by Hoseh (*248*).

Translations of the Soviet patent law enacted March 5, 1941, and of the regulations issued November 27, 1942, were published by Charles Prince, formerly Soviet Russian expert, U. S. Chamber of Commerce (*260*).

Swiss Patents

Swiss patents have become an increasingly rich source of chemical information, and are easy to search and a pleasure to read, thanks to the clear typography. As one leafs through the volumes, one encounters patents written in French, Italian, or German. This is a constant happy reminder that, as stated by the Encyclopaedia Britannica (1945 edition), "The Swiss Confederation is made up of 22 small states, differing from each other in nearly every point—religious, political, social, industrial, physical and linguistic; yet it forms a nation the patriotism of whose members is universally acknowledged." For over 300 years, Swiss of French, Italian, and German customs and language have lived peacefully together, while their cousins across the border periodically took up the sword against one another. There is no denying the success of this "little United Nations Organization."

It was during his period of employment at the Swiss Patent Office that Einstein worked out and first announced his theory of relativity, as well as other pioneering scientific achievements. That also happened to be about the time when the Swiss classification was revised. Swiss patents 1 to 39,400 (1888 to 1907) are classified under the old system, which contained 116 main classes. A translation of the headings of these classes appears in the second edition (1905) of "Key to the Classifications of the Patent Specifications of France, Germany, Austria, Netherlands, Norway, Denmark, Sweden, and Switzerland" (*183*).

The revised Swiss classification was adopted in January 1908 and has been in use since then. The headings of the 129 classes and their subclasses are given in English in the third edition of this bulletin (*183*).

In the old classification, many chemical patents appear under F, Miscellaneous Industries, Class 40 being entitled "40. Salt industry; manufacture of chemicals," and under K, Manufacture of scientific and technical apparatus etc., Class 59 being entitled "59. Physical, chemical, and electrolytic apparatus, etc."

In the new classification, Class G, Chemical Industries, includes the following subclasses:

36. Chemical processes and apparatus in general
37. Dyes, varnishes, lacquers, paints, adhesives
38. Fats and oils
39. Explosives, cartridges for mining purposes, match manufacture
40. Tanning, chemical section; tanning materials, impregnating and preserving leather
41. Chemical preparation of India rubber, gutta-percha, celluloid and plastic bodies in general
42. Manure preparation
43. Water purification for household or industrial purposes, disincrustants for boilers, preparation of mineral or gaseous waters, water distillation, sewage purification
44. Metal working, chemical

The patent periodical, *Patent-liste—Liste des brevets—Lista dei brevetti,* is issued twice a month. It contains a classified list of patents granted with accompanying data, a list of recently published patents, a classified list of patent assignments, and other patent notices. The indexes are rather complex, a noteworthy feature being that the name index of assignees lists foreign firms under the city of the home address.

One who reads widely in the patents of many countries soon acquires the feeling that patents, as means of exchanging information of progress between countries, stimulate international comity and understanding. This is particularly true of chemical patents which, like music and mathematics, are blessed with symbols and formulas that know no boundaries.

Over a century ago, C. M. Keller, examiner at the United States Patent Office, recognized the potentialities for progress in foreign as well as domestic inventions, when he wrote ("Report of the Commissioner of Patents for the Year 1844," by Henry L. Ellsworth, 28th Congress, 2nd Session Senate 75, page 464):

> In this report, as in the preceding, I shall not strictly confine myself to the inventions of the United States, but introduce such of the inventions of Europe, which have come to my notice, as I may deem worthy of public attention, either in their immediate applicability to our industry, or as containing the germs of future usefulness; for it often occurs that ideas which, in themselves, possess no practical usefulness, suggest and lead to the most important and useful inventions.

Bibliography

This bibliography illustrates the extensive aids which are available for explorations of chemical patent literature. For the convenience of the reader, it is presented under the following headings:

I. Patent searching
II. Special compilations of chemical patents
III. Chemical patent abstracts, lists, and encyclopedias

IV. Articles, books, and journals furnishing chemical patent references
V. Classification of patents
VI. Information on United States and foreign patents and patent laws

Bibliography

I. Patent Searching

(1) Amdur, L. H., "Patent Fundamentals," Clark Boardman, New York, 1948.
(2) Bailey, M. F., Lanham, B. E., Leibowitz, J., *J. Patent Office Soc.* **35**, 566–87 (1953). Mechanized searching in the U. S. Patent Office.
(3) Barrows, F. E., *Chem. & Met. Eng.* **24**, 423–8, 477–9, 517–21 (1921). Investigations of the chemical literature.
(4) Crane, E. J., "Guide to the Literature of Chemistry," 2nd ed., Wiley, New York, 1955.
(5) Deller, A. W., "Patent Law for Chemical and Metallurgical Industries," Chemical Catalog Co., New York, 1931.
(6) Egloff, Gustav, Davis, R. F., *Chem. Eng. News* **25**, 1046 (1947). Patent investigations.
(7) Green, J. H. S., *Research* **11**, 250–3 (1958).
(8) Lanham, B. E., *Ind. Eng. Chem.* **43**, 2494–6 (1952); *J. Patent Office Soc.* **34**, 315–23 (1952). Chemical patent searches.
(9) Lanham, B. E., Leibowitz, J., *Ibid.*, **40**, 86–109 (1958). Classification, searching, and mechanization in the U. S. Patent Office.
(10) Lanham, B. E., Leibowitz, J., Koller, H. R., *Ibid.*, **38**, 820–38 (1956). Advances in mechanization of patent searching, chemical field.
(11) Marx, C., *Chem. Age (London)* **31**, 398 (1923). Chemical patent searches.
(12) Mellon, M. G., "Chemical Publications," 3rd ed., McGraw-Hill, New York, 1958.
(13) Price, M. O., *Special Libraries* **31**, 118–28 (April 1940).
(14) Smith, J. F., *Chem. & Met. Eng.* **34**, 160 (1927). Chemical patent sources.
(15) Smith, J. F., *Ind. Eng. Chem.* **16**, 527 (1924). Chemical patent sources.
(16) Soule, B. A., "Library Guide for the Chemist," McGraw-Hill, New York, 1938.
(17) Untiedt, F. H., *Ind. Eng. Chem.* **21**, 689 (1929). Chemical patent search features.
(18) von Hohenhoff, E., *J. Patent Office Soc.* **17**, 808, 971 (1935); **18**, 49 (1936); "Bibliography of Journals, Books and Compilations (American and Foreign) Which List and Abstract Patents," reprint, Baltimore Special Libraries Association.
(19) Worischek, Arthur, "Searching Foreign Patents," introduction to Severance's "Manual of Foreign Patents," Patent Office Society, Washington, D. C., 1935.

II. Special Compilations of Chemical Patents

(20) Bräuer, A., D'Ans, J., "Fortschritte in der anorganisch-chemischen Industrie," 5 vols., Julius Springer, Berlin, 1877–1938.
(21) Faust, O., "Celluloseverbindungen," 2 vols., Edwards Bros., Ann Arbor, Mich., 1944.
(22) Friedlander, P., "Fortschritte der Teerfarben Fabrikation und verwandter Industriezweige," Julius Springer, Berlin, 1877–1930.

III. Chemical Patent Abstracts, Lists, and Encyclopedias

(23) Abegg, R., Auerbach, Fr., "Handbuch der anorganischen Chemie," 4 vols., S. Hirzel, Leipzig, 1905–20.
(24) Alexander, A. E., Johnson, P., "Colloid Science," 2 vols., Clarendon Press, Oxford, 1949.
(25) Allen, J. T., Washington, D. C., "Digest of U. S. Patents of Air, Caloric, Gas, and Oil Engines, 1789–1905," 5 vols., 1906.
(26) "Auslands Patentlisten auf den Gebieten der reinen und angewandten Chemie," Verein Deutscher Chemiker, Berlin, 1930–.
(27) Billiter, J., "Technische Elektrochemie," 4 vols., Wilhelm Knapp, Halle, Germany, 1923–8.
(28) Bräuer, A., Reitstötter, J., "Fortschritte des chemischen Apparatewesens," Akademische Verlagsgesellschaft, Leipzig, 1934–.
(29) *British Chemical Abstracts,* annual subject and author indexes, numerical patent lists, 1926–.
(30) Bur. Census, *Census Bull.* **210**; appendix to Census Reports, Vol. **10**, Twelfth Census of U. S. Manufacturers, Part 4, Special Reports on Selected Industries; Classified abstracts of chemical patents, 1836–1902.
(31) *Ceramic Abstracts,* 1922–, American Ceramic Society.
(32) *Chemical Abstracts,* Numerical patent indexes Vols. 1–30, 31–40, 41–50, annual since then.

(33) Chemical Foundation, New York, Index to Chemical Foundation Patents.
(34) Chemisch-technisches Ubersicht, Koethen, Germany, Abstract portion of *Chemiker-Zeitung*, 1882–.
(35) *Chem. Zentr.* (Berlin), 1830, German patents only until 1918, German and others since then.
(36) Chicago Section, American Chemical Society, "Abstracts of Chemical Patents Vested in Alien Property Custodian," classified and indexed by Science-Technology Group, Special Libraries Association, edited and published by Office of Alien Property Custodian, Washington, D. C., 1944.
(37) *Chimie et Industrie,* Extraites de Chimie, Abstract portion of *Chimie et Industrie, Paris,* 1917–.
(38) Creighton, H. J., Koehler, W. A., "Principles and Applications of Electrochemistry," 2 vols., Wiley, New York, 1943–4.
(39) Daniel, J., "Dictionnaire des Matières Explosives," Dunod, Paris, 1902.
(40) Daubert, B. F., "Fats, Oils, Detergents" (loose-leaf abstract service), Interscience, New York, 1944–.
(41) Doyle, A. M., "Digest of Patents Relating to Coal Tar Dyes and Allied Compounds, U. S. Patents Issued Prior to January 1, 1924," Chemical Publishing Co., Brooklyn, N. Y., 1926.
(42) Electronic Engineering Patent Index (annual classified digest), Electronics Research Publishing Co., New York, 1946–.
(43) Engelhardt, V., "Handbuch der technischen Elektrochemie," 3 vols., Akademische Verlagsgesellschaft, Leipzig, 1931–4.
(44) Finkelstein, J., Hauber, H., "Sabatier's die Katalyse in der organischen Chemie," Akademische Verlagsgesellschaft, Leipzig, 1927.
(45) Fremy, "Encyclopédie Chimique," 93 vols., index vol. 1899, Dunod, Paris, 1882–93.
(46) Furnas, C. C., "Rogers' Manual of Industrial Chemistry," 6th ed., Van Nostrand, New York, 1942.
(47) Glasstone, S., "Introduction to Electrochemistry," Van Nostrand, New York, 1942.
(48) Hackh-Grant, "Chemical Dictionary," 3rd ed., Blakiston Co., Philadelphia, 1944.
(49) Harris, Milton, Mark, H. F., "Natural and Synthetic Fibers" (loose-leaf abstract service), Interscience, New York, 1944–.
(50) Heilbron, I. M., Bunbury, H. M., "Dictionary of Organic Compounds," 3 vols., Oxford University Press, New York, 1946.
(51) Horwitz, D. D., *J. Patent Office Soc.,* **32,** 243–56 (1950). Table of chemical periodicals.
(52) Houben, J., "Fortschritte der Heilstoffchemie," Part 1, German Patents, Part 2, Literature, de Gruyter, Berlin, 1926–31.
(53) Jacobson, C. A., "Encyclopedia of Chemical Reactions," Vols. I, II, III, Reinhold, New York, 1946–9.
(54) "Jahresbericht über die Leistungen der chemischen Technologie," Wiegand, Barth, Leipzig, 1855–.
(55) Kirk, R. E., Othmer, D. F., "Encyclopedia of Chemical Technology," Vols. I, II, III, IV, V, Interscience, New York, 1947–50.
(56) Klosky, S., "Index of Oil-Shale Patents," Government Printing Office, Washington, 1950.
(57) Landrum, R. D., Carter, H. D., "Bibliography and Abstracts of Literature on Enamels," American Ceramic Society, 1929.
(58) Karo, W., "Kunstharze," Allgemeiner Industrie-Verlag, Berlin, 1932.
(59) Lange, O., "Die Zwischenprodukte der Teerfabrikation," Otto Spamer, Leipzig, 1920.
(60) LeBlanc, M., "Ergebnisse der angewandten physikalischen Chemie," 2 vols., Akademische Verlagsgesellschaft, Leipzig, 1931–5.
(61) Lewis, W. K., Squires, L., Broughton, G., "Industrial Chemistry of Colloidal and Amorphous Materials," Macmillan, New York, 1942.
(62) Mantell, C. L., "Industrial Electrochemistry," 2nd ed., McGraw-Hill, New York, 1940.
(63) Mark, H. F., Proskauer, E. S., "Resins, Rubbers, Plastics" (loose-leaf abstract service), Interscience, New York, 1942–.
(64) Marshall, A., "Dictionary of Explosives," Blakiston, Philadelphia, 1920.
(65) Mellor, J. W., "Comprehensive Treatise on Inorganic and Theoretical Chemistry," 16 vols., Longmans, Green, New York, 1937.
(66) Meyer, R. J., "Gmelin's Handbuch der anorganischen Chemie," 8th ed., Verlag Chemie, Berlin, 1924–35.
(67) Miall, S., Miall, L. M., "New Dictionary of Chemistry," 2nd ed., Longmans, Green, New York, 1949.
(68) Moissan, Pascal, Band, "Traité de Chimie Minérale," 12 vols., Masson et Cie., Paris, 1931–4.
(69) *Oil, Paint and Drug Reptr.,* 1918 Year Book, list of U. S. patents granted to Austrians and Germans.

(70) "Patent Applications in the Field of Fischer-Tropsch and Allied Reactions," 6 vols., C. A. Meyer & Co., New York, 1948–9.
(71) Prager, B., Jacobson, P., Richter, F., "Beilstein's Handbuch der organischen Chemie," 4th ed., 1st supplement 1928, Julius Springer, Berlin, 1918–35.
(72) Radt, F., "Elsevier's Encyclopedia of Organic Chemistry," Elsevier, New York, 1946–9.
(73) Regelsberger, F., "Chemische Technologie der Leichtmetalle und ihrer Legierungen," Otto Spamer, Leipzig, 1926.
(74) Reinglass, P., "Chemische Technologie der Legierungen," 2nd ed., Otto Spamer, Leipzig, 1926.
(75) Riegel, E. R., "Industrial Chemistry," 4th ed., Reinhold, New York, 1942.
(76) Rossman, J., "Electro-organic Chemistry in the Patent Office," Electrochemical Society, Preprint **84-11** (1943).
(77) Rossman, J., "Review of Patents on Electrolytic Methods for Making Powdered Metals," Electrochemical Society, Preprint **85-21** (1944).
(78) Ruhrchemie and I. G. Farbenindustrie, Patent Applications (oxo process), 6 vols., C. A. Meyer & Co., New York, 1948–9.
(79) *Ibid.*, wax oxidation.
(80) Sedlaczek, E., "Das Automobiltreibmittel der In- und Auslandes," Julius Springer, Berlin, 1927.
(81) Sedlaczek, E., "Die Krackverfahren unter Anwendung von Druck," Julius Springer, Berlin, 1929.
(82) Sedlaczek, E., "Die Mercerisierung-verfahren," Julius Springer, Berlin, 1928.
(83) Silbermann, H., "Fortschritte auf dem Gebiete der chemischen Technologie der Gespinstfasern 1885–1900," 2 vols., Kuehtmann, Dresden, 1902–3.
(84) Silbermann, H., "Hilfsapparate für den Farber und Koloristen," Max Jänecke, Leipzig, 1926.
(85) Suvern, K., "Kunstliche Seide," 5th ed., 1926, 1st supplement 1931, Julius Springer, Berlin.
(86) "Textilchemische Erfindungen," Ziemsen, Wittenberg, 1927–31.
(87) Thompson, M., "Theoretical and Applied Electrochemistry," Macmillan, New York, 1939.
(88) Thorpe, J. F., Whiteley, M. A., "Thorpe's Dictionary of Applied Chemistry," 4th ed., Vol. I 1937, Vol. X 1950, Longmans, Green, New York.
(89) Ullmann, F., "Enzyklopaedie der technischen Chemie," 10 vols. and index, Urban und Schwarzenberg, Berlin, 1928–34.
(90) U. S. Government, patent abstracts and lists issued by Dept. of Agriculture, Bureau of Chemistry and Solids; Dept. of Commerce, National Bureau of Standards, Office of Technical Services; Dept. of Interior, Bureau of Mines.
(91) Universal Oil Products Co., Chicago, "The Cracking Art," 1927–.
(92) Waeser, B., "Alkalien und Erdalkalien in ausgewahlten Kapiteln," T. Steinkopff, Dresden, 1931.
(93) Watt, S. D., "Dictionary of Chemistry," 4 vols., Longmans, Green, London, 1890–4.
(94) Watts, "Gmelin's Handbook of Chemistry," 18 vols. and 1 index vol., Cavendish Society, London, 1848–72.
(95) West, C. J., "Bibliography of Paper Making and United States Patents on Paper Making and Related Subjects, 1931," Technical Association of Pulp and Paper Industries, New York, 1932.
(96) Winther, A., "Zusammenstellung der Patente auf dem Gebiete der organischen Chemie, 1877–1905," 3 vols., Topelmann, Giessen, Germany, 1908–10.
(97) Worden, E. C., "Chemical Patents Index, U. S. Patents, 1915–24 Inclusive," 5 vols. with subject and inventor index and numerical list of patent, Chemical Catalog Co., New York, 1927–.
(98) Wurtz, A. D., "Dictionnaire de chimie pure et appliquée," 3 vols., 1874, 2 vols. 1st supplement, 7 vols. 2nd supplement, Hachette, Paris, 1907.

IV. Articles, Books, and Journals Furnishing Chemical Patent References

Items under this category are too numerous to attempt an extensive listing herein, especially in view of the existence of excellent bibliographies such as the one by von Hohenhoff (*18*) and the "List of Periodicals Abstracted by *Chemical Abstracts*" [**50,** 1J-314J (Nov. 25–Dec. 10, 1956)] and annual Supplements [**51,** 1J-27J (Nov. 10–25, 1957), **53.** 1J-32J (Dec. 10, 1959)], **52,** 1J-40J (Dec. 10, 1958). Valuable review articles have appeared in *Chemical Reviews* and the volumes of "Annual Survey of American Chemistry." Outstanding reviews, in some cases an annual feature in the January issue, have been published in the following journals. (Those marked with an asterisk regularly feature a patent abstract or patent list section.)

(99) _Abstract Bulletin,_ Aluminium Laboratories, Ltd., Kingston, Canada.
(100) *_American Dyestuff Reporter._
(101) *_Brennstoff-Chemie,_ Essen, Germany.
(102) *_Canadian Chemistry and Process Industries,_ Toronto, Canada.
(103) *_Chemical Age,_ London, England.
(104) _Chemical and Engineering News._
(105) *_Chemical Industries._
(106) _Chemical and Metallurgical Engineering._
(107) *_Chemiker-Zeitung,_ Koethen, Germany.
(108) *_Chemisch Weekblad,_ Amsterdam, Holland.
(109) *_Chimie et Industrie,_ Paris, France.
(110) *_Deutscher Farber-Zeitung,_ Wittenburg, Germany.
(111) *_Drug and Cosmetic Industry,_ New York.
(112) *_Fettchemische Umschau,_ Stuttgart, Germany.
(113) _Gazzetta chimica italiana,_ Rome, Italy.
(114) *_Gummi-Zeitung,_ Berlin, Germany.
(115) *_India Rubber Journal,_ London, England.
(116) _Industrial and Engineering Chemistry._
(117) *_Industrie Chimique,_ Paris, France.
(118) _Iron Age._
(119) *_Journal of the American Leather Chemists Association._
(120) *_Journal of the Society of Chemical Industry,_ London, England.
(121) *_Journal of the Society of Dyers and Colourists,_ England.
(122) *_Kolloid Zeitschrift,_ Dresden, Germany.
(123) *_Korrosion und Metallschutz,_ Berlin, Germany.
(124) _Materials and Methods._
(125) *_Melliand Textilberichte,_ Heidelberg, Germany.
(126) *_Metal Finishing._
(127) *_Metal Industry,_ London, England.
(128) *_Metal Industry,_ New York.
(129) *_Modern Plastics._
(130) *_Papier-Fabrikant,_ Berlin, Germany.
(131) *_Rayon and Melliand Textile Monthly,_ England.
(132) _Recueil des travaux chimiques,_ Amsterdam, Holland.
(133) *_Revue Generale des Matières Plastiques,_ Paris, France.
(134) *_Seifensieder Zeitung,_ Leipzig, Germany.
(135) *_Textile Institute Journal,_ Manchester, England.
(136) *_Transactions of the American Electrochemical Society._
(137) _Transactions of the Faraday Society,_ London, England.
(138) _Zeitschrift für angewandte Chemie,_ Berlin, Germany.
(139) *_Zeitschrift für anorganische und allgemeine Chemie,_ Leipzig, Germany.
(140) *_Zeitschrift für das gesammte Schiess- und Sprengstoffwesen,_ Munich, Germany
(141) *_Zellstoff und Papier,_ Berlin, Germany.

Many chemical patent references are to be found in books, which in turn are usually readily located through bibliographies, publishers' catalogs, or abstracts of book reviews. Many of the American Chemical Society monographs contain abundant patent references. The following list is illustrative of the variety that is available both as to breadth of field and the scope within the field.

CELLULOSE

(142) Avram, M. H., "The Rayon Industry," 2nd ed., Van Nostrand, New York, 1929.
(143) Halama, M., "Transparentfolien," Steglitz, Berlin, 1932.
(144) Hermans, P. H., "Physics and Chemistry of Cellulose Fibres," Elsevier, New York, 1949.
(145) Heuser, E., "The Chemistry of Cellulose," Wiley, New York, 1944.
(146) Hottenroth, V., "Artificial Silk," Isaac Pitman, London, 1928.
(147) Kausch, O. "Handbuch der Azetylzellulosen," J. F. Lehmann, Munich, 1933.
(148) Krueger, D., "Zelluloseazetate und die anderen organischen Ester der Zellulose," Th. Steinkopff, Dresden, 1933.
(149) Lipscomb, A. G., "Cellulose Acetate," E. Benn, London, 1933.
(150) Ott, E., "Cellulose and Cellulose Derivatives," Interscience, New York, 1943.
(151) Ott, E., Spurlin, H. M., Grafflin, M. W., "Cellulose and Cellulose Derivatives," 2nd ed., Interscience, New York, 1954.
(152) Schorger, A. W., "The Chemistry of Cellulose and Wood," McGraw-Hill, New York, 1926.
(153) Wheeler, E., "Manufacture of Artificial Silk," Van Nostrand, New York, 1931.
(154) Worden, E. C., "Nitrocellulose Industry," Van Nostrand, New York, 1911.

(155) Worden, E. C., "Technology of Cellulose Esters," Van Nostrand, New York, 1916–21.
(156) Worden, E. C., "Technology of Cellulose Ethers," 5 vols., Chemical Catalog Co., New York, 1933.
(157) Zart, A., "Herstellung und Eigenschaften der Kunstseide und Stapelfaser," Akademische Verlagsgesellschaft, Leipzig, 1935.

DRY CELLS

(158) Drotschmann, C., "Trockenbatterien," 3rd ed., Akademische Verlagsgesellschaft, Leipzig, 1945.
(159) Drucker, Finkelstein, "Galvanische Elemente und Akkumulatoren," Akademische Verlagsgesellschaft, Leipzig, 1932.
(160) Fery, C., "Piles Primaries et Accumulateurs," Baillière, Paris, 1925.
(161) Sholl, W. S., "The Dry Battery," Chas. Griffin, London, 1940.
(162) Vinal, G. W., "Primary Batteries," Wiley, New York, 1950.

EXPLOSIVES

(163) Beyling, C., Drekopf, K., "Sprengstoffe und Zundmittel," Julius Springer, Berlin, 1930.
(164) Colver, E., "High Explosives," Van Nostrand, New York, 1919.
(165) Davis, T. L., "Chemistry of Powder and Explosives," Wiley, New York, 1943.
(166) Escales, R., Stettbacher, A., "Initialexplosivstoffe," Velt & Co., Leipzig, 1917.
(167) Guttman, O., "Manufacture of Explosives," 2 vols., Macmillan, New York, 1895.
(168) Kast, H., "Spring- und Zundstoffe," Friedrich Vieweg & Sohn, Braunschweig, 1921.
(169) Marshall, A., "Explosives," 3 vols., 2nd ed., Blakiston Co., Philadelphia, 1932.
(170) Meyer, M., "Science of Explosives," T. Crowell Co., New York, 1943.
(171) Robinson, C. S., "Explosives," McGraw-Hill, New York, 1944.
(172) Stettbacher, A., "Die Schiess- und Sprengstoffe," 2nd ed., J. A. Barth, Leipzig, 1928.

RUBBER

(173) Bedford, C. W., Winkelmann, H. A., "Systematic Survey of Rubber Chemistry," Chemical Catalog Co., New York, 1923.
(174) Davis, C. C., Blake, J. T., "Chemistry and Technology of Rubber," Reinhold, New York, 1937.
(175) Genin, G., "Chimie et Technologie du Latex de Caoutchouc," *Rev. gen. caoutchouc*, Paris, 1934.
(176) Hauser, E. A., "Handbuch der gesammten Kautschuktechnologie," Union Deutsche Verlags., Berlin, 1935.
(177) Marchionna, F., "Latex and Its Industrial Applications," Rubber Age Publishing Co., New York, 1933.
(178) Stevens, H. P., "Rubber Latex," 2nd ed., Rubber Growers Association, London, 1933.

V. *Classification of Patents*

(179) Abridgement Class, Classification, and Index Key, showing abridgement classes, groups, and contents of index headings to which inventions are assigned in the official publications of the Patent Office (1927–32), H.M. Stationery Office, London.
(180) Bailey, M. F., *J. Patent Office Soc.* **28**, 463, 537 (1946). History of classification of patents.
(181) Ball, N. T., *Ibid.*, **29**, 409 (1947). German classification of patents.
(182) British Patent Office, "Fifty Years Subject Index, 1861–1910," H.M. Stationery Office, London, 1913–20.
(183) British Patent Office, "Key to the Classifications of the Patent Specifications of France, Germany, Austria, Norway, Denmark, Sweden, and Switzerland," 2nd ed. 1905, 3rd ed. 1915.
(184) *Bulletin Officiel de la Propriété Industrielle,* Paris, France, Bull. **3694**, Part 2 (Feb. 17, 1955).
(185) *Ibid.*, No. **3935** (Oct. 1, 1959).
(186) Classification des brevets d'invention appliquée à partir des brevets de l'année, Bureau de la propriété industrielle, Paris, 1904.
(187) Congress, Report of Investigation of U. S. Patent Office, H. R. Document 1110 (63rd Congress, 3rd session).
(188) "Gruppeneinteilung der Patentklassen," 2nd ed. 1910, 5th ed. 1933, Heymann, Berlin.

(189) "Gruppenliste der deutschen Patentschriften mit Angabe der zu jeder Klasse, Unterklasse und Gruppe gehorenden nummern.," 4th ed., Heymann, Berlin, 1934.
(190) Kuhlmann, N. E., "Alphabetical Index to German Classification," 1914 ed., Government Printing Office, Washington, 1919.
(191) Kuhlmann, N. E., "Manual of Classification of the French Patent Office (since 1904)," U. S. Patent Office.
(192) Lovett, G. A., "Manual of Classification of the German Patent Office," Government Printing Office, Washington, 1911.
(193) "Nummernliste der deutschen Patentschriften mit Angabe der Klassen, Unterklassen und Gruppen, hrsg. vom Reichspatentamt," 3rd ed., Heymann, Berlin, 1934.
(194) Rosa, M. C., *J. Patent Office Soc.* **31**, 414 (1949). Patent Office organization, viewpoint, and classification.
(195) *Ibid.*, **29**, 241 (1947). Problems of classifying chemical patents.
(196) "Stichworterverzeichnis, alphabetische Zusammenstellung technischer Gegenstande mit Angabe der dazugehorigen Patentklassen, Gruppen und Untergruppen," 4th ed., Heymann, Berlin, 1933.
(197) Swedish Patent Office, "Klassforteckning," December 1948.
(198) U. S. Patent Office, Classification Bulletins, class and subclass definitions, references to related subclasses.
(199) U. S. Patent Office, "Manual of Classification of Patents and Index to Classification," revised ed., April 1, 1949, maintained up to date.
(200) U. S. Patent Office, Subject-Matter Index for Inventions (Brevets d'Invention). Granted in France from 1791 to 1876, Inclusive," translated, compiled, and published under authority of the Commissioner of Patents, Government Printing Office, Washington, 1883.

VI. Information on Patents and Patent Laws

UNITED STATES

(201) Amdur, L. H., "Patent Office Rules and Practice" (loose-leaf, maintained up to date), Clark Boardman, New York, 1949.
(202) "American Patent System 1790–1940, Digest of History," Government Printing Office, Washington, 1940.
(203) Barrows, F. E., *Ind. Eng. Chem.* **30**, 1420 (1938). Present American patent system.
(204) Berle, A. K., De Camp, L. S., "Inventions and Their Management," 2nd ed., International Textbook, Scranton, Pa., 1947.
(205) Biesterfeld, C. H., "Patent Law for Lawyers, Students, Chemists, and Engineers," 2nd ed., Wiley, New York, 1949.
(206) Calvert, R., "Patent Practice and Management for Inventors and Executives," Scarsdale Press, Scarsdale, N. Y., 1950.
(207) Day, W. R., *Chem. Eng. News* **24**, 2617 (1946). How now chemical patents?
(208) Deller, A. W., "Walker on Patents," with annual cumulative supplement, Baker. Voorhis & Co., New York, 1937.
(209) Digest of Patents, United States, 1790 to Jan. 1, 1839, U. S. Patent Office, 1840.
(210) Ellis, R., "Patent Claims," Baker, Voorhis & Co., New York, 1949.
(211) Federico, P. J., *Chem. Eng. News* **25**, 840 (1947). Current activities toward revision of patent law.
(212) Fellmer, I. J., *Ibid.*, **25**, 400 (1947). Patents for chemists.
(213) *Ibid.*, p. 3354. Inventorship test in chemical priority conflicts.
(214) Fisher, C. M., *J. Patent Office Soc.* **29**, 622 (1947). Preparation and presentation of a case to the Patent Office.
(215) Fleischer, J., *Chem. Eng. News* **30**, 239 (1952). Growth of chemical patents.
(216) Gomory, A. B., *Ibid.*, **25**, 696 (1947). Research development and the patent right.
(217) Hoar, R. S., "Patent Tactics and Law," 3rd ed., Ronald Press, New York, 1950.
(218) Lotsch, J. L., "Walker on Patents," 2 vols., 6th ed., Baker, Voorhis & Co., New York, 1929.
(219) Nydick, A. J., *Chem. Eng. News* **25**, 664 (1947). U. S. patent system, its roots and origins.
(220) Ooms, C. W., *Ibid.*, **24**, 3027 (1946). American patent system and industrial research.
(221) Patent Act of 1952, *J. Patent Office Soc.* **34**, 545–83 (1952). Including committee report and notes.
(222) Potts, H. E., *Ibid.*, **23**, 163 (1941). Chemical patents.
(223) Rivise, C. W., *Ibid.*, **32**, 439, 591 (1950). Inventions in the chemical field.
(224) Rivise, C. W., "Preparation and Prosecution of Patent Applications," Michie, Charlottesville, Va., 1933.
(225) Rivise, C. W., Caesar, A. D., "Patentability and Validity," Michie, Charlottesville, Va., 1936.

(226) Rossman, J., "Law of Patents for Chemists," 2nd ed., Inventors Publishing Co., Washington, 1934.
(227) Rossman, J., *J. Chem. Educ.* **9,** 486 (1932). What the chemist should know about patents.
(228) Scher, V. A., "Patenting the Invention," Matthew Bender & Co., Albany, N. Y., 1948.
(229) "Shepard's Citations," quarterly lists of U. S. patents involved in or referred to in patent litigation, Colorado Springs, Colo., 1873–.
(230) Tashof, I. P., *Chem. Eng. News* **25,** 491 (1947). Patentability of uses in the chemical field.
(231) Thomas, E., "Chemical Inventions and Chemical Patents," Matthew Bender & Co., Albany, N. Y., 1950.
(232) Toulmin, H. A., "Patent Law for the Executive and Engineer," 2nd ed., Research Press, Dayton, Ohio, 1948.
(233) Tuska, C. D., "Patent Notes for Engineers," 5th ed., RCA Review, Princeton, N. J., 1954.
(234) "Underwood Card Digest of Patent Cases, 1918–," classified card summaries maintained up to date, Card Digest Co., Washington.
(235) U. S. Patent Office, "Manual of Patent Examining Procedure," Government Printing Office, Washington, Nov. 15, 1949.
(236) U. S. Patent Office, "Patent Laws (U. S.)," new editions periodically.
(237) U. S. Patent Office, "Rules of Practice of the U. S. Patent Office in Patent Cases," new editions periodically.
(238) U. S. Patent Office, U. S. Patents 1790–1873, subject matter index, 3 vols., 1874.
(239) *U. S. Patents Quarterly,* decisions of the Patent Office and courts in patent, trademark, and copyright cases, weekly advance sheets, bound in quarterly volumes, Vol. 1, 1929.
(240) Van Doren, L., *J. Chem. Educ.* **6,** 123–8, 536–40, 966–72 (1929). What the chemistry student should know about patent procedure.
(241) Wolcott, C. L., "Manual of Patent Office Procedure," 8th ed. 1940, supplement 1943, Patent Office Society, Washington, D. C.
(242) Woodling, G. V., "Inventions and Their Protection," 2nd ed., Matthew Bender & Co., Albany, N. Y., 1954.
(243) Young, G. H., *Chem. Eng. News* **25,** 594 (1947). Collaboration: Key to success for the inventor-attorney team.

FOREIGN

(244) Brown, J. L., "Industrial Property Protection throughout the World," Government Printing Office, Washington, D. C., 1936.
(245) Bureau voor Technische Adviezen, Amsterdam, "Manual for Handling of Applications for Patents, Designs, and Trade Marks throughout the World" (loose-leaf manual maintained up to date).
(246) Casalonga, A., *J. Patent Office Soc.* **42,** 630–9 (1960). Patentability in France of method for chemical product having therapeutic properties.
(247) Doorman, G., *Ibid.,* **30,** 225, 258, 347 (1948). Patent law in the Netherlands.
(248) Hoseh, M., *Ibid.,* **50,** 241–51 (1958). Patents of the U.S.S.R.
(249) Huttner, E., "Die Gesetze zum Schutze des gewerblichen Eigentums," Reichenberg, 1923.
(250) Jarratt, Wm., *J. Patent Office Soc.* **26,** 761 (1944). English patent system.
(251) Kemp, J. A., *Ibid.,* **32,** 851–60 (1950). Chemical patents in England and the 1949 Patents Act.
(252) Ladas, S. P., "International Protection of Industrial Property," Harvard University Press, Cambridge, Mass., 1930.
(253) Langner, Perry, Card & Langner, New York and Chicago, "Foreign Patents," 4th ed., 1951.
(254) Lindenmeyer, H. F., *J. Patent Office Soc.* **36,** 463–81 (1954).
(255) Meinhard, P., "Invention, Patents, and Monopoly," Stevens and Sons, London, 1946.
(256) Michel, A. J., New York, "Introduction to the Principal National Patent Systems," 1936.
(257) Michel, A. J., New York, "The World's Patent Laws," 1947.
(258) Muller, E., "Chemie und Kontinentales Patentrecht," Verlag Chemie, Berlin, 1932.
(259) Potts, H. E., "Patents and Chemical Research," University of Liverpool, England, 1921.
(260) Prince, Charles, *J. Patent Office Soc.* **28,** 261, 367 (1946). The new Soviet patent law.
(261) Sadtler, R., *Chem. Eng. News* **10,** 133 (1932). Canadian patent laws and practice.
(262 *Ibid.,* **16,** 190 (1938). Working requirements and costs of foreign chemical patents.

(263) Severance, B., "Manual of Foreign Patents," Patent Office Society, Washington, 1935.
(264) Singer, B., Chicago, Ill., "Patent Laws of the World," 5th ed., 1930.
(265) Spencer, R., Chereau, L., *J. Patent Office Soc.* **42**, 640–3 (1960). France to grant patents for pharmaceuticals.
(266) Tolpin, J. G., *Chem. Eng. News* **25**, 434 (1947). Patents in the U.S.S.R.
(267) Vojacek, J., "Survey of the Principal National Patent Systems," Prentice-Hall, New York, 1936.
(268) Weidlich, Blum, "Das Schweizerische Patentrecht," Stämpfli & Cie., Bern, 1934.
(269) West, P. B., *J. Patent Office Soc.* **42**, 621–9 (1960). German analogy process doctrine.
(270) White, W. W., Ravenscroft, B. G., "Patents throughout the World" (loose-leaf book maintained up to date), 2nd ed., Trade Activities, Inc., New York, 1948.

BASED on paper presented before Division of Chemical Literature, Symposium on Searching the Chemical Literature, 117th Meeting, ACS, Detroit, Mich., April 1950. Revised 1960.

Techniques Employed in Making Literature Searches for a Patent Department

THELMA HOFFMAN, GABRIELE WOHLAUER, and RUTH CROSS
Shell Development Co., Emeryville, Calif

Methods and sources employed in making literature and patent searches for the patent department of a chemical research organization are discussed. Searches are classified according to the purpose they are designed to serve and the techniques employed vary accordingly. Patent searches to determine patentability, state of the art, infringement, and validity are described.

The rapidly increasing mass of scientific literature has made the problem of searching through it for a particular compound, reaction, or process, one to be handled only by a specialist. In the literature-searching groups described, specialization is carried to such a point that patents are searched by the staff of the patent library while all other published literature is covered by the members of the technical library staff, who also make literature searches for other divisions of the research organization.

Members of the staffs of both libraries are chemists who are well trained in organic chemistry and who have a reading knowledge at least of French and German. In practice, most foreign languages in which scientific articles appear can be read by some member of the staff. The personal characteristics of the people doing this type of work are most important, inasmuch as perseverance, integrity, good judgment, ability to analyze a problem, and ingenuity or chemical intuition are just as necessary as proper academic background. The qualities required for people working in literature and patent searching are neatly summed up by stating that the "literature searcher is not a librarian, a bibliographer, a subject specialist, an abstracter, a translator, a critic, an editor or a writer. However, a literature searcher must be well grounded in the techniques of all those professions or work categories" (*1*). It has been said that "the first great principle in learning to use a library is to acquire the knack of saving time" (*7*). Individuals with the characteristics mentioned gradually develop this knack, which is made up of familiarity with the tools, skill in using indexes or patents, knowledge of how to take short cuts safely, judgment in what should be included, the ability to read rapidly, and increased ease in handling foreign languages.

Most of the requests from the patent department for literature and patent searches fall into four general classes: patentability, state of the art, infringement, and validity. Because patentability searches are requested most frequently, they are considered first and in considerable detail.

Patentability Searches

When the results of laboratory research reach the patent department by memorandum or letter or orally, the patent attorney to whom the case is assigned usually requests both patent and literature searches. The patent department is divided into five sections—organic chemistry, macromolecular chemistry, petroleum exploration and production, petroleum technology, and mechanical and general. Each section is headed by a group leader. Requests for searches originate with the member of the patent department to whom the case has been assigned and are approved by the group leader, who has an over-all picture of the work being done in the section as well as of the research under way in the laboratories. Thus it is sometimes possible to combine several searches, or broaden one search so that it can take the place of several which might otherwise become necessary later. Requests are made on standard forms. Different forms are used, depending on whether a patent search or a literature search is requested. Pertinent information already available to the patent attorney is indicated in the request, so that the searcher may build up the picture as quickly as possible. After the request for a search has been assigned to a particular member of either library staff, the first step is always a complete survey of the problem, using company reports, correspondence, and general references to supply the background. A conference with the patent attorney requesting the search follows, if necessary. In this way the searcher gains a complete understanding of the scope of the investigation, points to be emphasized, and related material to be included.

In the patent library the first step in this type of search is to consult an index of searches already completed, and in some cases it proves necessary only to bring an earlier search up to date. An extensive collection of United States and foreign patents is maintained. All of the United States patents and some of the foreign patents are classified and filed according to the system of the United States Patent Office, as given in the "Manual of Classification of Patents" and the *Classification Bulletins,* which may be purchased through the Office of the Commissioner of Patents (3). The recent foreign patents are classified and filed according to the Netherlands classification system (5). Each patent is abstracted and copies of the abstract are indexed under patent number, inventor, assignee, and in a cross-reference abstract file; the patent copies are filed according to the classification used. Subscriptions to the *Official Gazette, United States Patent Office,* the *Canadian Patent Office Record, Derwent Petrochemicals Patents Journal,* and *Derwent Belgian Patents Report* are helpful in providing prompt information about currently issuing patents. Special indexes are kept on subjects of particular interest in cases where the patent art may be widely scattered. Unisort edge-punched cards are adaptable for files of this type pertaining to a narrow field.

After the index of earlier searches and special indexes have been checked, the files of patents and the cross-reference file of abstracts are systematically searched in selected subclasses of the United States classification system (3) and the Netherlands system (5). If too many patents appear to be pertinent, a conference with the patent attorney may be needed to narrow the field to be searched. Upon completion of the search, the patents are arranged in numerical order by countries and sent to the patent attorney together with a report in which the sources searched and the pertinent patents found are listed. If a large number of patents is sent, they are usually arranged logically—for example, in the case of a catalytic process the patents may be arranged according to the catalyst used. A duplicate copy of the report is indexed and filed in the patent library for future reference.

Since it is impractical to maintain complete files of patents on all subjects, searches requested in fields where there is no patent art on file or where the file is incomplete are sent to firms in Washington, D.C., specializing in making patent searches in the U.S. Patent Office, where a complete set of United States patents and a large collection of foreign patents are available (4).

Techniques. Patentability searches conducted by the library staff are of two types—a brief preliminary examination, and a regular patentability search in cases where the subject is of sustained interest. Techniques involved in making regular patentability searches are common to most types of searches and so may well be described first and in detail.

In the technical library the starting point of all searches is the file of index slips which the library has accumulated. This file includes references in periodicals, government publications, material put out by associations and societies, trade literature, books, literature searches previously made, and miscellaneous material. As in the case of patent searches, an earlier investigation brought up to date may take care of the request or some portion of it. Standard reference works in the field in question are then consulted. Abstract journals are covered next. This step in the search is of the greatest importance, as it serves as a key to the periodical literature. An abstract is not regarded as a substitute for the article abstracted; in all but a brief preliminary examination the original reference is read if at all possible.

Sources. The nature of the problem determines which of the abstract journals and indexes should be used, and in a regular patentability search it is usually necessary to use several different ones. The principal abstract journals and indexes to be consulted for a particular search are carefully selected from a list which includes *Chemical Abstracts, Chemisches Zentralblatt, British Abstracts, Engineering Index,* and *Industrial Arts Index* which currently is superseded in part by *Applied Science and Technology Index.* For searches in the organic chemistry field "Beilstein's Handbuch der Organischen Chemie" is frequently found to be of great value. Other tools which might be mentioned are the abstracts appearing in the *Journal of the Institute of Petroleum* and in *Petroleum Refiner,* the *Bibliography of Petroleum and Allied Substances* (compiled for a time by the United States Bureau of Mines) for a search in the field of petroleum, and *Experiment Station Record, Biological Abstracts, Bibliography of Agriculture,* and *Agricultural Index* for problems dealing with agriculture.

Abstracts of interest are located through subject, formula, author, and patent indexes—given here in order of decreasing importance in use and value. In their "Guide to the Literature of Chemistry" Crane and co-authors (2) say, "Skill in literature searching involves skill in index using, and efficient index using is an art in itself—something to be acquired." Patent indexes are relatively simple to use. The Special Libraries index to patents in *Chemical Abstracts* (8) makes it possible to find the abstracts in *Chemical Abstracts* in the years before a patent index was included in that journal. The patent index of *Chemisches Zentralblatt* is particularly useful in finding equivalent patents in foreign countries. Author indexes are used in a regular search only when the work of one or two men has been found to be of particular interest. Formula indexes, found in both *Chemical Abstracts* and *Chemisches Zentralblatt,* are most useful at the beginning of a search in the field of organic chemistry as an aid in working out nomenclature of the compounds under investigation. One whole class of complex compounds was found by a member of the library staff to be known after the laboratory chemist, less skilled in the intricacies of indexes, had concluded that it was novel. A complex compound with a number of functional groups may be classified in the subject index under any one of several different headings, and for patentability searches the formula index of *Chemical Abstracts* is customarily used to find the proper entry in the subject index. The formula and subject indexes of *Chemisches Zentralblatt* are both used for all compounds and constitute a valuable supplement to *Chemical Abstracts*. They provide additional references, usually to foreign literature or patents, which either are not abstracted or are obscurely indexed in *Chemical Abstracts*. The proper use of subject indexes calls for a broad knowledge of chemistry, a complete understanding of the problem under investigation, familiarity with the particular subject index, and considerable ingenuity. Each subject index has its own idiosyncrasies and this is particularly true of the index of *British Abstracts*, where the entries are key words rather than subjects.

Three new publications are currently being evaluated for their usefulness in locating new published literature which has not yet appeared in the abstract journals and review articles abstracted in *Chemical Abstracts: Chemical Titles, Bibliography of Chemical Reviews,* and *Index Chemicus*. The first two are new services provided by *Chemical Abstracts* and it is hoped that they will bridge the gap between the publication date of an article and the appearance of the corresponding annual index of *Chemical Abstracts* by means of which the abstract of the original article may be found in *Chemical Abstracts*. *Index Chemicus* is a compilation of new compounds disclosed in the current literature and the corresponding references. This new journal is published by the Institute of Scientific Information, Philadelphia, Pa.

In conducting a patentability search in the field of organic chemistry, *Chemical Abstracts* would be used, first starting with the latest volume and working backward. This would be followed by *Chemisches Zentralblatt*, using the formula index first and then the subject index of the latest volume and working back to 1919. This year was selected because the main volumes of Beilstein cover the period up to that time, and because in that year *Chemisches Zentralblatt* began a wider coverage of technical articles. When the abstract journal indicates that something of interest may be found in the original article, the reference, together with the *Chemical Abstracts* or *Chemisches Zentralblatt* reference, is copied on a slip together with a brief note of the information to be sought in the original article. Patent references are omitted in patentability searches unless the request specifies that they should be included for some particular reason, inasmuch as parallel searches are usually conducted in the two libraries. After work with the first abstract journal has been completed, the working slips are sorted by periodical to eliminate duplication and for convenience later in consulting the originals. As the search progresses, other abstract journals, bibliographies, footnotes, and review articles provide more references for this collection of "to be read" slips. If a reference to a certain article is found in *Chemical Abstracts, Chemisches Zentralblatt,* and Beilstein, all three references are noted. It is understood that in all searches except those of a preliminary nature the original is to be read and, in the relatively small number of cases where the article cannot be obtained or where the language is one that cannot be read, the written report indicates that the information is based on abstracts. In such a case all available abstracts are read.

References in periodicals not available locally are secured on microfilm and an extensive file of such material is gradually being built.

Search Report. The search report submitted by the technical library to the patent attorney after all the references have been read consists of extracts pertinent to the problem taken from the original articles. Extracts are usually arranged in order of importance. Related material is often included at the end of the report. The only general rules for assembling the material are that the arrangement be a logical one and one which will make the material as easy as possible for the attorney to use. A chronological arrangement is used only when it is significant—for example, in the literature dealing with the development of a certain process. If there is much material, it is separated according to subject matter and a table of contents is included. Often it is necessary to say "no material found." This is a source of satisfaction to the patent attorney in the case of patentability searches, but never to the library staff. The original articles are not sent with the report, but are available to the patent attorney upon request. The reports are not critical, except for the fact that apparent errors are noted.

Brief Form. The preliminary examination or brief form of the patentability search calls for greater skill and experience on the part of the searcher, because much less time is allotted to it and only the most promising sources are consulted. Familiarity with the various periodicals and works of reference and well developed skill in using the indexes of the abstract journals are essential. In this type of literature check, if the problem is one of novelty, one single good reference showing that the compound or process is already known is sufficient. Books, especially those like "Organo-Metallic Chemistry" by Zeiss and "Catalytic Oxidation in the Vapor Phase" by Marek and Hahn, encyclopedias such as Thorpe, Ullmann, and Kirk-Othmer, bibliographies such as "Bibliography of Organic Sulfur Compounds" by Borgstrom and others, are particularly important in this type of search. Occasionally the answer may even be found in a book like "The Chemical Formulary." If no material is found in the brief preliminary examination, a regular patentability search may be requested later but, because of records kept by the library on all searches, no duplication of effort is involved.

State-of-the-Art, Infringement, and Validity Searches

The foregoing gives a general idea of how searches are conducted in our libraries. State-of-the-art searches may be considered as extended patentability searches and are made in a similar manner. They are much more time-consuming because of the broader field to be covered. Infringement searches are carried out in the patent library by collecting for consideration by the patent attorney the pertinent United States patents issued in the last 17 years. Infringement and validity searches, because of their importance, are carried out by the most experienced members of the group. Validity searches in both libraries call for the most exhaustive investigation. Every patent and every footnote which might possibly have bearing on the case is investigated. Early works such as *Dinglers Polytechnisches Journal, Fortschritte der Chemie,* Fehling's "Neues Handwörterbuch der Chemie," and Erlenmeyer's "Handwörterbuch der Chemie" are given special attention. In validity searches it is sometimes necessary to go through an early or obscure periodical on the particular subject page by page. In this type of investigation the public availability date is of paramount importance. If a good reference is found which does not bear a sufficiently early publication date, investigation may produce a still earlier brief announcement or note concerning the work in another periodical. In one validity search where a technical article was important evidence, it was necessary to use affidavits to prove the date on which this publication was actually available to the public in a library, since this important date is sometimes much later than that appearing on the magazine itself (*6*).

Miscellaneous Searches

In addition to the four general types of searches discussed, other types of information are frequently requested by the patent department. Such requests are not usually made on the regular search forms but are made and answered informally. While the regular searches are assigned according to a flexible schedule, these other requests for information usually require an immediate answer if the information is to be of use; they are handled accordingly. These short and specific requests are handled by more experienced members of the library staff because the answers are usually desired within the shortest period possible. In the patent library these requests may take the form of a request for a specific patent when the information concerning it is incomplete or incorrect. Lists of patents by a certain inventor or patents assigned to a company on a particular process may be requested. The inventor and assignee files of index slips and the "Index of Patents issued from the United States Patent Office," published annually, are invaluable in answering these requests. For such requests the patent library does not make and index a full report; results are written or typed on brief "Patent Request" forms and filed chronologically without indexing or classification.

In the technical library these brief requests are of various kinds, some of which may be of interest. It is sometimes advantageous in connection with interference actions to have a chronological pattern of the activities of a man whose patent application is involved in the interference, in order to approximate the period of invention. When the technical library receives such a request it may be answered quickly if the man is listed in "American Men of Science" or other similar biographical works. If he does not appear in any such volume, the path to be followed is tortuous. A large collection of lists of memberships of scientific and technical societies covering a period of years is most useful in finding the affiliations of the person in question. Patents and periodical articles also give such information. Even such odd references as city and telephone directories may be used. It is an interesting game to fill in the blank periods and present a continuous picture of a man's activities. Company relationships and ownership are of interest to the patent department as well as to the other members of the research organization. All current periodicals and other publications such as *U.S. Government Research Reports, Current Chemical Papers,* and *Dissertation Abstracts* are reviewed as they are received in the technical library, and among the types of information recorded on index slips is anything which would add to our knowledge of the structure of companies in the chemical and petroleum fields. Index slips, filed under the names of all companies involved, cover information obtained from such diverse sources as news items in periodicals, company correspondence, Congressional hearings, and statements filed with the Securities and Exchange Commission. Questions involving ownership can usually be answered by the index slips together with Moody's Industrials or Standard-Poors.

Members of the staff of the technical library rapidly become experts on matters of nomenclature, and many questions concerning structure, formulas, and naming of compounds reach this group. Often the composition or manufacturer of a trade-named product is requested. In addition to such sources of information as the lists in "Thomas' Register," *Chemical Week's* "Buyer's Guide Issue," Haynes' "Chemical Trade Names and Commercial Synonyms," Zimmerman and Lavine's "Handbook of Material Trade-Names," the Special Libraries Association's "Trade Name Index," and Gardiner's "Synonyms and Tradenames," the supplementary index compiled by the technical library over a period of years is most useful. In answering requests for physical properties of compounds, references such as International Critical Tables, Landolt-Börnstein, Seidell, Lecat, Beilstein, dictionaries, and handbooks are consulted first. If the information is not found through such sources, it may be necessary to check the abstract journals. Such special collections on the properties of hydrocarbons as those of Doss, Egloff, and Faraday and the work of the American Petroleum Institute and the National Bureau of Standards usually make it unnecessary to go to the abstract journals for information in this field. In order to decide in which foreign countries patents should be filed, the technical library may be asked to prepare a brief review of the economics and development of a certain industry in the countries in question. Definitions or statements of fact may be needed to support a point or convince a patent examiner. Dictionaries and reference books are usually used for such information, as it is important that answers be obtained from well-known and authoritative sources.

Summary

Searches made by the two libraries have a direct bearing on the effective production of the patent department. Such a simple bit of information as azeotropic composition may be needed to convince the patent examiner that a separation process will function as claimed in the patent application. Most of the applications rejected are anticipated by or do not distinguish in a patentable sense over prior art. In addition to preventing the filing of applications which would be rejected on patent or literature references, good patentability searches are needed by the patent attorney to aid him in judging the proper scope of his claims, so that the result will be a strong patent which cannot later be proved invalid.

A state-of-the-art investigation is of great value when the whole field of activity is being reviewed, because it gives a picture of the patent situation and industrial development in the field, and shows potential competitors and their economic and patent positions. Infringement searches are made to aid a patent attorney to determine whether any process to be used or compositions to be marketed might infringe any patent claims. Validity searches are made to gage the strength of a patent offered for sale or a patent which is blocking activity in a field of interest to the organization. Most exhaustive of all searches are those validity searches called for when court action has been taken in a case of alleged patent infringement. Here, as in the other cases, success may depend on the close cooperation of the two libraries with the patent department and millions of dollars may hinge on one reference in an obscure journal, or an old foreign patent.

Literature Cited

(1) Anderson, F. J., *Special Libraries* **51,** 557–8 (1960).
(2) Crane, E. J., Patterson, A. M., Marr, E. B., "Guide to the Literature of Chemistry," 2nd ed., Wiley, New York, 1957.
(3) Lanham, B. E., *Ind. Eng. Chem.* **43,** 2494–6 (1951).
(4) Lindenmeyer, H. F., "What Does the Patent Office Scientific Library Have to Offer the Chemist?", Division of Chemical Literature, 125th meeting, ACS, Kansas City, Mo., March 31, 1954.

(5) Patent Council (Octrooiraad), Netherlands Patent Office, The Hague, Netherlands, "Indeling der Techniek in Uitvindingsklassen," 1950.
(6) Sabrosky, C. W., *Science* **98**, 473 (1943).
(7) Soule, B. A., "Library Guide for the Chemist," McGraw-Hill, New York, 1938.
(8) Special Libraries Assoc., "Index to Patents in *Chemical Abstracts* 1907–1936."

BASED on paper presented before Division of Chemical Education, Symposium on Chemical Literature, at the 111th Meeting, ACS, Atlantic City, N.J., April 1947. Revised 1961.

Preparing Literature and Patent Surveys

MILBURN P. DOSS, *Texaco Research Center, Box 509, Beacon, N.Y.*

GERTRUDE A. MUNAFO, *Texaco Development Corp., 135 East 42nd St., New York 17, N. Y.*

The literature and patents in various fields are surveyed by the technical libraries of Texaco Inc., prior to laboratory research. These surveys are made from as broad a viewpoint as possible and are mainly noncritical, since they are later critically reviewed by the individuals who are to do the research work. A detailed account is given of the techniques employed in making these surveys.

The value of library research as a foundation for laboratory research has been increasingly recognized. Its importance, which has been discussed in various American Chemical Society symposia on library techniques, has frequently been emphasized by leaders in industrial as well as academic research (*4, 6*).

This paper describes the techniques employed by Texaco Inc., in making extensive patent and literature surveys as a background and basis for laboratory research. These techniques are fundamentally applicable to most searches relating to chemistry or any phase of the petroleum industry.

Noncritical Surveys

The comprehensive surveys made by Texaco are entirely noncritical—i.e., all references to the subject are included and presented in a form which offers the reader the most convenient access to the greatest amount of information. These reports are passed to the laboratory personnel, usually the project leader of the laboratory research problem, who can then prepare a critical review with his recommendations as to the most promising course for the laboratory work. This has been found to be the most suitable and economic procedure, because it not only saves the time of the laboratory worker but also yields a more comprehensive search, prepared in minimal time by personnel trained and skilled in this particular phase of research. When a laboratory investigator prepares his own survey it is most frequently of such a restricted, critical nature that it may not be at all suitable if the course of the investigation is changed or if its scope is broadened. Furthermore, the project may be transferred to another worker who has different ideas as to the mode of attack. Much of the searching done by the predecessor, which is frequently not mentioned in his report or even recorded in his notes, must then be repeated. The trained literature searcher also includes references of possibly minor interest from the research standpoint but which may be of considerable importance to the patent department in the prosecution of patent applications.

Scope

For this type of survey the scope is made as broad as time will permit, because too often, near or after the completion of a search, the scope of the research work is extended, thus rendering it necessary to repeat most of the literature search to relocate references previously omitted. If a request is received for literature and patents on the chlorination of methane, for example, an attempt is made to extend the scope to the chlorination of the lower paraffins, and, if possible, to the halogenation of all paraffins. This is especially desirable if later, as a result of laboratory research, a new angle of approach or related compounds appear more promising, or patent applications are considered; often the general field or even a specific modification of the process or product is of more interest than that originally suggested.

Collection of Abstracts

After the scope of the search is established and outlined, the next step in its preparation is the collection of all abstracts already available in the library's extensive card files. Texaco has been abstracting the literature and patents in the chemical, petroleum, and related fields for the past 40 years and as a result has approximately 500,000 abstracts which are filed according to a detailed classified system. In spite of extensive cross referencing of the abstracts, it is not possible to obtain all the abstract information on a specified subject in any one section, although at least 90% of the abstracts would probably be found in the most pertinent section and its subdivisions. It is, therefore, necessary to check a number of sections to assemble all of the abstract cards on a given subject. Previous literature and patent surveys on related subjects are also examined for abstracts of interest; these are copied on cards and added to the collection. For a survey on desulfurizing, for example, a check is made through any surveys of processes known to be used for removal of sulfur compounds, such as clay treating or solvent refining. All these abstract cards are then arranged in two groups—articles and patents—the articles alphabetically by first author and the patents chronologically for each country. Anonymous articles are arranged according to the journal title in a separate section preceding the author group.

To render it unnecessary to use the cards themselves for checking against new material, all references are entered in a loose-leaf notebook by author or by patent number. A highly abbreviated form of reference is sufficient in this notebook—for example, "Brown, Am2053" indicates an article by G. C. Brown *et al.* in the *Journal of the American Chemical Society* on page 2053. It is not necessary to give in this check book the volume number or year for journals that use consecutive paging throughout a volume, as it is highly unlikely that another article by the same first author on the same subject would appear in the same journal on the same page of two separate volumes. Only in the case of journals paging each issue separately is it necessary to add the date—e.g., Nelson, O&G, 11/6/56, 71 for a reference in the *Oil and Gas Journal* by Roy Nelson. The abbreviated entries in the notebook are quick and simple to prepare and enable the searcher to check much more rapidly and conveniently, especially when checking references in related fields in other libraries such as the Engineering Societies Library or the New York Academy of Medicine. Two simple code marks are used in this notebook; a dash before the page number of the reference indicates that a satisfactory abstract has not yet been obtained, and an X after the page indicates that checking the original article or patent proved that the reference is not of interest for the search. The latter mark avoids much repetition of checking, especially during an extensive search. When supplements to the survey are later prepared, this notebook is of particular utility for rapid checking.

Selection of Sources

When these abstracts have been assembled and the references have been listed in the notebook, the next step is the selection of the sources to be checked. These are chosen from four main groups: (1) the major abstract journals, (2) classified patents, (3) the thoroughly catalogued books and pamphlets in the Texaco libraries, and (4) a very extensive list, that has been compiled and is under constant expansion, of special sources of information, each item bearing a brief note as to the field(s) covered and any unusual types of information therein. This listing provides a ready reference not only to the field of information that are not readily apparent from the nature of the source but also to the best sources in clearly identifiable fields. Because of the wide scope of interests in the petroleum industry and the ever-expanding source literature, it has been found most advantageous to review this special source list prior to every survey. A few examples from this list are given in Table I.

Table I. Special Source List

Author	*Title and Publisher*	*Coverage*
Abderhalden, E.	"Handbuch der biologischen Arbeitsmethoden" (1928–1930)	Excellent reviews on colloidal solutions, halogenation, alkylation, saponification, sulfonation, organometallic compounds
	"Annual Review of Physical Chemistry," Vol. I (1950), Annual Reviews, Inc.	Plastics, irradiation, copolymerization, chelates, ion exchange, etc.
Asinger, F.	"Chemie und Technologie der Paraffine" (1956) "Chemie und Technologie der Monoolefine" (1957)	Excellent reviews of CO hydrogenation, chlorination, nitration, sulfochlorination, oxidation, dehydrogenation, extractive distillation, hydration, synthetic lubricants, etc.
Brooks, B. T., *et al.*, eds.	"Chemistry of Petroleum Hydrocarbons," Vol. I (1954), Vol. II (1955), Vol. III (1955)	Nitration and sulfonation of aromatics, Diels-Alder condensation, polyethylene, molecular complexes, CO-paraffin reaction, detergents, etc.
Ellis, C.	"Synthetic Resins," Vols. I and II (1935) "Hydrogenation," 3rd ed. (1930) "Chemistry of Petroleum Derivatives," Vol. I (1934), Vol. II (1937)	Various topics

Table I. Special Source List (*Continued*)

Author	*Title and Publisher*	*Coverage*
Engler, C., and Hoefer, H.	"Das Erdoel," 1st ed. (1913–1925), 2nd ed. (1929–1930)	Hundreds of references to early literature. Searcher should consult not only volume which relates to specific subject but also indexes of other volumes—volume covering ultilization as well as volume on treating for acid treating
Faith, W. L., *et al.*	"Industrial Chemicals," 2nd ed. (1957)	Some 141 chemicals giving method or methods of preparing each, material and energy requirements, flow sheet of reaction, use pattern, properties, economic aspects, statistics, manufacturers, and plant sites
Faraday, J. E.	"Encyclopedia of Hydrocarbon Compounds," Vols. I–XIII (1946 to date)	Hydrocarbon preparation
Fischer, F., ed.	"Gesammelte Abhandlungen zur Kentnis der Kohle," Vols. I–X (1917–1930)	Good reviews on hydrocarbon oxidation, acetylene polymerization, etc.
	Journal of the Institute of Petroleum	Excellent articles and lengthy abstracts, but inadequate index. Annual "Reports on the Progress of Naphthology" appeared in the journal during 1923–1934. "Reviews of Petroleum Technology" 1935–1946, and "Petroleum Technology," 1947–1954.
Kissling, R.	*Chemische Umschau*	Annual surveys
Kobe, K. A., and McKetta, J. J., eds.	"Advances in Petroleum Chemistry and Refining," Vol. I (1958), Vol. II (1959), Vol. III (1960)	Excellent reviews of azeotropic and extractive distillation, oxo process, polymers, fractionating trays, separation by crystallization radioisotopes, radiation processing, detergents, hydrazine preparation, liquid thermal diffusion, isomerization, acetylene manufacture, etc.
Krczil, F.	"Kurzes Handbuch der Polymerisationstechnik," Vols. I–IV (1940–1944)	Literature and patents on polymerization, also many uses of such products as polybutene and polyethylene; particularly good for foreign patents
	Mechanical Engineering	Excellent annual reviews on lubrication
Naphtali, M.	"Leichte Kohlenwasserstofföle" (1928)	Cracking and treating; table of contents and subject index are surprisingly good
	Petroleum Zeitschrift für die gesamten Interessen der Erdöl-Industrie und des Mineralöl Handels	Subject index is inadequate but annual surveys by Singer and others in early years should be checked
Sedlazcek, E.	"Automobiltreibmittel" (1927)	Section on treating
	Seifensieder-Zeitung in Gemeinschaft auf Kriegsdauer mit Allgemeine Ol- und Fett-Zeitung und Mineralöle	Many references to naphthenic acids, soluble oils, lubricating greases, etc.; fairly good subject index
Topchiev, A. V., *et al.*	"Boron Fluoride and Its Compounds as Catalysts in Organic Chemistry" (1959)	Excellent surveys of olefin hydration, alkylation, isomerization, polymerization, disproportionation, hydrocarbon separation, coordination compounds etc.

Table I. Special Source List (Continued)

Author	*Title and Publisher*	*Coverage*
Wagner, R.	"Jahresbericht über die Leistungen der organischen Chemie"	From around 1850, cover applied and pure chemistry. Excellent abstracts of patents and literature, some not found in *Chemisches Zentralblatt;* subject index fairly adequate. Wagner has a rather complete German patent number index in the chemical field.
Liebig, J., and Kopp, H.	"Jahresbericht über die Fortschritte der Chemie"	

The selected sources are then evaluated—that is, sources expected to give the most information are listed first. This order would naturally depend on the subject being surveyed. In one case *Chemical Abstracts* would be first; in another, some special treatise on the subject, either a monograph, such as Bailey's "Retardation of Chemical Reactions" (*2*), or perhaps a series of journal articles of a bibliographical nature, such as Pritzker's survey of synthetic lubricating oils (*9*) or the annual fatty oil surveys made by Piskur (*8*) might be checked first.

Concurrently with the preliminary arrangement of source materials, a list of key words is compiled for use in checking the abstract journals—for example, although *Chemical Abstracts* has a fine subject index, the searcher must nevertheless look under a number of headings. In the case of the chlorination of methane, one cannot rely solely on the entries under "methane" and "chlorination," but must check "halogenation," "paraffins," "hydrocarbons," "natural gas," and all the products that might be obtained by the reaction.

This list of key words must often be revised and amplified during the course of the search, especially when checking indexes covering a wide range of years or various abstract journals, particularly British or foreign language publications. Connotations and concepts as well as entries vary over a period of years in the same journal as well as between journals and most especially those from different countries. Merely translating the entries into the pertinent language will not be adequate. In many instances to obtain thorough coverage the most pertinent divisions of an abstract journal such as *Chemical Abstracts* or *World-Wide Oil & Gas Abstracts* will also be checked item by item. The foregoing is not to be construed as a criticism of *Chemical Abstracts,* as the impossibility of arranging all subject listing under one heading is obvious. The same caution applies to a far greater extent to other abstract journals such as *British Abstracts, Chemisches Zentralblatt, Fuel Abstracts, Synthetic Liquid Fuel Abstracts, Science Abstracts,* the *U. S. Government Research Reports,* etc.

In addition to the abstract journals, the available indexes of the Technical Oil Mission (TOM), the Field Information Agency, Technical (FIAT), and the British Intelligence Objectives Sub-committee (BIOS) are often checked. The indexes of journals specializing in the field of the search—e.g., *Nucleonics, and Electronics*—might be searched as well as the abstract journal in the field—e.g., *Nuclear Science Abstracts.* In many instances these specialized journals are leafed through page by page. In a search on refining fatty oils, for example, the *Journal of the American Oil Chemists' Society* would be paged.

Patent Searching

For patent references, in addition to those obtained from the abstract sources, selected classes of United States patents, which are maintained in the same subclasses as in the United States Patent Office, are checked. The classes to be checked are determined by consulting the appropriate Classification Bulletins as well as "The Manual of Classification" and the "Index to Classification" of the U. S. Patent Office. The index comprises an alphabetical list of subject headings referring to the appropriate subclasses whose descriptive titles are given in the manual. Since the titles are necessarily brief in the manual, the Classification Bulletin should be consulated for the class and subclass definitions. The bulletins also contain useful explanatory notes and search notes which direct the searcher to related subject matter in other classes and subclasses. Bulletin 200, Revision No. 1, for Class 260, Chemistry, Carbon Compounds, Patent Office, Department of Commerce, Washington, D. C., 1956, contains an excellent discussion of the basis of classification, the rule of superiority, and the rules of cross referencing. The classes of a number of representative patents obtained from the abstracts or other sources are also considered. The Patent Office cross references and the references cited on the more pertinent patents are also checked. Supplementary sources in the patent field that should be consulted are Worden's "Chemical Patents Index" (*11*), "Abstracts of Chemical Patents Vested in the Alien Property Custodian" (*5*), and von Hohenhoff's "Bibliography of Journals, Books and Compilations Which List and Abstract Patents" (*10*).

For additional foreign patents and specifications laid open to inspection, the *Derwent patents gazettes* and *journals* are a valuable aid. *The Petrochemicals Patents Journal* published by Derwent Information Service, London, contains abstracts of British specifications published prior to grant, and German, Indian, Australian, and South African specifications laid open to public inspection in the fields of general organic and general inorganic chemistry, plastics, metal finishing, petrochemicals, and plant. "The Derwent Belgian Patents Report" gives very detailed abstracts of all Belgian patents falling within these same classes, and in the field of textiles, dyeing, and cellulose.

Before the search is completed the originals of practically all articles and most available patents are examined, not only to amplify the abstracts, particularly by adding details on the special field of interest, but also to check any references cited by the author.

Preparation and Arrangement of Abstracts

Unless the article is of a review nature, lengthy abstracts are prepared in which particular notation is made of any data and graphs; a descriptive title is written, and key words in the abstract are underlined. In all cases the company or university affiliation of the authors is shown, as it often indicates the basis for their viewpoint or the link from one work to another. On the abstracts of the United States patents, corresponding foreign patents (not necessarily equivalents) are recorded.

After the abstracts have been edited, the next step is to determine how they should be arranged in the report—alphabetically by author, chronologically, or subdivided by subjects. In case subdivision by subjects is used, the abstracts within each division may be arranged either chronologically or alphabetically. Patent abstracts may be grouped together at the end of each year and are often arranged according to the assignee. In all cases, those who will have occasion to use the survey are consulted to determine the most suitable arrangement for them, because each system has obvious advantages.

Facilities for Library Research

The ready availability of sufficient and suitable source material is a very important requirement. While some industrial libraries have available on their shelves only the abstract journals and the main reference sources and rely on public and other outside libraries for other publications, using outside sources would be very costly in time of personnel. Typing facilities are not readily available at most public libraries and it thus becomes necessary to write in longhand the data required; furthermore, on checking the information later, it may be necessary to make another trip to the library to supplement the data first obtained. Consequently, it has been the aim to have available in the Texaco libraries not only all the main abstract journals, American, British, French, and German, reference works and encyclopedias, but also practically all texts relating to Texaco's particular fields of interest.

It is not sufficient merely to have such material on the library shelves; it must also be carefully indexed. All new books and pamphlets are examined carefully, particularly for information that would not ordinarily be expected in such publications, and are thoroughly cataloged. In "The Chemistry of the Non-Benzenoid Hydrocarbons" by Brooks, for example, there are references to naphthenic acids, production of fatty acids by wax oxidation, and synthetic lubricating oils. In "Colloid Chemistry" (*1*) there are chapters on the Geiger-Müller x-ray spectrometer, electron microscopy, catalysis and its industrial applications, soil stabilization, polythene, and potential nuclear energy. In "Catalysis" (*7*) there are lengthy discussions of alkylation, polymerization, hydroreforming, chemisorption, hydrogenation, ammonia synthesis, methanol synthesis, oxo reaction, hydrocarbon oxidation, hydrodesulfurization of petroleum fractions, hydration and dehydration, etc. This catalog information is typed on 3 × 5 cards; on some books as many as 40 or 50 cards may be required. In this way an extremely useful file of information has been built up that might otherwise be overlooked, since valuable data sometimes appear in unexpected places.

Abstracting and Filing Systems

The Technical Literature Section issues two weekly abstract bulletins, one covering articles and the other patents. These abstracts are prepared from two different viewpoints—to furnish the reader information on current developments and to accumulate data to be used later in the searches. Consequently it has been found necessary to make rather lengthy abstracts, especially to achieve the second aim. All abstracts are reproduced on 5 × 8 cards and are filed by author, company, and classified subject. One abstract may be filed under as many as 10 to 12 subject classifications. The filing system is the classified type (not alphabetical) and covers the entire field of science and technology. The catalog cards are filed in a separate file but according to the same classification system. Books on the shelves are also arranged by this system. One alphabetical guide to the index therefore serves all three. Consequently, in beginning a search or looking up data, the alphabetical index is consulted to locate the decimal number of the subject. The searcher then consults the abstracts of articles and patents, the book catalog cards, and the books on the shelves under this decimal classification. The information already available thus serves as an excellent basis for the searches.

For the patent searching, in addition to the hundreds of subclasses of patents maintained by the TLS and by Texaco Development Corp., many of the attorneys in the Patent Division maintain special collections of patents, both United States and foreign, on the specific fields in which they are interested, such as solvent refining, well logging, and alkylation. These are cataloged by and accessible to the search staff of TDC.

Conclusion

Because the preparation of these lengthy surveys usually requires months, and the information is generally desired for immediate use, the logical procedure would be the constant preparation of basic surveys on the fundamental processes, products, and reactions of interest in order to have them available when needed. All specialized topics could not be anticipated, but a great deal of information from these basic reports could be used which would expedite the preparation of these special reports. Basic surveys could be made, for example, on the halogenation, oxidation, nitration, and sulfonation of hydrocarbons, refining processes such as sulfur and wax removal, additives for improving the properties of various products, and preparation of motor fuels from heavier and lighter fractions and their rearrangement by isomerization. As long as hydrocarbons serve as the building blocks, information will be desired on these reactions and processes, whether the hydrocarbons originate from petroleum, oil shale, coal, or natural gas.

Literature Cited

(1) Alexander, Jerome, ed., "Colloid Chemistry," Vol. VI, Reinhold, New York, 1946.
(2) Bailey, K. C., "Retardation of Chemical Reactions," Longmans, Green, New York, 1937.
(3) Brooks, B. T., "Chemistry of the Non-Benzenoid Hydrocarbons," 2nd ed., Reinhold, New York, 1950.
(4) Bush, Vannevar, Chairman, "Report to the Secretary of Commerce by the Advisory Committee on Application of Machines to Patent Office Operations," Department of Commerce, Washington, D. C., Jan. 22, 1954.
(5) Chicago Section, ACS, "Abstracts of Chemical Patents Vested in the Alien Property Custodian," Vols. I, II, 1944.
(6) Coulson, T., *J. Franklin Inst.* **241**, 187–93 (1946).
(7) Emmett, P. H., ed., "Catalysis," Vols. I–VII, Reinhold, New York, 1954–60.
(8) Piskur, M. M., *Oil and Soap* **12** to **23** (1935–46); *J. Am. Oil Chem. Soc.* **24** to **36** (1947–58).
(9) Pritzker, G. G., *Natl. Petrol. News* **38** (32), R 606, R 608, R 610, R 612 (1946); *Petrol. Processing* **1** (1), 58–9, 61–4 (1946); **2** (3), 205–6, 208; (4) 291–3, 295–6 (1947).
(10) Von Hohenhoff, Elsa, *J. Patent Office Soc.* (October 1935–February 1936).
(11) Worden, E. C., "Chemical Patents Index," Chemical Catalog Co., New York, 1927–1934.

BASED on paper presented before Division of Chemical Education, Symposium on Chemical Literature, 111th Meeting, ACS, Atlantic City, N. J., April 1947. Revised 1960.

Library Techniques in Searching

D. F. BROWN[1]
Revised by M. D. SCHOENGOLD
Esso Research and Engineering Co., Linden, N. J.

A review of some suggested procedures for successful technical literature and patent searching techniques as applied at Esso Research and Engineering Co.

Lord Rayleigh once said that "by a fiction as remarkable as any to be found in law, what has once been published (no matter what the language) is usually spoken of as known, and it is often forgotten that the rediscovery in the library may be a more difficult and uncertain process than the first discovery in the laboratory" (*32*).

It has frequently been said, however, that the cheapest research is that done in the library; many chemists can probably confirm this statement from their own experience. It is because of this that the informed chemist seldom thinks of embaıking upon a new research program in the laboratory before he has ascertained what information already exists that may have some bearing upon his problem. The value of such library research has already been ably discussed (*10, 11, 14, 22, 24, 32, 52*).

Many articles and books describe the numerous tools and techniques available to the searcher in any well-equipped library. A partial list of these is appended to this paper. Outstanding among these are the books by Crane, Patterson, and Marr (*14*), Mellon (*32*), and Soule (*50*), in each of which indexes to the chemical literature are listed and their use is explained. In addition, these books emphasize the importance of systematic planning of the search and give helpful suggestions regarding the mechanics of successful searching techniques. This paper reviews some of the procedures suggested by these excellent summaries as they have been applied in the Technical Information Division of Esso Research and Engineering Co.

In this organization the research man may come to the library for the prior art—journal articles, patents, books, etc.—that will assist him in his work. He is free to use the library files (which he often does), or he may ask the Technical Information Division to help him gather the information he needs.

A library search may be made for various purposes. The chemist or engineer may request a complete report of published articles and patents relating to a particular or general field. If so, the request is for an art search and the task of the searcher is to collect, digest, and annotate all the published information in books,

[1] Deceased.

periodicals, or the patent literature that is relevant to the field defined. The patent attorney may want to know if the invention he is trying to protect in a new patent application has sufficient novelty to be patentable; he asks for a novelty search. He may wish to know whether a contemplated use of a certain product, process, or piece of equipment is already covered by an existing patent so that use of it would therefore infringe; he requests an infringement search. He may know of a patent which does cover an invention the company wishes to use; he then requests a validity search to determine the value of the existing patent. He may ask only for an index search to determine what patents or articles have been published over the name of a particular individual or company.

The various types of searches and the techniques and sources best adapted to each have been ably discussed by others (*39, 51*). This paper discusses only the art search. But the volume of literature for even a very limited field is today so great that it is appalling. The method of attack and the time to be spent, therefore, must depend upon the importance of the problem. If the problem is of sufficient importance, the extended time required to make a complete search will be justified, but a less important problem may merely require scanning those sections of the art most likely to contain pertinent references. In any search, however, the initial step is the same; the problem must be analyzed, and the sources to be examined must be determined.

It is absolutely essential that the searcher understand the nature of the problem. He asks himself what the elements of the request are. Is it a question of a single-step process or a simple compound, or are there many steps with varying degrees of dependence? If so, what are they? If it is a new product, is it a new species or is it generic in nature? How broadly must the search be made to cover all relevant material? What analogous procedures or equivalent products must be considered? It is usually helpful, unless the request is very simple, to reduce the analysis to a written outline accompanied by a brief list of the sources to be examined before the actual search is begun.

At this stage of the search, consultation with the person making the request is very helpful. As a result of this consultation, any error or misconception in the analysis of the request should become apparent. Furthermore, the limits of the search may be set more realistically as the magnitude of the search is made apparent.

Hypothetical Art Search

Consider a hypothetical request for an art search as it might be made to the library, and the procedures that would be followed in the prosecution of the search. Assume that Dr. John Doe has requested help in connection with research he is about to start on the Fischer-Tropsch synthesis. He first requests the art on hydrogenation. This, obviously, is a very broad field, with numerous references in all the major sources—books, monographs, general and special texts, encyclopedias, etc.; indexes such as *Chemical Abstracts* and *Engineering Index*; special files such as card file indexes and clipping files; and patents. Table I shows how this field may be subdivided.

Dr. Doe has not realized how broad a field of search he is requesting until this is pointed out to him at the consultation. He sees the necessity, therefore, for stating his question more explicitly, in order to reduce the scope of the search to only such art as is likely to pertain to his particular problem. He explains that his problem is concerned specifically with the Fischer-Tropsch synthesis.

Table I. Hydrogenation Classification

Hydrogenation of
1. Specific materials
   a. Animal and vegetable oils
   b. Mineral oils
      (1) Petroleum
      (2) Shale oils
      (3) Bitumens
   c. Coal, lignite, peat, etc.
   d. Oxides of carbon
   e. Miscellaneous carbon compounds
   f. Inorganic compounds
2. Use of hydrogen
   a. As a reducing agent
   b. In purification processes
3. Raw materials and their production
   a. Hydrogen
   b. Synthesis gas, etc.
4. Use and/or properties of hydrogenation products
5. Apparatus
6. Catalysts

Although more limited in scope than the first request, this is still a very broad field, and a vast amount of literature has been written on the subject. This may be seen from the outline in Table II.

Table II. Fischer Synthesis

1. Processes
   a. Fixed bed catalyst
   b. Fluidized catalyst
   c. Other
2. Operating conditions
   a. Temperature
   b. Pressure
   c. Contact time, flow velocity, etc.
3. Products
   a. Hydrocarbons
   b. Oxygenated compounds
      (1) Alcohols
      (2) Aldehydes, etc.
   c. Properties
   d. Refining
4. Raw materials and their preparation
5. Apparatus
6. Catalysts

After further discussion, Dr. Doe admits that he is interested only in the wax products obtained in the synthesis reaction and, finally, that his particular problem is to study the effect of catalysts on the yield of such products. His problem is now defined, and the searcher can proceed with the analysis and outline of material to be examined as previously described.

The analysis will result in an outline something like that shown in Table III.

Table III. Effect of Catalyst Composition on Wax Product in Fischer Synthesis

1. Nickel catalysts
2. Cobalt catalysts
3. Iron catalysts
4. Promoters
5. Other catalysts and catalyst mixtures
6. Catalyst preparation
7. Catalyst regeneration
8. Economic studies

With the question defined, the next step is to outline the art to be examined. Here the searcher's training and experience are important. He ascertains from Dr. Doe that economic data are not required at the present time and that the field to be examined may be limited to the technological aspects of the problem. The searcher will recall from memory a few of the books, monographs, encyclopedias, or general texts that should be examined in the search. Memory still plays an important part in the activities of a searcher, but memory alone should not be depended upon in preparing this section of his outline. He will consult the library catalog. If a special card index is available, he may consult this first and may possibly find enough information there to avoid the necessity for consulting further sources. But if the card index is not sufficiently complete, or if he wishes to acquire more background in the preparation for the search, the searcher will go first to the monographs, encyclopedias, and the general texts on the subject located through the catalog.

Most chemists are familiar with the library catalog. It consists of a card or cards carrying bibliographic data for each title on the library shelves. It may be a dictionary catalog containing cards filed alphabetically for each author and subject, or it may be only an author index to the books plus a shelf-list section. This shelf list consists of one card for each title, arranged in the classification order in which the books are filed on the shelves. One advantage of using a shelf list over visual examination of the books on the shelf is that the cards do not circulate. Thus, a book may be missed because it is out in circulation or misfiled at the time the shelf section is examined.

Examination of the catalog shelf-list section for titles in the field of hydrogenation reveals a number of texts in this field—e.g., "Hydrogenation of Organic Substances" by C. Ellis, and "The Fischer-Tropsch and Related Syntheses" by H. A. Storch *et al.* Ellis' book, Chapter 55, "Reduction of Carbon Oxides," is specific to the problem in question. All the other texts listed in this section should, of course, be examined also, well as the Kirk-Othmer, Ullmann, and Thorpe encyclopedias, and the books on catalysis.

Many leads for further searching will be found in these books, both as to related fields of subject matter that should be examined and to specific references to the prior literature in books, periodicals, and patents. These may be numerous; if so, it is wise to record each pertinent reference as noted, preferably on a separate card, so that the cards can be kept in alphabetical order by author, or in numerical order by patent number, and serve as a check list as the search progresses. Time wasted in recording duplicate references can be eliminated by such a check list.

In recording references during a search it is wise to make a complete record of each reference as it is noted for the first time, so as to avoid, in so far as possible, the necessity for going back again for additional data. In an extensive search such as the one discussed here, a 3 × 5 card, a 4 × 6 inch card, or hand-sorted punched cards are preferred for each reference. Complete bibliographical data are recorded, together with an abstract. The abstract should be aimed specifically at the purpose of the search, and need not be a complete abstract of the original article.

In an upper corner of the card should be given the author or authors for a literature reference, and the patent number, inventor, or assignee for a patent. If significant dates (filing, issued, published, or convention date) are given, one or more of these with the names is usually included in this corner of the card. The abstract should contain all the significant data likely to be included in the final report. If the reference is noted from another publication, the secondary publication reference should also be indicated. It is important to put down complete bibliographical reference data. Abbreviations that are not fairly obvious should be avoided. Others may have to use the notes at some time in the future, and the few additional seconds required to make the reference clearly understandable may save hours in searching for it later on. The abstract may be brief or extended, according to the preference of the searcher, but it should at least indicate the type of information contained in the article, and why the reference is considered pertinent. A time saver is to word the abstract so that it can be copied into the final report.

When the textbooks and monographs have been examined, the searcher should be sufficiently oriented into the search to permit preparation of an adequate list of subject headings for use in examining the various literature indexes. Such a list for the hypothetical case considered here might start as indicated in Table IV.

With such a list of subject headings, the searcher is now ready to begin his

Table IV. Subject Headings

Catalysis
Catalysts
Carbon oxides
Cobalt
Fischer-Tropsch
Hydrocarbons
Hydrocarbon synthesis
Hydrogenation
Iron
Nickel
Ruthenium
Synthesis

examination of the journal and patent literature. Assume that he wishes to start with the journals.

The original list of indexes to be examined should be reviewed at this point and revised if necessary on the basis of the additional knowledge obtained in the review of the books and the like. In fact, both the list of sources to be examined and the subject headings to be used should be repeatedly checked and revised as the search progresses. The searcher may wish to start the indexes with the special card index in the library, if this is sufficiently complete. If a more exhaustive search is required, the searcher would start from here with the most comprehensive indexes available.

Most technical libraries will have an index such as *Chemical Abstracts, Chemisches Zentralblatt, British Chemical Abstracts,* and its predecessors, *Journal of the Society of Chemical Industry* and *Journal of the Chemical Society, Wagner's Jahresberichte, Liebig-Kopps Jahresberichte, Science Abstracts, Physikalische Berichte,* and *Engineering Index.* In examining each of these indexes it is important to determine which would be most likely to yield the greatest return for the time invested in searching it. It is also important in examining these indexes, or even in going from volume to volume in the same index, constantly to review the list of subject headings which the searcher has compiled. Checks should be made of all the cross references noted in the indexes, to make certain that the right subject headings are being used each time. This is necessary because the editors who prepare these indexes revise their subject headings from year to year.

There are many routines by which this examination of the indexes can be systemized. The one preferred by the writers consists in listing at the top of a sheet of paper all the headings to be used for the volume being examined. Space is left for the insertion of additional headings as the need for them may be dis-

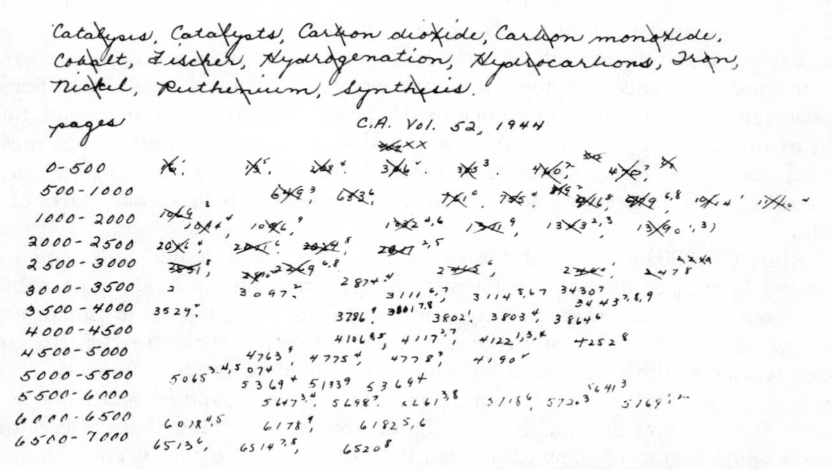

Figure 1. Work sheet for examining Chemical Abstracts

covered later. The page references as indicated in the index are then tabulated on the sheet, spaced sufficiently to permit arrangement in numerical order as additional pages are noted under the successive headings in the index. When all the pages have been listed in this way, in at least approximate numerical order, the searcher can go through the volume systematically and examine each reference listed, checking it off as he does so.

A specimen check sheet of this sort is shown in Figure 1. In this instance the references in a volume of *Chemical Abstracts* are listed in approximately numerical order. Such a sheet can usually be easily expanded to contain all the references noted in a cumulative index, such as the *Chemical Abstracts* Decennial Index.

If the subject is very important or if the period to be covered is such that the indexes are not available, it is necessary to page the volume itself, or certain portions of it. It may even be necessary to page certain primary periodicals that are most specific to the field of the search.

Ultimately all the references noted from the index journals have been added to the growing file of pertinent references, the original articles have been consulted for additional information whenever this is necessary, in the judgment of the searcher, and additional references have been noted from the bibliographies and footnotes in the original articles. A final check should then be made to determine if any other bibliographies, indexes, trade catalogs, government documents, or theses should be examined.

Memory still plays an important part in the activities of the searcher. It is well to become familiar with the basic reference books in the fields of company interest. This may easily be done by browsing, paging through the new books received in the library, reading book reviews, etc. Another technique is to check through certain review journals regularly and to list review articles that might be of possible future interest. This list might easily be classified by subject, the classification system being as broad or narrow as experience dictates.

Patent Literature

A point is finally reached where the searcher decides that all of the indexes, books, pamphlets, and periodical literature have been examined, in so far as the importance of the search justifies the time spent on it. There still remains a vast and most important body of art—the patent literature.

Patents make up one of the principal storehouses of information concerning the technical advances in the industrial world. Technical men have become increasingly aware of the importance of the patent literature. Evidence of this is seen in the fact that *Chemical Abstracts* makes a concerted effort to abstract all United States and foreign patents of possible interest to the chemist, and in the numerous patent-abstracting services that have sprung up in various parts of the world.

Almost 3,000,000 United States patents have been issued and copies are arranged in subject files at the Patent Office, Washington, D. C. The subjects range from safety pins to harvesting combines, from hand lotions to processes for cracking petroleum, and from making synthetic rubber to making nylon stockings. If one wishes to develop something new in any field of product, process, or mechanical art or device, one cannot ignore the patent literature, particularly the United States patent art, for there is almost always something there which bears some resemblance to his new idea, even if it does not anticipate it completely.

How does one examine this enormous body of art? It is not as complicated as it may seem. In the chemical field, much of it is well indexed in the abstract journals such as *Chemical Abstracts*. Therefore, much of the patent art may have been gathered when the indexes to these journals were examined.

It is not wise, however, to rely solely on abstracts or abridgments for the collection of patent art. The patent copies themselves should be examined.

The United States Patent Office classifies its patents into some 350 main classes, each of which is divided into many subclasses. There are now about 45,000 of these subclasses. Titles of the classes and subclasses are listed in the "Manual of Classification of Patents" (*54*). Revision of this classification is a continuous process. As classes are revised and new definitions for them are written, these are published first in the *Official Gazette of the U. S. Patent Office* and later in the *Classification Bulletin* issued at intervals by the Patent Office.

To search the United States patent art, therefore, the first step is to examine the "Manual of Classification," together with the definitions furnished in the *Classification Bulletins* in order to determine, if possible, which classes will contain the art to be examined. The only classified sets of patents available to the public in this country are in the Patent Office search room in Washington. Some companies, therefore, maintain partial sets in their own libraries. These may be readily maintained by subscribing to the classes of special interest. In this way, copies of the patents classified by the Patent Office into these classes are automatically received.

There are other ways of obtaining United States patent information, such as the Uniterm Index to United States Chemical Patents, and the various other private agencies which supply copies of the patents, or of the most important claim on some sort of punched card.

In connection with the search under discussion, reference to the Classification Manual reveals that class 260, and subclass 439, 449.5 and particularly 449.6, are directly pertinent to Dr. Doe's problem. More subclasses may, perhaps, be selected from the manual. Furthermore, in going through the patents in any particular subclass the searcher will find cross-referenced patents from other classes. These often reveal important classes to search which had not appeared obvious from the list of classes in the manual. Sometimes, also, additional classes to be searched are located by looking up the classification of a relevant patent which had been discovered by accident from the index journals or recalled from memory.

Some searchers have been known to rely upon abstract publications for patent references, but this is not safe. An important patent reference may be missed completely in the abstract publication, or the abstractor may have failed to indicate the clue that permits recognition of the relevancy of the original patent to the point being searched. The disclosure in the patent may be so incidental or obscure that the abstractor could not be expected to have included it in his brief condensation. The reverse may also be true. The abstract may contain a statement, overlooked by the searcher when he examined the original, which may make the patent a valuable reference. In a thorough search the original patent copies in the classified sets should be examined, and the abstracts to these same patents should be noted as they are found in the abstract publications. This serves as a check to ensure against overlooking relevant references.

After the United States patents have been examined, the foreign patent art still remains to be covered. Here again the only sets of classified foreign patents available to the public are to be found in the Scientific Library of the United States Patent Office, which maintains both numerical and classified sets of patents from most of the foreign countries which print them. These include Austrian, French, Dutch, German, and Swiss patents. The patent copies in these classified sets are arranged as originally classified in the country of origin, and manuals explaining these classifications are available in the Scientific Library. The procedure for using them is the same as for examination of the United States patent art. Dependence upon abstracts of foreign patents is even more to be avoided than in the case of United States patents.

Eventually, the searcher finds that he has examined every source which his experience tells him is likely to contain valuable references. He then assembles his list of references with such data for each as he plans to report.

The report can now be written. It should contain a clearly stated definition of the object of the search and a description of the sources searched and the period covered, sufficiently detailed to permit the future reader of the report to decide whether additional searching should be attempted, and if so, to avoid searching again the sources already covered. How the references themselves are to be reported depends upon the searcher's preference and his understanding of the preferences of those who will later use the report. The report should indicate, either in a separate discussion or in the abstract of the individual reference cited. why each reference is cited.

Such an exhaustive search as is here outlined briefly is very time-consuming and is justified only by extreme importance of the problem. Most searchers are shorter and less thorough, but whether short or long, the elements are the same (Table V).

Table V. Steps in Conducting a Search

I. Define the problem to be searched, preferably in writing.
II. Outline the sources to be examined; list the most important first.
III. Set up a list of subject headings and revise it as the search progresses.
IV. Enlarge the scope as necessary by adding new sources indicated by the clues that appear as the search progresses.
V. Systematize the references as they are found.
VI. Assemble the references and make the report.

The ability to search accurately and efficiently is a special one and seems to be inherent rather than acquired. A knowledge of subject matter and the best sources for specific subjects can be acquired, as can the routines to be followed in making the search. But the ability to recognize infallibly and quickly the relevancy or nonrelevancy of subject matter examined depends upon an alert and imaginative mind and discriminating judgment, as well as technological skill. Thus it is important that the mind not wander as the search progresses. If the search is being made at the request of another, the scope of the search should be clearly defined, so that time will not be wasted in gathering irrelevant or unnecessary art. An adequate background should be provided by the one who requests a search, so that the searcher will understand why the required information was requested and how it will be used. This is essential if he is to apply his imagination in recognizing the relevancy of the references to be examined.

This view has been confirmed by others. Thus, Lewton (*30*) states that the searcher should have a complete knowledge of sources and the ability to evaluate them. In addition, the type of work demands extensive technical training and understanding of research concepts and viewpoints. "The gift of applying the general to the specific, imagination to form the nonobvious correlation and see possibilities, and ability to interpret abstract scientific ideas into terms of commercial understanding are required to carry on desk research. In fact, it takes the same qualities and processes of mind-analysis of problems into factors, outlining the logical steps in mode of attack, evaluation of tools and techniques to be employed as is required by a leader or director of research."

Adams (*1*) states that some of the qualifications of a research bibliographer are an analytical mind, active interest in reading, love for creative thinking, and technical training.

The Larger Problem

The topic we are considering here is but a fragment of a much larger problem which demands corrective action in the near future. Recorded experience as it now exists in the literature is expanding at a great rate and it is not well organized. As this expansion continues, the difficulties of searching increase. Many people and organizations are working on the problem of coping with this problem, to improve indexing procedures, to speed up the appearance of abstracts, to increase the speed of searching, to increase the depth of indexing, and to provide mechanical translations. Perhaps an entirely new method will be found for communicating information, a method which will not require the human eye to read. But no matter what new methods are evolved, it will always take a human being to analyze the information as it relates to the problem at hand. Machines will in time relieve the human being of the burdensome task of finding the information, but they will never do the final analysis for him.

Bibliography

(1) Adams, F. W., *J. Chem. Educ.* **16,** 581–3 (1939). Opportunities for women as research bibliographers.
(2) American Chemical Society, *Ibid.,* **21,** 315–46 (1944). Symposium on technical library techniques.
(3) Anon., *Industritidning. Norden,* No. **53,** 425 (Dec. 30, 1936). Value of technical literature for inventors.
(4) Arend, A. G., *Petrol. Times* **47,** 84 (Feb. 20, 1943). Studying foreign petroleum literature.
(5) Aslin, N. S., Nicol, H., *Mfg. Perfumer* **1,** 190–1 (March 1937). Library aids to industry. World list of periodicals.
(6) Berolzheimer, D. D., *Chemist* **13,** No. 2, 426–33 (1936). Searching chemical and allied literature.
(7) Bradford, S. C., *Engineering* **140,** 202–3 (Aug. 23, 1935), 230–2 (Aug. 30, 1935). Organization of a library service in science and technology.
(8) Brightman, R., *Ind. Chemist* **12,** 396–400 (September 1936). Organization of information for industry.
(9) Cochran, S. W., "Recent Progress in Patent Classification," Paper 30, Division of Chemical Education, Symposium on Chemical Literature, 111th Meeting, ACS, Atlantic City, N. J., April 1947.
(10) Connolly, A. G., *J. Chem. Educ.* **20,** 531–3 (1943). Symposium on technical library techniques.
(11) Coulson, T., *J. Franklin Inst.* **241,** No. 3, 187–93 (March 1946). Neglected aspect of research.
(12) Crane, E. J., *Ind. Eng. Chem., News Ed.* **16,** 353 (1938). In the abstract.
(13) Crane, E. J., *Special Libraries* **31,** 260–4 (July–August 1940). Abstracting and indexing scientific and technical literature.
(14) Crane, E. J., Patterson, A. M., Marr, E. B., "Guide to the Literature of Chemistry," 2nd ed., Wiley, New York, 1957.
(15) Culhan, P. J., *J. Chem. Educ.* **20,** 601–2 (1943). Importance of scientific literature in patent applications.
(16) Deller, A. W., *Special Libraries* **31,** 151–4 (May–June 1940).
(17) Dexter, G. H., *Mech. Eng.* **59,** 845–9 (November 1937). The library as an engineering tool.
(18) Dyson, G. M., "Chemical Literature," Longmans, Green, London, 1951.
(19) Egloff, G., Alexander, M., Van Arsdell, P., *J. Chem. Educ.* **20,** 393–8 (1943).

(20) Ellis, G. P., *Research (London)* **11,** 276–8 (1958). Literature problems in organic chemistry.
(21) Fizette, M. Y., Jones, B. E., Gibson, R. W., Jr., *Special Libraries* **49,** 253–5 (July-August 1958). The bibliographic research team.
(22) Foreman, P., *Hydro News (Toronto)* **32,** 9–11, 25 (April 1925). Knowledge is power.
(23) Gilbert, C. L., Gray, C., "Classification of Literature in the Technical Department of an Oil Co.," Brit. Soc. Int. Bibliography, Sept. 26, 1944; *Petroleum* **T.221** (December 1944) (abstract).
(24) Hammond, C. R., *Power Plant Eng.* **50,** No. 9, 69, 85 (1946). Is science's Waterloo at the library?
(25) Harden, F., *J. Chem. Educ.* **21,** 326–32 (1944). Use of government publications in chemical research.
(26) Henion, G. F., *Ibid.,* **21,** 33–5 (1944). Searching the literature of organic compounds. Use of Richter's "Lexikon der Kohlenstoffverbindungen," Stelzner's "Literatur-Register der organische Chemie," Formula Indexes of *Chemical Abstracts* and *Chemisches Zentralblatt,* and Beilstein's "Handbuch der organische Chemie" is explained.
(27) Hopp, R. H., *Special Libraries* **37,** 291–3 (November 1946). Bibliography compilation in technical fields.
(28) Kobe, K. A., "Chemical Engineering Reports. How to Search the Literature and Prepare a Report," 4th ed., Interscience, New York, 1957.
(29) Leighty, J. A., *Special Libraries,* **31,** 264–6 (July–August 1940). What the research worker expects of the librarian.
(30) Lewton, L. O., *Chem. & Met. Eng.* **53,** No. 3, 112–3, 116 (March 1946). Libraries —advance scouts for research.
(31) Lewton, L. O., *J. Chem. Educ.* **28,** 487–91; 539–43 (1951). Art of searching the literature.
(32) Mellon, M. G., "Chemical Publications, Their Nature and Use," 3rd ed., McGraw-Hill, New York, 1958.
(33) Nicol, H., *Am. Perfumer* **2,** 20–1 (April 1937). Abstracts, bibliographies, and translations.
(34) Oatfield, H., Emilio, B. R., *Am. Documentation* **9,** 238–76 (1958). Some aspects of searching in the pharmaceutical literature. Reference fringe benefits.
(35) Olsen, G. F., "Functions and Advantages of a Company Technical Library," A.I.M.E. Meeting Paper, Los Angeles, Oct. 19, 1939; *Mining Met. Soc. Bull.* **21,** 333–4 (July 1940).
(36) Ostrold, H., "Bibliographic Aids for Literature Research," Inst. of Agriculture Library, Univ. of Minnesota, St. Paul, 1957.
(37) Potter, D. J. C., Bassett, F. J., *Chem. in Can* **9,** 39–44 (1957). Use of indexes for searching chemical literature.
(38) Premo, J. G., *J. Chem. Educ.* **35,** No. 7, 353 (July 1958). A simplified procedure for searching U. S. chemical patents.
(39) Price, M. O., *Special Libraries* **31,** 118–28 (April 1940). Patent searching, with special reference to chemical patents.
(40) Read, T. T., Laist, J. W., *Mining Met. Soc. Bull.* **27,** No. 427, 396–7 (July 1946). The institute's library and how to use it. Short description of the Engineering Societies' Library and its services.
(41) Rostler, K. S., *Rubber Age* **82,** 678–88 (1958). Rubber compounding information; sources, indexing, retrieving.
(42) Schaler, C., *Special Libraries* **32,** 270–3 (September 1941). Technique of meeting information needs of a patent department of any industry.
(43) Schmitz, W., *Z. Ver. deut. Ing.* **80,** 1271–3 (Oct. 17, 1936). How to find technical literature.
(44) Sewell, W., *Special Libraries* **48,** 189–93 (May–June 1957). Retrieval of therapeutic information: Using abstract and index publications.
(45) Short, M. A., *Research* **10,** 313–18 (August 1957). Searching the literature of physical and organic chemistry.
(46) Singer, T. E. R., *Rec. Chem. Progr.* **18,** No. 1, 11–29 (1957). Need for imagination and skepticism when making literature searches.
(47) Smith, W. W., *J. Chem. Educ.* **20,** 602–4 (1943). Symposium on technical library techniques.
(48) Soule, B. A., *Ibid.,* **19,** 508–9 (1942). Frozen assets. Putting chemical knowledge to work.
(49) *Ibid.,* **21,** 333–5 (1944). Finding the literature.
(50) Soule, B. A., "Library Guide for the Chemist," McGraw-Hill, New York, 1938.
(51) Stores, C. D., *Special Libraries* **40,** No. 3, 88–92 (March 1949). Patent searching.
(52) Strieby, I. M., Cole, B. J., *Chem. Inds.* **57,** No. 7, 1064–8 (1945). Finding facts for a chemical clientele.
(53) Tolpin, J. G., *J. Chem. Educ.* **23,** 485–9 (1946). Searching the Russian technical literature.

(54) U. S. Patent Office, Washington, D. C., "Manual of Classification of Patents."
(55) Van Luik, J., associates, "Searching the Chemical and Chemical Engineering Literature with an Analysis of 229 Journals and Handbooks," 2nd ed., Purdue Univ., Lafayette, Ind., 1957.
(56) Wright, J. E., "Manual of Special Library Technique with Particular Reference to the Technical Special Libraries of Commercial and Government Establishments," Aslib, London, 1945.

BASED on paper presented before the Division of Chemical Education, Symposium on Chemical Literature, 111th Meeting, ACS, Atlantic City, N. J., April 1947. Revised 1960.

Continuous Collection and Classification of Data as an Aid in Preparing Surveys

JOHN C. LANE[1] **and JOHN METSCHL**

Gulf Research & Development Co., Pittsburgh, Pa.

This paper outlines a scheme for preparing literature and patent surveys with a near minimum of time expenditure and a high degree of completeness. The scheme consists primarily of the continuous collection, classification, and filing of current literature and patents. As a result of this operation, surveys may be prepared directly from filed material without arduous searching through the abstract journals. Stenographic personnel may be utilized for much of the work to reduce the cost of the operation and conserve the time of technical personnel.

If literature and patent surveys are to serve as guides for research programs, it is frequently essential and always highly desirable to prepare them in the shortest possible time, so that the speedy development of an idea will result in a competitive advantage. A patent may be obtained or a market may be captured if a process can be brought to completion before a competitor's; yet a hastily contrived survey may be useless. Some reference overlooked may contain the key to success or failure.

Thus the two main requirements of literature and patent surveys are that they be sufficiently comprehensive and that they be completed within as short a time as is consistent with adequate coverage. These two requirements are, by nature, somewhat opposed, and it is possible to satisfy both simultaneously only by conducting a survey as efficiently as possible.

Inasmuch as collection of material usually requires by far the largest amount of time consumed in the preparation of literature and patent surveys, and entirely determines the coverage, increasing the efficiency of the collection step is of paramount importance. The present paper outlines a scheme for preparing surveys with a near minimum of time expenditure and a high degree of completeness, by continuous collection, classification, and filing of current literature and patents.

Classification

Smooth functioning of this scheme involves the teamwork of several sections

[1] Present address, Ethyl Corp., Ferndale 20, Detroit, Mich.

and a number of individuals, each section contributing its services according to its facilities and each individual according to his particular training. The backbone of the entire scheme is the index classification system developed by Gulf Research & Development Co.'s fellowship at Mellon Institute; by use of this system both the literature and the patents are classified and filed for ready reference.

The 9 main divisions shown in Table I, Divisions B through J, classify material pertinent to the petroleum products, while the other divisions provide classifications for all other material relating to the petroleum industry.

Table I. Main Divisions of Mellon Institute File Index System

A. Miscellaneous	L. Chemistry and chemical composition
B. Gas	M. Physical properties
C. Gasoline and other motor fuels	N. Testing, analysis, and specifications
D. Kerosine	O. Equipment
E. Gas oil, fuel oil, and fuels	P, Q, R. Open
F. Lubricants and lubrication	S. Production, pipelines, and storage
G. Wax and petrolatum	T. Distillation
H. Asphalt and coke	U. Treating chemically
I. Crude oils	V. Treating physically
J. By-products and miscellaneous petroleum products	W. Cracking

Each main division is subdivided into as many classes as are required by the amount and type of information to be classified. Table II shows the breakdown of the lubricants and lubrication division. The first letter in the file designation for each class is that of the main division, in this case F for lubricants and lubrication. The second letter indicates the particular class within the main division. A number of classes are provided for lubricant products, while others exist for classification of information relating to production, specifications, testing, etc. Each class is further divided as extensively as has proved to be useful. Since the system was initiated prior to 1927, it is not surprising that a number of subclasses have since been added, as have some classes and even a few main divisions.

Table II. Breakdown of Typical Main Division of File Index System

FA. Miscellaneous, general	FM. Greases and soaps, transmission, chassis, extreme pressure lubricants
FB. Nonviscous oils. Textile oils	FN. Properties and composition
FC. Turbine oils	FO. Theory of lubrication
FD. Industrial lubricants	FP. Specifications (of petroleum lubricants)
FE. Motor oils	FR. Preparation
FF. Open	FS. Equipment
FG. Cutting and emulsifying oils	
FH. Cylinder and bright stocks, car journal, black oils	
FI. Compounded lubricants, thickened lubricants, additions	

Table III shows how the classes are broken down into subclasses. The FI class has been taken as an example to continue the account of the breakdown of the F main division. The subclasses are designated by number and further divisions by lower case letters. The paragraph just under the class heading indicates briefly and rather incompletely the type of material filed under the class. However, subclasses may be added as needs dictate.

Filing

Both the literature and patents are continuously classified and filed by use of this classification system. A card file, a reprint file, and a patent file are maintained. The card file contains references to all or almost all of the existing material on each subject; the reprint file contains the full text of a large number of the best articles on each subject; and the patent file holds all pertinent patents classified by subject matter. Thus it is possible, at a moment's notice, to extract the classifications desired, and find instantly at hand all the material necessary for a complete survey.

Table III. Breakdown of Typical Class of File Index System

FI. Compounded Lubricants, Thickened Lubricants, Additions
(See also MC–4a, GB–2a, LH–4)

Additions of compounds for improving lubricating oils, viscosity improvement, increasing film strength, pour-point depression, oiliness agents, compounded oils, synthetic oils, fatty acids as lubricants, linseed oil, rapeseed oil (including blown), castor oil and castor oil blends, rubber in lubricants, tin compounds, Exanol, Paratone, Vistones, etc., penetrating oils, electrochemical oils.

FI–1. General (miscellaneous)
  FI–1a. Graphite lubricants
    Aquadag, Oildag, graphite, analysis theory of graphite lubrication
FI–2. Improving viscosity and viscosity index
FI–3. Oiliness, extreme pressure, film strength
FI–4. Anticorrosion agents
FI–5. Antioxidants
FI–6. Detergents
  Sludge dispersers
  Carbon preventives
FI–7. Anti-ring-sticking agents

Although these files are great timesavers when a survey is to be prepared, they require surprisingly little time to maintain in current condition. Division of effort prevents taking more than a small fraction of any one person's time, and stenographic help is employed as far as possible.

Selection of Material

At Mellon Institute, the senior fellow makes selections from a number of outstanding periodicals, including *Chemical Abstracts, Journal of the American Chemical Society, Industrial and Engineering Chemistry, Chemical Engineering, Petroleum Refiner, S. A. E. Journal, Petroleum Engineer,* and *Petroleum Processing.* He indicates whether a card is to be made for an article, whether it is to be clipped and added to the reprint file, or both. This work is done in his odd moments. Another member of the fellowship, who also heads the library at Gulf Research & Development Co., classifies the senior fellow's selections according to the index system described. Taking *Chemical Abstracts* as an example, about 2 hours of classification are required per issue, and an average of around 100 abstracts are classified. This amounts to only a little over 1 minute per abstract.

From this point, the additions to the files become a stenographic job. For articles in journals other than *Chemical Abstracts,* cards listing the bibliographic data, but containing no abstract, are made and filed under the indicated classification, and selected articles are clipped and filed. In the case of *Chemical Abstracts,* the abstracts themselves are clipped, pasted on cards, and filed according to classification. These *Chemical Abstracts* cards replace the cards containing only bibliographic data, the latter serving an interim purpose in keeping the file up to date. Thus, as far as the literature is concerned, the card file is as complete as the coverage of *Chemical Abstracts,* and the reprint file contains articles from the leading journals in the field.

The patent phase of the work is handled somewhat differently but in an equally efficient manner. The head of the Patent Section of Gulf Research & Development Co. examines each copy of the *Official Gazette of the United States Patent Office* for patents of interest. He then obtains copies of the patents, roughly classifies them, and sends them to qualified persons at the research laboratories for abstracting. Since each man receives only patents which directly pertain to his specialty, the abstracting involves a minimum of mental effort—hence time. The patents, accompanied by copies of the abstracts, are then sent to Mellon Institute for classification and filing in a manner analogous to the way in which the literature is handled.

Information Bulletins

These procedures serve a number of purposes in addition to maintaining the files. For example, the selections made in *Chemical Abstracts* are checked for completeness of coverage both at Mellon Institute and at Gulf Research, and a mimeographed bulletin is prepared for each issue; it contains all the abstracts considered by the selectors to be of interest to Gulf Research personnel. This bulletin, prepared by the Information Section, is so arranged that individual abstracts can be clipped from it, pasted on file cards, and added to each man's personal file. The patent abstracts are published monthly in a mimeographed bulletin put out by the Patent Section. Thus, the entire technical personnel of the company is kept abreast of current developments in the field, and each man may build a personal file to suit his particular needs.

The Information Section, whose chief function is the preparation of literature and patent surveys, utilizes all the previously mentioned facilities and, in addition, has adopted several other aids. One of the most valuable of these is the use of standardized abstract forms in conducting a search. Separate forms are available for periodical, book, and patent references. The periodical and patent forms are illustrated in Figure 1.

Abstract Forms

The fact that each item of information always appears in the same place on the abstract form simplifies, by systematization, both collection of the information and its subsequent utilization. Much of the "leg work" and "pencil pushing" connected with collection of search information may, therefore, be relegated to stenographic personnel. When it becomes necessary to make a detailed search for abstracts pertaining to some given subject, a technical man needs only to consult an index—for example, the *Chemical Abstracts* index—jot down the page number of each pertinent abstract, and hand it to a copy girl who locates each abstract for him by marking the places with bits of paper. He then quickly skims the abstracts to judge their pertinence and by supplying authors' names or patent numbers indicates which abstracts are to be copied on forms. Figure 2 typifies the information provided on the completed notation sheet. The copy girl types the selected abstracts on the standard forms and files the completed forms in loose-leaf binders for future use. The loose-leaf feature permits arrangement of the literature references alphabetically by author and the patent references by country and patent number; such an arrangement is made at the conclusion of the search. Also, the references

CLASSIFIED SUBJECT: Cat. Cracking | PROJECT NUMBER | FILE NUMBER

PATENTEE: M. Sutton and C. W. Nysewander | COUNTRY AND PATENT NO.: U. S. 2,379,550
ASSIGNEE: Standard Oil Company of Indiana
TITLE: Introduction of Make-Up Catalyst.

OFFICIAL GAZETTE: VOL. PP. DATE | ABSTR. REFS.: C. A. | VOL. 39 | PP. 4458 | DATE 1945
DISCLAIMER TO CLAIMS NO.:
DECISIONS:
CORRESPONDING PATENTS OTHER COUNTRIES: | DRAWINGS: | DATE ISSUED: July 3, 1945
CLAIMS: | APPLICATION FILED:
REISSUE OR SIMILAR PATENTS: | CLASS NO.:
ORIGINAL AVAILABLE AT: | CALL NO.: | APPLICATION SERIAL NO.: | CONVENTION DATE:

ABSTRACT: The method of introducing fresh catalyst material into an $AlCl_3$-hydrocarbon conversion zone operating at superatmospheric pressure is described. This comprises withdrawing a portion of the partially spent liquid $AlCl_3$-hydrocarbon complex from the conversion zone and adding $AlCl_3$ until the complex has the consistency of ordinary toothpaste, followed by incorporation of the paste into the reaction zone by means of pressure. The $AlCl_3$ shows no tendency to settle out in this paste.

DATE EXAMINED: BY: PURPOSE OF SEARCH: CONT'D:

ABSTRACT BLANK FOR PATENTS AND FILED APPLICATIONS

CLASSIFIED SUBJECT: Cat. Cracking | PROJECT NUMBER | FILE NUMBER

AUTHOR: Goldtrap, W. A. and Skinner, B. Phillips Petroleum Company
TITLE: Refinery Conversion for Premium Motor Fuels.

ORIG. REFS.	VOL.	NO.	PAGES	DATE
Petroleum Engr.	16	7	174-82	1945
ABSTR. REF.: C. A.	40		4198	1946

ABSTRACT: A discussion of the catalytic cracking, gas reversion, and catalytic polymerization processes for increasing the output of high-octane gasoline components.

DATE EXAMINED: BY: PURPOSE OF SEARCH: CONT'D:

ABSTRACT BLANK FOR PERIODICALS AND REGULARLY ISSUED PROCEEDINGS

Figure 1. Standardized abstract forms for patent and periodical references

are checked for pertinence and completeness, and each abstract is given a reference number. If the search form of presentation is to be followed, the typist can immediately begin stenciling from the abstract books while the technical man prepares a subject index to the search.

Use of loose-leaf abstract forms is of particular value in the continuous collection of data for supplements to existing searches or surveys. As two of its services, the Information Section issues a *Weekly Literature Notification Bulletin,* which calls attention to articles of interest in the current literature, and the *Chemical Abstracts* bulletin already mentioned. During the preparation of each, abstract forms are filled out for all articles on subjects for which supplements will eventually be required. In the case of the literature notification bulletin, only bibliographic data are recorded on the forms, but in the case of the *Chemical Abstracts* bulletin, the abstracts are also included. When the supplement is to be prepared, all that is required is to add available material, if any, from sources other than *Chemical Ab-*

SYNTHINE SURVEY
CHEMICAL ABSTRACTS 38 (1944)

238^{4} — MELLER
~~366^{4}~~
~~375^{8}~~
470^{2} — GER. 728,766
470^{3} — GER. 729,290
~~624^{5}~~ —
633^{6} — GER. 731,295
751^{8} — GER. 732,719
949^{6} — FISCHER
~~1083^{3}~~
~~1084^{1}~~
1089^{5} — FISCHER
1094^{4} — GER. 733,749
1096^{9} — GER. 733,841
~~1102^{9}~~
~~1332^{4}~~
1342^{1} — EIDUS
1343^{2} — GER. 734,993
1343^{3} — GER. 734,218
~~1616^{4}~~
1621^{6} — FISCHER

2478^{3} — FISCHER
2478^{3} — GER. 716,836
2478^{4} — BR. 551,312
2478^{5} — GER. 717,693
2810^{7} — GER. 735,276
3111^{6} — PIGNOT
3114^{5} — GER. 736,844
3114^{6} — GER. 736,701
3443^{7} — KIMPFLIN
3786^{9} — U.S. Re. 22,415
3801^{7} — U.S. 2,338,805
3801^{8} — U.S. 2,338,475
3802^{1} — GER. 736,922
3864^{6} — SPIRK
4106^{4} — GER. 738,368
~~4106^{6}~~
4122^{3} — U.S. 2,339,927
4122^{4} — GER. 735,662
4122^{5} — GER. 738,091
4778^{7} — U.S. 2,345,957
5065^{4} — CAN. 421,168

Figure 2. Notation sheet supplied copy girl to fill out standard abstract forms

stracts and begin typing. Figure 3 shows how selections for supplements requiring search and surveys are made, simultaneously, with selections for the *Weekly Literature Notification Bulletin* and the addition of articles to the section's files. The only time technical skill is required is when the selections are made. After they are recorded on the form shown in Figure 3, a stenographer fills out the forms, makes additions to the files, and prepares the bulletin. During the page by page check of *Chemical Abstracts* for the abstract bulletin, notations are made of all abstracts to be added to the supplement books on the standardized forms, and the stenographer who prepares the bulletin does this. Figure 4 shows a typical notation sheet for this operation.

Advantages of System

In all these methods for facilitating the preparation of searches and surveys, the work has been reduced to the stenographic level wherever possible. This is important both to keep the over-all cost down and to conserve the time of the technical personnel for other duties. Technical time has been further conserved by combining functions—for example, making selections for the supplement abstract books at the time when the literature notation and *Chemical Abstracts* bulletins are being prepared.

JOURNAL PETROLEUM REFINER 8-46

Page No.	Weekly Bulletin Subject	Abstract Forms	File
87	PETROL. SUBST.	SYNTHINE	87-98
99	SYNTHESIS, GEN.	HYDROG. SYNTHINE	99-108
109	CRKG. & REFORM.	———	———
111	DESULF.	———	———
115	CRKG. & REFORM.	CAT. CRKG.	115-18
119	LUBES & Additives	———	119-29
130	UNIT OPERATIONS	———	———
136	FUELS	POLYMERIZATION ALKYLATION	136-42
143	REFINING, GEN.	———	———
154	ECONOMICS	———	154-8
196	REFINING, GEN.	———	196-8
200	CRKG. & REFORMING	———	200
200	ISOMERIZATION	ISOM.	200
202	ALKYLATION	ALK.	202-3
204	POLYMERIZATION	———	204
206	REFINING, GEN.	———	206-12

Inf. Section Form 4

Figure 3. Combining preparation of weekly bulletin with file expansion operations

The final test of any scheme, system, or process is—what does it offer? The continuous collection, classification, and filing of literature and patents as outlined

CHEMICAL ABSTRACTS, 9-20-46

PAGE NO.	IDENTIFICATION	CLASSIFICATION
5393^6	PALFRAY	HYDROG.
5442^2	HOWES	NAPH. ISOM.
5442^5	MYERS	" "
5448^6	DAVIS	DIESEL FUELS
5552^5	HILL	CAT. CRACKING
5552^5	VILAND	" "
5552^6	CAULEY	" "
5552^7	PETERSON	" "
5552^9	FOSTER	CAT. CRACKING
		SYNTHINE
		LUBE ADDITIVES
		SYNTHET. LUBES
5553^2	BERG	NAPH. ISOM.
5554^2	TAO-SEN KING	SYN. LUBES
5554^8	KAUPPI	" "
5556^8	LAY	CAT. CRACKING
5556^9	THAYER	" "
5556^9	MOORE	NAPH. ISOM.
5557^6	WARSLEY	SYN. LUBES
5558^7	WARRICK	NAPH. ISOM.
5559^2	MATUSZAK	" "

Figure 4. Notation sheet for making additions to supplement books during preparation of Chemical Abstracts bulletin

afford advantages far in excess of the relatively small amounts of time and money spent.

First, and perhaps most important, the existence of up-to-date, comprehensive files, logically classified by an index system, makes possible rapid preparation of literature and patent surveys directly from filed material without need for searching the abstract journals. Collection of material, usually the most arduous step and the step most susceptible to errors of haste and omission, is obviated, with savings of time and money.

Almost equally important, members of the organization can use the same files to prepare technical papers and books. Here the advantages are manifold; subject classifications may be removed from the files one by one as needed and taken home or to the office for individual use. In many cases, the article file suffices for the work in question. However, the card file is available when more comprehensive coverage is needed. In essence, the card file is a portable condensation of *Chemical Abstracts* arranged by subject matter. Extraction of a subject classification from this file and removing it to the office for study are equivalent to transporting some 40 volumes (or roughly 130 separate bindings) of *Chemical Abstracts* to the same place and then searching for one subject out of thousands.

How effective the files are may be judged from the fact that "The Chemical Technology of Petroleum" was written almost exclusively from them. This book, by W. A. Gruse and D. R. Stevens of Gulf's Mellon Institute fellowship, is widely known and highly regarded throughout the petroleum industry. It is only one example of the way in which the files have rendered yeoman service. Other examples include numerous technical papers and at least one other book.

Finally, the fact that the card, literature, and patent files are up to date at all times makes the issuance of a supplement to existing information, whether survey, article, or book, only a matter of writing. The briefest possible answer to the question, "What does the scheme offer?" is simply time—time saved from laborious searching—technical time conserved for technical work.

Summary

The over-all scheme was devised purely from the standpoint of the needs of Gulf Research & Development Co. Certain operations, such as the preparation of bulletins concurrently with making selections for the files, have been discussed only to make the picture complete and to illustrate how time may be conserved by combining collection of material for the files with other existing operations. The salient feature of the scheme is the continuous collection, classification, and filing of literature and patents. This operation has been found most helpful in the preparation of surveys and is passed on to others for whatever use they may care to make of it.

Based on a paper presented before the Division of Chemical Education, Symposium on Chemical Literature, at the 111th Meeting, ACS, Atlantic City, N. J., April 1947. Revised **1960.**

The Literature Report

IRLENE ROEMER STEPHENS[1]
Celanese Corp., Summit, N. J.

The literature report presents all references pertaining to the research problem under consideration. It may be a bibliography, an annotated bibliography, a bibliography with abstracts, or a critical literature report. Some organizations specify the desirability of the scientist's conducting his own survey for, it is reasoned, he only is thoroughly acquainted with the problem and, therefore, he only can efficiently analyze the literature. In some cases, a cooperative search is specified. In other cases, the survey is conducted and the literature finally presented to the scientist. When writing the literature report, the searcher must keep constantly in mind the purpose of the report and the function it is to serve. Perhaps the best technical writing is being done by persons at the top of their professions who have done important work, understand its meaning, and write about it with confidence. They are bold enough to write simple, direct English.

After the literature search is completed, accumulated information must be organized, correlated, analyzed, and summarized if it is to be useful. Often, interpretation is also in order.

At the very outset, it is well to remember that the literature report is designed to meet certain definite requirements just as any structure is destined to carry its load. The form which the literature report will take depends upon the purpose the report is to serve. It has been said that most of the structural faults of technical reports result from the author's being so concerned with what he is writing that he neglects to worry enough about how and for whom he is writing. This brings us back to the beginning, the initiation of the search, for it is here that the foundation for the literature report is laid.

The suggestion of bringing together the literature worker and the research worker on a personal basis seems likely to produce beneficial results—both to the research worker in improving his understanding of literature searching, and to the literature worker in a better appreciation of requirements—since man's progress is

[1] Present address, Maplewood, N. J.

not even bounded by his vivid imagination. Such a discussion of the problem at hand is even more productive, if the scientist is experienced in using the library effectively (*10*). It is here, in the preliminary discussion, that the scientist explains the problem. Often, the subject of the search is narrowed as a result of a mutual interchange of ideas between the scientist and the literature worker. Here we see synergism, as applied to creative thinking, in action: $2 + 2 = 5$ (or more) (*43*). The literature worker becomes thoroughly familiar with the problem. Then he and the scientist break down the problem, analyze it, digest it, and formulate a plan of attack.

This preliminary discussion will also be the basis for the decision as to the kind of literature report which will be made. If, in his discussion of the problem with the literature worker, the scientist recognizes that the literature worker has a grasp and understanding of the subject area under investigation, it is likely that he will request a critical survey and, consequently, a critical report with interpretation of accumulated references. According to many published statements of research directors, the most common and serious deficiency of chemists is the inability to present the results of an investigation. The chemist may decide that the literature worker is equipped to search out and report literature pertinent to the problem at hand. ". . . The chemist may very well find that someone else possesses, to a degree that chemists cannot reasonably achieve, the useful skill to present chemical ideas and conclusions . . ." (*22*).

The vital research function performed by the literature worker is magnified, in the eyes of many people, when it is realized that the scientist no longer burdened by literature searches is now free to think and work. Hopefully, his thinking is creative in its performance for ". . . never before in our history has such a premium been put upon creative thinking—in both pure and applied science. Our highly competitive economy makes industrial progress essential. Each industry strives to find ways to make its current products and methods of production obsolete . . ." (*44*). The literature worker plays a part in industrial progress. It grows with increased participation and understanding of the research process. He must have the quality of sympathy—the ability to consider the problem as it is presented by the scientist and to consider the mind of the recipient of the report.

Types of Literature Reports

The form of the report is determined when the search is started. There are several possibilities.

The Bibliography. At the end of the search, one stage of intelligent appraisal of the literature on a specified subject has been accomplished—that of sorting out pertinent references. If the results of the search are to be useful, the references must be organized. Decisions must be made as to whether references are to be presented in topical or chronological arrangement. The arrangement chosen will depend both on the purposes of the search, as defined by the scientist requesting it, and on the actual references traced. Usually some sort of classification is in order.

Annotated Bibliography. The annotated bibliography is identical in its possible forms to the bibliography, with the added advantage of having a descriptive sentence or two added for each bibliographic entry. This augmentation of the title increases the value of the report and saves time for the researcher.

Bibliography with Abstracts. A frequently requested and very usual form of the literature report is that of the bibliography with abstracts. In its simplest form, the abstract included is the abstract which appeared in *Chemical Abstracts* or in *Chemisches Zentralblatt*, or the author summary of articles traced through indexing tools. A subject arrangement is ordinarily specified. This arrangement requires classification and cross-classification of the accumulated references. Ordinarily, an author index of references is advisable in a report, no matter what its length.

Critical Literature Report. The bibliographic report, in any of its forms, may best be regarded as a noncritical report. Selectivity, based on an understanding of the subject involved, is exercised in searching. Thought is involved in organizing and classifying the references. However, little analysis and, certainly, no interpretation is exercised. The critical literature report puts more responsibility on the reporter. The crux of the matter emphasized in the problem must be clearly stated. The accumulated references must be carefully reviewed, analyzed, and finally classified. The quality of the final report is enhanced by a systematic stick-to-itivism on the part of the writer. If it has been requested, and particularly if the researcher, himself, is preparing the literature report for his supervisor, interpretation should accompany the report.

Interpretation of literature search results presupposes a thorough acquaintance with the problem under investigation. Between the organization of the references and the final interpretation of data in report form there is a stage of highly intelligent appraisal. Sound and objective evaluation must be exercised. Occasionally, intuitive evaluation is involved in making recommendations. The intuition referred to here can be described as the spontaneous, integrated result of past experience, logical reasoning, and personal preference (*38*). Hence, decisions which are based in part upon intuition are less secure, in general, than those based upon a simple balancing of accumulated evidences.

Any literature report should be as current in nature as possible with available periodical indexes. The scope of the search should be clearly defined in the report to avoid misunderstanding the extent of the search. The up-to-datedness is, perhaps, more vital in the patent search than in any other. Yet, currency is desirable in all searches. Certainly its importance cannot be contested in the case of the economic literature report, alternatively referred to as the cost estimation report (*41*). The exhaustive—and exhausting—general search aimed at catching everything on the designated subject should be current if it is to serve its purpose to the utmost, as should the processing equipment literature report. Something vital might have been written just last month—or last week, as a matter of fact. How disappointing and unforgivable to miss it!

Of course, it is apparent that the "what's new" type of literature report is, by its very nature, current. In this type, current news items are selected and presented either as coordinated commentaries or in order of appearance in selected newspapers and periodicals.

In the critical literature report, published abstracts are useful as guides to literature, but it is well to remember that they are not authoritative.

References which from abstracts appear to be pertinent to the problem should be referred to in their original form. When the final abstract is included in the literature report, clarification and amplification of misleading or involved chemical terminology, notational systems, trivial names, and trade-mark names should be made parenthetically. To establish these facts, one may refer to standard rules for naming organic and inorganic compounds as followed by the American Chemical Society (*8, 17–19*). These added notations will make it easier for the investigator to interpret the data.

Who Writes the Literature Report?

There are many different practices in searching the literature. Some organizations specify the desirability of having the scientist conduct his own survey for, it is reasoned, he is the only one thoroughly acquainted with his problem. He, alone, will recognize leads not anticipated in the preliminary definition of the problem; thus he can exercise utmost efficiency in cutting through irrelevant material, and only he can analyze the literature resulting from an intensive search.

It is reasoned that the researcher is perfectly able to do his own reporting as well as his own literature searching (*6, 51*). It is thought by some that ". . . a deficiency in skill of writing a lucid report on the part of technical men is more accurately the lack of ability to think at the professional level . . ." (*29*). It is supposed by some that the habits of care in handling laboratory materials and meticulous accuracy in statements about quality, which are natural to the technologist, would enable him to use a similar approach in the use of words and to obey rules for arranging subject matter. And so, sometimes the researcher conducts his own survey. In this case, the literature group might carry out a preliminary bibliographic search as an aid to the scientist.

In other cases, a cooperative search is specified. The problem is defined and discussed not only at the outset of the search, but periodically. The responsibility for the search lies with the senior investigator (*50*). The literature group performs the mechanics but under the watchful direction of the researcher.

On other occasions, the survey is conducted and the literature organized logically, summarized, and presented to the scientist. Sometimes, when specified at the outset, interpretation of traced references is appended. This latter practice is becoming acceptable as skilled scientific people move into the literature field. However, it should be emphasized that the function of the literature report most often is to present all references listed in standard tools available to the searcher on a specified subject in a logical and well organized form, so that the scientist may more readily analyze and interpret reported literature in his area of interest. Good interpretations can be produced by a nontechnical individual, if he is equipped with unusual shrewdness. He is handicapped, however, by his dependence upon what he is given and told—he can ask questions, but he can rarely check for himself from first principles. Experience suggests that the interpreter having sound knowledge of his subject is, on the whole, better equipped to interpret accurately and quickly and without bothering other people. His besetting sin—at least his temptation—is to impose upon the writing of others a technical viewpoint of his own.

This distortion of the author's viewpoint is sometimes observed in abstracts, where introduction of a subjective approach may not affect the facts but is likely to upset the balance of their presentation.

Writing the Literature Report

One of the commonest and most serious faults in technical and scientific writing is to bury the important fundamental ideas under a mass of detail. We all say, "Don't bury ideas in excess verbiage, keep it simple!" When writing the literature report it is well to keep constantly in mind the purpose of the report and the function which it is to serve. It is more important to allay doubt and avoid ambiguity than to provide variety and elegance. Both jargon and clichés are inappropriate. Jargon is nothing less than technical slang and is in bad taste where other descriptive terms are available. Clichés indicate that the author is the servant of the language and not its master. In writing the report it is wise to remember that it must revolve around its specific purpose.

It would seem to me that the best technical writing is being done by persons at the top of their professions who have done important work, understand its meaning, and write about it with confidence. They are bold enough to write simple, direct English. Concepts are complex. We should not add to their complexity with vague, indirect language. We should write simply, clearly, coherently, accurately, in neat, precise language; avoid ambiguities, padding, and fogging. We should put ourselves in the place of the chemist or executive who reads our report as a stranger. The research content is always vital and is the part that counts.

Organization. One of the main defects of report writing results from the inability of the report writer to present facts in logical order. Ordinarily the final products of the literature search will be on cards. There are several methods of organizing the accumulated references. First of all, after a cursory examination of the references, an outline should be set up. This outline will undoubtedly be revised several times in the course of organizing the references. Any one of three methods of organization is applicable and provides an arrangement suitable for analyzing the literature.

1. The subject of the reference can be indicated on the reference card, using Roman numerals or letters and Arabic numerals of the outline.
2. References can be randomly numbered and these numbers placed on sheets corresponding to sections of the outline.
3. "If punched cards are used to record the data collected and are coded in accordance with the outline, the cards should be numbered to correspond with the bibliography, since the cards pertaining to each phase of the subject can then be sorted out as required . . ." (*48*).

Format of the Literature Report. No set method of arrangement would be appropriate for all kinds of reports. The format of noncritical literature reports has been briefly discussed. The bibliographic report which is arranged topically should be cross-referenced and should have an author index. Under each subject, either a chronological or an alphabetical arrangement is acceptable. The chronological arrangement may have the greater advantage. It may be considered advisable to include photostats of articles which were particularly comprehensive. It is to be remembered that the scientist will analyze and interpret the presented data. Its systematic arrangement will aid his study.

The critical report may be arranged in one of several ways. Whether references in the bibliography-with-abstracts are arranged alphabetically by the author's name, topically with references alphabetically arranged, or topically with references chronologically arranged is not a vital matter so long as a consistent practice is followed. Certain essential components should be included:

1. The covering memorandum. The report should be sent with a covering memorandum which outlines the problem as it was presented at the start of the search. A detailed listing of the major tools used for the search should be included. This memorandum is of the nature of an introduction.

2. Title page.

3. Table of contents.

4. Summary, abstract of contents.

5. Descriptive section. Here a description of reactions or processes involved is presented. This section will vary depending on the subject of the survey.

6. Interpretation of data, only when clearly specified. This section is sometimes excluded, for the scientist most often prefers to make his own interpretations based on his critical analysis of the presented data.

7. Bibliography. The bibliography is organized in one of the several arrangements described for bibliographies.

Style. Style is the mode of expressing thought in language. It is the quality which gives distinctive character and excellence to artistic expression. The effectiveness of a report depends to a large extent on the style of its architecture. Absence of clarity is a serious matter since it rebukes utilitarian standards. Clarity of thought precisely set down may result in no more than a flat desert of undistinguished sentences, but at least there are no obscurities.

Review of the Report. Systematic procedures for critical examination of the literature report should be practiced.

Some consider that good writing is rewriting. Certainly revision should not be ignored as a means of making the introduction or summary more effective, nor should one ignore the possible advantage of review by another as insurance against discontinuity and ineffective presentation. It is gratifying if the report provides answers to the problems which prompted the request for a literature survey. However, this is not the test of an effective report. Negative results are significant. When questions are not answered through the literature, the investigator may plan his laboratory research accordingly.

Conclusion

The literature report, like any written report, is a measure of the intellect of the person writing that report. If that is so, and I believe it to be so, it behooves us to approach the written word as a record which unmasks us. The writing of the literature report should be approached accordingly.

Bibliography

(1) Arnold, C. K., "Technical Writing Manual," Electronic Periodicals, Inc., Cleveland, Ohio, 1959.
(2) Barzun, Jacque, Graff, H. F., "The Modern Researcher," Harcourt, New York, 1957.
(3) Bjorksten, J., *Chem. Inds.* **60**, 407 (1947). Specifications for a good research report.
(4) Cady, E. L., "Creative Communication," Reinhold, New York, 1956.
(5) Case Institute, "Chemist's Profile Redrawn," Case Institute Survey, 1959.
(6) *Chem. & Ind.* (London) **1959**, 269. Technical writing; an unnecessary new specialism (editorial).
(7) Cherry, C., "On Human Communication," Wiley, New York, 1957.
(8) Christiansen, J. A., *J. Am. Chem. Soc.* **82**, 5517–22 (1960). Manual of physicochemical symbols and technology (IUPAC).
(9) Ellis, A., *Sci. Monthly* **66**, 427 (1948). Application of scientific principles of scientific publications.
(10) *Endeavour* **9**, 53 (April 1950). Accessibility of knowledge.
(11) *Engineer* **198**, 171 (July 30, 1954). The technical interpreter.
(12) Fieser, L. F., Fieser, Mary, "Style Guide for Chemists," Reinhold, New York, 1960.
(13) Flesch R., Lass, A. H., "The Way to Write," 2nd ed., McGraw-Hill, New York, 1955.
(14) Godfrey, J. W., Parr, G., "The Technical Writer," Wiley, New York, 1958.
(15) Gunning, R., "The Technique of Clear Writing," McGraw-Hill, New York, 1952.
(16) Harwell, G. C., "Technical Communication," Macmillan, New York, 1960.
(17) International Union of Pure and Applied Chemistry, *J. Am. Chem. Soc.* **82**, 5575–84 (1960) Definitive rules for the nomenclature of amino acids, steroids, vitamins, and carotenoids (IUPAC).
(18) International Union of Pure and Applied Chemistry, *J. Am. Chem. Soc.* **82**, 5545–74 (1960). Definitive rules for the nomenclature of organic chemistry (IUPAC).

(19) *Ibid.*, **82,** 5523–44 (1960). Nomenclature of Inorganic Chemistry, American version with comments (IUPAC).
(20) Killeffer, D. H., *Chem. Eng. News* **35,** 18–19 (Aug. 15, 157). U. S. needs science writers.
(21) *Ibid.*, pp. 60–2 (April 26, 1957). Chemistry's fourth estate.
(22) Killeffer, D. H., *Chemist* **32,** 271 (1955). Working with technical writers.
(23) Kobe, K. A., "Chemical Engineering Reports," 4th ed., Interscience, New York, 1957.
(24) Mandel, Siegfried, "Writing in Industry," Vol. I, Polytechnic Institute of Brooklyn, Plenum Press, Brooklyn, N. Y., 1960.
(25) Marder, Daniel, "The Craft of Technical Writing," Macmillan, New York, 1960.
(26) Marple, H. A., *Chem. Eng. News* **35,** 82 (April 8; Part II, 1957). Writing for the chemical industry.
(27) Mathis, H. M., *Chem. Eng. Progr.* **48,** 585 (1952). Plea for simplicity.
(28) Nelson, J. R., "Writing the Technical Report," 3rd ed., McGraw-Hill, New York, 1952.
(29) Nichols, W. T., *Chem. Eng. News* **26,** 602 (1948). The technical report bugaboo.
(30) Norgaard, Margaret, "A Technical Writer's Handbook," Harper, New York, 1959.
(31) Piper, H., Davie, F., "Guide to Technical Reports," Reinhart, New York, 1958.
(32) Rhodes, F. H., Johnson, H. F., "Technical Report Writing," McGraw-Hill, New York, 1955.
(33) Sherman, T. A., "Modern Technical Writing," Prentice-Hall, Englewood Cliffs, N. J., 1957.
(34) Singer, T. E. R., *Record Chem. Progr.* **18,** 11–29 (1957). Need for imagination and skepticism when making literature searches.
(35) Singer, T. E. R., ed., "Information and Communication Practice in Industry," Reinhold, New York, 1958.
(36) Soc. Tech. Writers and Editors, "Review of Literature on Technical Writing," Soc. of Technical Writers and Editors, Washington, D. C.
(37) Souther, J. H., "Technical Report Writing," Wiley, New York, 1957.
(38) Stanly, A. L., *Mech. Eng.* **77,** 778 (1955). Evaluating intangibles for executive decision.
(39) Steel, E. M., "Readable Writing," Macmillan, New York, 1950.
(40) Stephens, I. R., *Ind. Eng. Chem.* **48,** 32A–33A (October 1956). Chemical industry cost estimating.
(41) Stephens, I. R., "Technical Writing," chap. in "Information and Communication Practice in Industry," T. E. R. Singer, ed., Reinhold, New York, 1958.
(42) Stephens, I. R., Reyling, P., "Editing Technical Reports," chap. in "Technical Editing," B. H. Weil, ed., Reinhold, New York, 1958.
(43) Stuber, P. J., *Chem. Eng. News* **33,** 4930 (Nov. 14, 1955). Synergism: 2 + 2 = 5 (or more).
(44) Thomas, C. A., *Ind. Labs.* **6,** 68 (October 1955). Creativity in science.
(45) Trelease, S. F., "The Scientific Paper," Williams & Wilkins, Baltimore, 1947.
(46) Waldo, W. H., "Better Report Writing," Reinhold, New York, 1957.
(47) Weil, B. H., ed., "Technical Editing," Reinhold, New York, 1958.
(48) Weil, B. H., ed., "The Technical Report, Its Preparation, Processing and Use in Industry and Government," Reinhold, New York, 1954.
(49) Weil, B. H., Lane, J. C., *Chem. Eng. News* **34,** 6244 (Dec. 17, 1956). Psychological barriers to writing.
(50) Williamson, M. A., *Ind. Labs.* **10,** 33 (December 1959). Professional man and the obligation of authorship.
(51) Williamson, M. A., *Research and Development* **11,** 105–6 (April 1960), 63–6 (May 1960), 91–2 (June 1960), 75–6 (July 1960). Transforming report writing from a chore to benefit.
(52) Wilson J. H., *Chem. Eng. News* **32,** 3898 (Sept. 27, 1954). Who cares who writes it.
(53) Wilson, J. H., *J. Chem. Educ.* **34,** 447–9 (1959). Our constantly changing language.

BASED on paper presented before Division of Chemical Literature, Symposium on Searching the Chemical Literature, 130th Meeting, ACS, Atlantic City, N. J., Septembeer 1956. Revised 1960.

Searching Chemical Information Mechanically

ALLEN KENT

Center for Documentation and Communication Research,
School of Library Science, Western Reserve University, Cleveland, Ohio

HARRIET A. GEER

Research Information and Planning Department,
Research Division, Parke, Davis and Co., Ann Arbor, Mich.

Searching for recorded chemical information is of increasing economic importance in connection with business, research, sales, and other activities. In most searching operations, costs of retrieving information must be matched against not only the potential benefits but also the costs of regenerating the desired information. Many organizations have found it feasible to develop systems and to utilize various types of equipment for the mechanized searching of chemical information. Typical systems are reviewed.

The complexity of the scientific and technical literature which reports new developments presents increasingly difficult problems. Publications in such diverse fields as chemistry, biology, geology, engineering, and physics are of interest to the chemical industry. With the continuing diversification of scientific and technical research, the problem of ensuring effective use of recorded information both in publications and in company reports will become increasingly acute.

Industrial and governmental recognition of this problem has brought the development of innovations to extend and supplement traditional library procedures and techniques. Foremost among these innovations have been mechanical aids to literature searching, ranging from hand-sorted punched cards to computers. Hand in hand with the development of mechanical aids has been the development of suitable systems for the analysis and recording of subject matter on the new literature searching media. The development of a searching system and selection of a suitable mechanical aid are engineering matters (*1*, p. 1). Thus, various types of systems will find different realms of usefulness in the literature searching field, depending upon various engineering factors.

Specific input considerations to be taken into account in engineering new retrieval systems are (*28*):

1. Economic or other justification for installation of systems for retrieval of a specific body of information
2. Physical characteristics of the system
   a. Character of available files, as to number of documents and average number of "aspects" per document
   b. Expected rate of growth
   c. Necessary speed of reply in answering questions
3. Breadth of subject matter to be encompassed by the information retrieval system
4. Compatibility of a new system with comprehensive centralized retrieval
5. Extent to which the system should be designed for conversion to more sophisticated equipment

The searching and correlating requirements of a new system may be categorized into several levels. Examples of the various levels are:

1. Searching for information by means of an accession number or other code number. This involves identification of documents or reports when their serial number is known and requires simply a file or listing by number.
2. Reference type of searching. This may involve searching the literature exhaustively on the basis of well-known and well-understood terminology in a field where there is agreement as to both basic concepts and the meaning of the terminology of the field. On the other hand, it may be necessary to make searches where well-designed indexes do not exist and in fields where good agreement on basic concepts and on the meaning of the terminology has not been achieved. Lastly, the search may be in restricted fields—e.g., within the report literature of an individual organization, where service is to restricted technical personnel in the organization.
3. Creative literature searching. Here the record is used as a research tool and the information obtained from the record by the literature scientist feeds into the research project and forms the basis for further insight into research problems.

Information-retrieval systems engineered to serve the various levels of literature searching may be drastically different from one another. Appraisal of the potential information-retrieval requirements of the foreseeable future may be a critical consideration in engineering a new system.

Machine Literature Searching

"Machine literature searching" has been used to cover a wide variety of systems employing relatively simple mechanical equipment to highly complex machines. A mechanized literature research center under government sponsorship has been discussed, but at present there are no definite plans for installing a single over-all center of this type in the United States. A central organization along these lines, described in some detail by V. P. Cherenin in a publication from the Institute of Scientific Information of the Academy of Sciences of the U.S.S.R., is now in operation (*30*). Chemical Abstracts Service is investigating the problems and possible value of a central searching system at *Chemical Abstracts* (*21*). Jacques Samain (*49*, p. 478) reports that the Centre National de la Recherche Scientifique, which publishes *Bulletin Signaletique* containing some 130,000 abstracts annually, has undertaken to establish a central service. A centralized searching operation has been developed for the American Society for Metals and other organizations by J. W. Perry and coworkers (*29*; *49*, pp. 407, 435). In addition, a large number of industrial and governmental installations have put into practice various types of machine literature searching systems and searching equipment (*16*). Most of the operational systems have been preceded by extensive periods of research, development, and pilot runs. Some mechanized systems in chemistry and related fields are reviewed below.

Opinions differ concerning the value of machines and their use in information-retrieval systems. It becomes important, therefore, to attempt to measure the worth of the various systems. In investigating the criteria for evaluating mechanized information-retrieval systems, judgment might be based on two levels—"systems" and "mechanical." The systems level involves consideration of indexing, correlating, and identification possibilities and characteristics. The mechanical level involves consideration of factors such as speed of scanning, correlating ability, amount of internal storage, and delivery of material. The searching time may be shortened either by increasing the speed of scanning or by eliminating from consideration large portions of the file which are of no probable interest in a particular search. The latter case, however, may often constitute an anomaly, since the reason for preparing comprehensive systems is to permit cross fertilization of ideas from one field to another, and the elimination without inspection of large portions of the file in certain searches on a probability basis avoids the "total search." Engineering considerations (the economic or other importance of a particular search) will determine the type and comprehensiveness of the search to be made in a particular situation. Therefore, it appears advantageous to provide for the ability to conduct total scanning when it is considered advisable.

Machines for Information Retrieval. In this discussion the functions of machines in this field are considered from three points of view—manipulative requirements, storage capacity, and delivery of material. The capabilities of six main classes of machines are presented in Table I in terms of these functions.

Machine Language. In the design of a machine literature searching system, one problem is selecting an appropriate machine language. The term "machine language" in this context may be defined as an appropriate means for recording meaningful symbols (letters, words, numbers, etc.) on a searching medium—punched cards, photographic film, or other recording means. There are several levels of sophistication for machine language.

Direct Translation. This is the least sophisticated method of generating machine language. Machine language is obtained by translating the symbols of the source language on a symbol-for-symbol basis. An example is the translation of a numeral into a punch in a predetermined position in a column of a punched card. No meaning is attributed to the machine symbol that was not inherent in the source symbol. Nor may economy of symbols be achieved by this direct translation. This type of machine language is said to involve the recording on the searching medium in "open" language.

Indirect Translation. The machine language is generated by translating the symbols of the source language into a code—for example, translating the name of an inventory item to a code number. No meaning is attributed to the individual symbols of the code that was not inherent in the source "word." However, the translation to code was performed to achieve economy of symbols, or to facilitate machine searching operations. In this type of language, a code dictionary is required to record the code equivalents for the open language index data.

Systematic Codification. Special significance is attributed to the codes used for machine language, since they record meaning that would not be evident if the original open language were recorded directly on a search medium. This level of sophistication may be achieved in several ways:

Classification Numbers. Recording the various hierarchies of classification which are designated by the numerical or alphabetical symbols in the classification code permits searching for concepts or ideas on the basis of parts of the code as well as the total code (*37, 38*).

Notation Systems. Specific aspects of significance may be recorded independently within a unique code representation, as is done by several codes for molecular structure. Thus searching operations may be directed to the total compound, to various substituent groups, or to individual symbols or combinations (*15*).

Generic Codes. Generic, functional, or other significant aspects may be recorded for independent searching within unique or nonunique codes. Examples are "semantic" codes (*37*) and Universal decimal classification.

Machine language is not necessarily a code which can be recognized as easily as a combination of numerals or other symbols. Thus, machine language is implied when a hand-sorted punched card is notched in a certain position to record a certain aspect of subject matter contained in a particular document; or when a hole is punched in a certain position in a peek-a-boo type of system (*50*), or a document number as recorded in a certain position by pen, pencil, or stamp, as in the Uniterm system (*45*).

Review of Mechanized Systems

This paper does not attempt to describe all the installations which have been used in searching for stored chemical information but rather notes certain typical ones which give a picture of the present status of mechanical methods. For the most part, successfully operating installations have been limited to individual or industrial files covering a somewhat restricted field, although developments in projects of the U. S. Patent Office, Australian Patent Office, and American Society for Metals embrace wider areas of subject matter.

The individual or company file is often an ideal package for a mechanical application. In many instances, the file has only recently reached a size where the human memory is no longer able to retain the desired information. At this point the rewards of coding can be enjoyed within a short time. Here the danger lies in underestimating the ultimate size of the file and using a system which will soon fail to accommodate the accumulated data. Although this question should be carefully studied, if a system gives every indication of being able to handle the material for 15 to 20 years, it is wise to try it even if it later becomes outmoded. Much valuable experience is gained in use and use alone, as one discovers the ways in which a system may be altered to provide greater benefits to users. If a well-considered plan is used in setting up the scheme initially, it may be possible to convert to a more complex searching device or system with minimum effort.

Edge-Notched Cards. If it seems relatively certain that the total file will not exceed 10,000 cards, the Keysort or edge-notched cards may fill the needs. Many uses of these are described by Casey *et al.* (*8*). A card may represent the document, as was the case in an early application of punched cards described by Cox, Bailey, and Casey (*17*). Here a single card containing an abstract of the information was prepared for each document, and author, date, and subject were coded around the edge of the card. Some details of chemical structure may be included in the coding of the information, but detailed coding of structure is not possible, especially when several compounds are included in a single document. To describe

Table 1[a]. Capabilities of Machines

Name of Systems or Equipment	Examples	Manipulative
1. Hand-sorted punched cards	McBee cards, E-Z sort cards, Flexisort cards (*8*)	Desired cards selected by manual manipulation of needles in holes or slots. Multiple needles may be used with certain auxiliary devices
2. Hand-manipulated aspect cards		
Number matching	Uniterm cards (*45*)	Columns of numbers on one aspect card matched visually against numbers on another aspect card
Identification of pattern coincidence	Batten cards (*7*, p. 169), Uniterm cards, Termatrex (*25*)	Aspect cards superimposed, and desired document numbers detected visually by light passing through coincident holes
3. Machine-sorted punched cards		
Fixed field	Remington Rand, IBM, and Powers Samas Standard sorters and collators	Punched cards maintained in drawers and fed into machine in stacks of up to 500
Intermediate	IBM 101 (*22*)	
Free field	IBM Luhn scanner (*13*), experimental IBM × 794 (*14*)	
4. Machine-manipulated aspect cards		Coincidence numbers detected mechanically or by activation of light-sensitive terminal
Number matching	Experimental machines developed on ONR funds	
Pattern coincidence	Peek-a-boo (NBS)	
5. Tape-reading devices		Tapes stored on reels, entries scanned electronically or by mechanical feelers. Entries may be transferred automatically to duplicate or output tapes.
Magnetic tape	IBM 700 series, Remington Rand Univac series digital computer (*3*), General Electric 250 (*27*)	
Punched paper tape	WRU Selector (*33–36*)	
6. Photographic film devices		
Fixed field	Rapid Selector (*42*)	Film stored on reels and transferred to other reels as scanned
Intermediate	Filmorex (*49*, p. 478)	Unit pieces of film manipulated and scanned
Free field	Minicard (*46; 49*, p. 488), Photoscopic storage device (International Telemeter) (*24*)	Encoded information on film scanned in sequence, stored on unit pieces of film or rolls, or disks

[a] Reprinted with modifications from (*26*).

Storage		
Indexing Possibilities	*Number of Documents*	*Delivery*
Direct coding. Limited by number of holes in cards (up to about 200) *Superimposed coding.* Limited in number of index entries (2 to about 20) *Relationships.* Not convenient to record complex relationships among index entries	Limited by tolerance of user to needling operation (1000 to 10,000)	Actual card containing abstracts, indexes, and bibliographic information
Limited by increasing number of false combinations as depth of indexing increases	Limited in convenient use by quantity of document numbers that can be recorded on single aspect card	Document number identified, serves as entree to document file arranged in accession number order
Similar to hand-sorted punched cards above	Limited by tolerance of user to sorting operations in fixed fields. Use of multiple file, increases capacity (7, p. 149)	Document number identified, serves as entree to document file. Limited bibliographic material or data may be printed on face of card or recorded on microfilm insert
Similar to hand-sorted punched cards above. Simple relationships may be recorded	More convenient than above; effective file up to 50,000	
Unlimited number of index entries per document. Certain relationships among index entries may be recorded	Limited by tolerance of user to quantity of cards (up to 75,000)	
Same as for hand-manipulated aspect cards	Same as for hand-manipulated aspect cards. For unit card approach, limited by tolerance of user to quantities of cards handled	Same as for hand-manipulated aspect cards, matrix film under development by NBS
Unlimited number of index entries per document. Unlimited complexity of relationships among index entries	Limited by time available for search as opposed to scope of search desired	Document number identified, serves as entree to document file. Entire encoded message or abstract may be reproduced if desired
Six index entries per document (no relationship)	Same as 5	Selected film or film card contains coded information, as well as microscopy of document. For photoscopic storage device, same as 5
Twenty index entries per document (no relationship)		
Unlimited number of index entries (complexity of relationship not yet developed to limit).		

structure in more detail, the compound may be designated as the unit and a card prepared for each compound. This procedure has been commonly used in coding the structural components of compounds in a company file of chemicals. In many instances, the individual organization has devised its own code for describing the structural fragments of a compound. During the war, Wiselogle and associates developed a classification system (*5*) for arranging in an organized fashion the drugs tested as antimalarials. They later adapted this system to edge-notched cards; and installations using this adaptation or some modification of it are in operation at Squibb, Grasselli Division of Du Pont, and Metal and Thermit (*33*). The immediate availability of the information when the sort is completed is one great advantage of edge-notched cards. However, for a large file (15,000 or more cards) sorting becomes physically cumbersome and machine sorting is essential. The McBee Co. has made available a device containing a row of needles which permits sorting two or more holes at a time. This is satisfactory in searching for a "logical product"—for example, for A and B. However, it cannot be applied in a single sort to a search for the "logical sum"—for example, for A or B—which is often desired in searches for analogs of a given structure. Mooers (*32*) has developed an electric vibrator (Zator Selector), which sorts 800 Zator edge-notched cards per minute. This reduces the tediousness and time of sorting.

Infrared spectra have been made available on Keysort cards under the auspices of the National Research Council (*12*). The large space in the center of edge-notched cards which is not used for holes and notches permits recording the spectrum in graphic form. Although sorting becomes cumbersome as the file increases in size, it is very convenient to have a search lead directly to the actual data desired—in this case, the infrared spectrum.

Crandall and Brown (*18*) describe the application of Keysort cards to recording information in the field of petroleum products. Crandall has also explored the possibilities of the Hollerith-type card and has worked out a method for using to advantage the best characteristics of each device.

IBM and Remington Rand Machine-Sorted Punched Cards. It is generally agreed that, although IBM and Remington Rand accounting machines possess certain individual differences, their performances are much the same. Several organizations have employed IBM or Remington Rand cards for recording chemical structural information as well as activity and properties of the compounds in restricted fields. Whereas punched cards of this type do not contain the pertinent information in a readily recognizable form, the cards obtained from a search may be mechanically arranged in various orders according to the values of the categories punched on the card. In some instances users have employed Ditto, Multilith, Ozalid coating, or some other duplicating process to transfer information to the IBM card. If the card is damaged in any way, the information must be transcribed onto a new card. Others rely upon a subsidiary file which contains the information arranged in document or compound-number order. When this file consists of an Ozalid or Multilith master, the information is easily reproducible. Often a punched card file with the chemical name of a compound punched on it is used as subsidiary to a structure file. If the file is large, the cards with the chemical name punched on them will probably be pulled and refiled by hand rather than by collation, but the names may be readily duplicated mechanically in a tabulated list or on punched cards. Both the Dow Chemical Co. and Sloan-Kettering Institute for Cancer Research have used the chemical name punched and printed on the card. The use of a specific notation such as the Dyson or Wiswesser also allows mechanical reproduction of structural information. Mechanical reproducing of information coded on punched cards is a definite problem which justifies attention; possibly the microfilm insert may prove useful in this capacity.

The inability to search in more than one column at a time with the simple sorter has been minimized by reducing either the number of columns on the card which must be searched or the number of cards which must be passed through the machine. So-called direct coding assigns definite meaning to a single hole. If the number of index items is sufficiently limited, the information may be recorded by direct coding. In this case, all cards containing a hole punched for the information sought may be located by a single pass of the cards. Both Dow and Parke-Davis use direct coding to represent the chemical structure on IBM cards and employ the simple sorter for structural searches. The use of fixed fields—i.e., assigning a specific column or columns for recording a definite type of information—also limits the space on the card which must be searched. The number of cards which need to be examined may be decreased in certain searches by the use of prefiling—e.g., according to seniority of elements and structural groups when coding chemical structure. The use of multiple files—i.e., a card filed under each property punched on the card--also decreases the number of cards which must be searched. Actually most installations use a combination of these methods.

Many projects have applied IBM cards usefully with only the simple sorter as a searching device. At the instigation of Kuentzel (*8*, p. 175; *31*), infrared spectral maxima were punched on IBM cards along with a code for the structure of the compound. These cards may be purchased from the American Society for Testing Materials. The U. S. Patent Office (*49*, p. 447) also offers for sale IBM cards on which information on the structure of steroid compounds described in U. S. patents is punched according to a code devised by the U. S. Patent Office staff. Smith (*44*) has coded some 50,000 compounds on IBM cards according to the Wiswesser notation. Although this code specifically describes the chemical structure and is punched on the card by use of "free fields," Smith was able to search satisfactorily by employing auxiliary direct coding in several columns. Peakes has described (*1*, p. 149; *49*, p. 306) the development which the Bakelite file underwent over a period of about 10 years. By the use of multiple files, some 50,000 indexed items have been handled with a relatively simple machine installation, and searches are carried out on the simple sorter.

The Chemical-Biological Coordination Center, established in 1946, studied the application of accounting-type equipment to information retrieval in the chemical-biological field. Chemical and biological codes (*9–11*) were developed and published. It was an operational organization for more than five years, but was discontinued in 1957 because of lack of financial support. Multiple files, requiring extensive use of the collator, permitted the selection of certain information by hand. In this respect it resembled multiple 3 × 5 inch card files, but the IBM cards could then be collated with other groups or sorted and arranged according to characteristics punched on the cards. Baker, Wright, and Opler (*4*) have described use of the collator for identifying mixtures by means of infrared absorption spectra.

The Ethyl Corp. (*1*, p. 173) has a Remington-Rand installation for indexing the properties of fuel and lubricant additives. Both chemical structure and additive properties are coded on a single card. The use of the selective sorter, which will permit sorting in 12 adjacent columns simultaneously, and well-organized prefiling of the cards have made this an extremely workable file without the introduction of more complex machines. Company reports and patents are coded at present.

Several pharmaceutical companies (Merck, Sharp and Dohme; Smith, Kline and French; and Schering Corp.) have applied the IBM 101 electronic statistical machine to literature searching (*8*, p. 232; *41; 49*, p. 240). The number of columns which may be searched simultaneously depends upon the number of punches appearing in a single column, but as many as 60 columns may be examined at one pass of the cards. The 101 is a versatile machine which cuts down the searching time as compared with the simple sorter. A similar machine called ILAS was developed for searching coded steroid structures (*49*, p. 447) in the U. S. Patent Office.

Dyson in conjunction with the Hollerith Co. of Great Britain developed a machine which sorted punched cards horizontally and permitted searching the entire card on a single pass. IBM later built the Luhn machine (*13, 20*), which was also capable of sorting the entire card at a single pass. Consideration was given to making a redesigned version of this machine commercially available, but the demand seemed insufficient to make it economically practical. The principles of this machine are being made available in the Western Reserve University searching selector (*35, 36*) and in the General Electric Co. GE-250 information searching machine.

In all fairness, in a survey of machine methods which are in operation, those abandoned because of dissatisfaction should be included. Ashthorpe (*2*) describes difficulties encountered at the Atomic Energy Research Establishment in Harwell. After two years in operation and the accumulation of 6500 Hollerith-type cards, the installation was abandoned and a multiple file of visually located index cards was established. The punched-card installation was completely dependent upon a single file of punched cards arranged in random order. It was impossible to ascertain how a document previously coded had been indexed without resorting to the punched card file. In almost all operations now used, supplementary hand files permit the rapid location of certain specific information. Ashthorpe gives an excellent description of the difficulties and frustration which may come from too complete dependence on a single punched-card file. It is a very instructive article for those embarking into the mechanical field.

The "Peek-A-Boo" Method. The peek-a-boo method is a relatively simple way of recording and retrieving information and has been used both here and in Europe. Batten (*7*, p. 169) applied it to specialized files for patent searching by using Hollerith cards which contain 960 holes. This system was applied by a group at the National Bureau of Standards to the recording of information in instrumentation (*50*). Each document was assigned a position on a 5 × 8 inch card, and each index heading was assigned a card. By precise usage of the space, as many as 18,000 different positions were placed on a single card. For each subject indexed in a document, a hole was drilled in the subject card at the document position. Documents containing information on more than one specified subject can be readily located by visually inspecting the cards in front of a bright light. A light spot indicates that the subjects specified are treated in the same document. Wachtel (*47*) has used an IBM card in this way for recording properties of nuclides. Jonker Business Machines (*25*) is now selling Termatrex-10 and -40 machines, which will accommodate 10,000 and 40,000 documents per card, respectively. Taube and his group have developed a machine which employs a photoelectric cell to locate documents containing the indicated uniterms (*45*).

Photographic Film Devices. The Rapid Selector was proposed by Bush and the performance of an experimental model was studied in considerable detail by Shaw (*42, 43*). The original model permitted the coding of six index subjects for each frame of film which contained the abstract of a document. The film passed through the machine at the rate of 500 feet per minute or 330 frames per second and a single subject could be searched for in one passage of the film. When the pattern of the dots, which were used to code the subject matter, matched those of the selector, the film in this frame was photographed on a second roll of film. Adjusting the movement of the second film to permit several exposures in rapid succession while the film with the original material was moving at 500 feet per minute proved to be one of the more difficult problems in the design of this equipment. In the experimental work, abstracts from *Chemical Abstracts* were filmed and coded by numbers assigned to the subject index headings. This allowed all of the desired material from a search of several years of *Chemical Abstracts* to be made available immediately in printed form. As yet no practical application appears to have been made of the Rapid Selector.

Samain (*49*, p. 478) employs a rectangular microfilm containing the reproduction of an abstract or document and a pattern of dots which permits the coding of 20 five-digit code designations. These microfilms may be searched by machine at the rate of 700 per minute. The microfilms obtained from a search may be read directly in a microfilm reader or filmed for later reference.

The Eastman Kodak Co.'s Minicard (*46; 49*, p. 488) has combined the characteristics of punched cards and a photographic film. The Minicard is a 16 × 32 mm. photographic film with a slot provided for transference on a metal stick from storage to the machines. Sorting, including handling, may be accomplished at a rate of 1800 cards per minute. The card may be divided as the user wishes between actual reproduction of the original material and the coding area, which consists of columns containing patterns of dots. Up to 12 images may be reproduced on a Minicard with ample space remaining for coding the material. Possible applications of this device to information retrieval are being explored.

Electronic Computers. Several groups have been actively investigating the application of computers to the information-retrieval field, and some routine applications have been made. The Bendix G-15D, a small digital computer, is now being used by the Patent Division of the Du Pont Textile Fibers Department (*23*) for report index searching. Some 14,000 reports, a high proportion of which was converted from marginal punched cards without recoding, have been entered in the system. Operation of this installation for several months has shown it to be a practical method of storing and retrieving information. The Patent Division shared the G-15D with the research laboratory, which used about 80% of the computer capacity.

Perry and coworkers (*40; 49*, pp. 407, 435) developed a paper tape machine, the Western Reserve Selector, for searching abstracts prepared for the American Society for Metals. Its principles are now being incorporated by the General Electric Co. in the GE-250 (*27*).

The IBM 704 has been applied to routine reporting of the biological activity of compounds tested in the Monsanto Laboratories (*48*). Chemical structure, represented in a pictorial fashion, and biological activity are entered in the computer. As new biological data are obtained the computer matches them with the stored structure and prints out lists arranged in any desired order. In addition to the preparation of reports, it is possible to search the structure file for types of chemical compounds and to search the biological file for degree of activity. It is not economically feasible to use a computer of this complexity on a full-time basis for information retrieval. The Monsanto group uses only a small portion of the computer capacity for this purpose.

Norton and Opler (*34*) developed a chemical code for computer usage. This code specifically describes the structure but is not easily converted to the chemical structure by visual inspection. Opler (*1*, p. 31) has done considerable exploratory work on the application of computers to the information-retrieval field, including conversion of machine language into a form which is easily recognized by humans A group at the Midwest Research Institute is now using the Norton-Opler code on the IBM 704 to study physical properties *vs.* structure and usage (*6*).

Several other computer applications have been reported or are under investigation. Among these are the U. S. Patent Office and National Bureau of Standards joint project (*39*) and chemical structure searching using the GKD chemical code on the Electronic Structural Correlator (*19*).

Prospectus

This paper has summarized systems and equipment as applied to mechanized literature searching in the field of chemistry, and has enumerated the considerations involved in engineering a mechanized system to fit a particular requirement. Detailed engineering procedures have not been presented. It has not been considered feasible to make the literature references entirely current. A more complete bibliography is available (*8*).

The future of machine literature searching appears to be showing three definite trends:

Proliferation of a large number of mechanized systems in narrow subject fields. The searching media tend to be centered in accounting-type punched-card equipment, or "standard" digital computers which were obtained by the organizations chiefly for business applications, and searching inefficiencies can be tolerated because of complete amortization of equipment cost on nonlibrary applications.

Development of specialized equipment and systems for centralized literature processing activities. This trend has led individual organizations to devote much attention to engineering their private systems so that they will be compatible with foreseeable developments in centralized and wholesale literature encoding activities on the professional society level.

Investigation of means for converting the results of previously processed (abstracted, indexed, classified) information into a form amenable to machine searching.

Literature Cited

(1) American Chemical Society, Division of Chemical Literature, "Advances in Documentation and Library Science," Vol. **1**, "Progress Report in Chemical Literature Retrieval," G. L. Peakes, Allen Kent, J. W. Perry, eds., Interscience, New York, 1957.
(2) Ashthorpe, H. D., *ASLIB Proc.* **4**, 101–04 (1952).
(3) Bagley, P. R., Digital Computer Laboratory, Mass. Inst. Technology, Rept. **R-200** (Nov. 1, 1951).
(4) Baker, A. W., Wright, Norman, Opler, Ascher, *Anal. Chem.* **25**, 1457–60 (1953).
(5) Buhle, E. L., Hartnell, E. D., Moore, A. M., Wiselogle, L. R., Wiselogle, F. Y., *J. Chem. Educ.* **23**, 375–91 (1946).
(6) Carpenter, R. A., Bolze, C. C., Findley, L. D., *Am. Document.* **10**, 138–43 (1959).
(7) Casey, R. S., Perry, J. W., "Punched Cards. Their Applications to Science and Industry," 1st ed., Reinhold, New York, 1951.
(8) Casey, R. S., Perry, J. W., Berry, M. M., Kent, Allen, "Punched Cards. Their Applications to Science and Industry," 2nd ed., Reinhold, New York, 1958.
(9) Chemical-Biological Coordination Center, National Academy of Sciences–National Research Council, Biology Code, P. G. Seitner, G. A. Livingston, A. S. Williams, eds., Publ. **790** (1960).

(10) *Ibid.*, "Key to the Biology Code," Publ. **790K.**
(11) Chemical-Biological Coordination Center, National Research Council, "Method of Coding Chemicals for Correlation and Classification," 1950.
(12) *Chem. Eng. News* **30,** 1092–4 (1952).
(13) *Ibid.*, pp. 2806–10.
(14) *Ibid.*, **32,** 866–9, 891 (1954).
(15) *Ibid.*, **33,** 2838–43 (1955).
(16) *Chem. Week*, 74–82 (Feb. 20, 1960).
(17) Cox, G. J., Bailey, C. F. Casey, R. S., *Chem. Eng. News* **23,** 1623–26 (1945).
(18) Crandall, G. S., Brown, B. M., *J. Chem. Educ.* **25,** 195–9 (1948).
(19) Davison, W. H. T., Gordon, M., *Am. Document.* **8,** 202–10 (1957).
(20) Dyson, G. M., *Chem. Ind.* (*London*) **1954,** 440–9.
(21) Dyson, G. M., Division of Chemical Literature, 138th Meeting, ACS, New York, N. Y., September 1960.
(22) Garfield, Eugene, *Am. Document.* **5,** 7–12 (1954).
(23) Grandine, J. D., 2nd, Starr, E. M., Putscher, R. E., Division of Chemical Literature, 136th Meeting, ACS, Atlantic City, N. J., September 1959.
(24) International Telemeter Corp., Los Angeles, Calif., Bull. **R-77** (March 15, 1955).
(25) Jonker, Frederick, *Am. Document,* **11,** 305–15 (1960).
(26) Kent, Allen, *Ibid.*, **8,** 150–1 (1957).
(27) Kent, Allen, ed., "Information Retrieval and Translation," Vol. **1,** Chap. 1, Interscience, New York, 1960.
(28) Kent, Allen, Tech. Note. **10,** Contract No. AF49(638)-357 Western Reserve University School of Library Science, Rept. **AFOSA TN 59–1140** (Oct. 16, 1959).
(29) Kent, Allen, Booth, R. E., Perry, J. W., *Metal Progr.* **71** (No. 2), 71–5 (1957).
(30) Kent, Allen, Iberall, A. S., *Am. Document.* **10,** 1–19 (1959).
(31) Kuentzel, L. E., *Anal. Chem.* **23,** 1413–18 (1951).
(32) Mooers, C. N., *Am. Document.* **2,** 20–32 (1951).
(33) Moran, M. K., *Ibid.*, **11,** 222–8 (1960).
(34) Norton, T. R., Opler, A., "Manual for Coding Organic Compounds for Use with a Mechanized Searching System," Dow Chemical Co., Midland, Mich., May 27, 1953 (revised March 1956).
(35) Perry, J. W., Kent, Allen, *Appl. Mechanics Revs.* **9,** 457–60 (1956).
(36) Perry, J. W., Kent, Allen, Center for Documentation and Communication Research, Western Reserve Univ., *Newsletter,* No. **2** (August 1956).
(37) Perry, J. W., Kent, Allen, "Tools for Machine Literature Searching" (Semantic Code Dictionary, Equipment, Procedures), Interscience, New York, 1958.
(38) Perry, J. W., Kent, Allen, Berry, M. M., "Machine Literature Searching," Interscience, New York, 1956.
(39) Pfeffer, Harold, Koller, H. R., Marden, E. C., *Am. Document.* **10,** 20–6 (1959).
(40) Rees, Janet, Kent, Allen, *Ibid.*, **9,** 277–303 (1958).
(41) Rockwell, H. E., Hayne, R. L., Garfield, Eugene, *Federation Proc.* **16,** 726–31 (1957).
(42) Shaw, R. R., *Am. Document.* **1,** 194–6 (1954).
(43) Shaw, R. R., *J. Document.* **5,** 164–71 (1949).
(44) Smith, E. G., *Science* **131,** 142–6 (1960).
(45) Taube, M., *et al.*, "Studies in Coordinate Indexing," Documentation, Inc., Washington, D. C., 1955–58.
(46) Tyler, A. W., Myers, W. L., Kuipers, J. W., *Am. Document.* **6,** 18–30 (1955).
(47) Wachtel, Irma, *Ibid.*, **3,** 56–7 (1952).
(48) Waldo, W. H., Gordon, R. S., Porter, J. D., *Ibid.*, **9,** 28–31 (1958).
(49) Western Reserve University, School of Library Science, "Advances in Documentation and Library Science," Vol. **II,** "Information Systems in Documentation," J. H. Shera, Allen Kent, J. W. Perry, eds., Interscience, New York, 1957.
(50) Wildhack, W. A., Stern, Joshua, Smith, Julian, *Am. Document.* **5,** 223–37 (1954).

Based on paper presented before Division of Chemical Literature, Symposium on Searching the Chemical Literature, 130th Meeting, ACS, Atlantic City, N. J., September 1956. Revised 1960.

The Chemists' Club Library

ANNE D. DUCA
Library, The Chemists' Club, New York 17, N. Y.

The Chemists' Club Library's collection of 60,000 volumes is almost entirely restricted to chemical literature. Particular emphasis is placed on specialized phases of the chemical industry, notably biographical and portrait material, prizes and awards listings, the CCDA and CMRA publications, the Society of Cosmetic Chemists collection, watermarks and hand-made papers, the Natta reports, and company histories. Special services of the library are described.

The Chemists' Club Library stands unique among technical libraries in the New York metropolitan area because its collection of 60,000 volumes is almost entirely restricted to chemical literature. It includes on its shelves complete sets of all standard authors and periodicals which through the years have become bibles for the chemist and the research worker. Our current periodicals titles number about 500, including society and trade publications within our field; only those house organs of a strictly technical nature are kept permanently. We have representative books and periodicals on textiles and dyes, petroleum, glass, paper, pharmacy, paint, leather, plastics, rubber, soaps and perfumery, fats, and essential oils. No attempt is made to house a good collection of learned societies or of medicine, since the former are adequately covered in the New York Public Library and the latter in the New York Academy of Medicine Library.

Our library stacks are open to the technical public from 9 A.M. to 5 P.M., Monday through Friday, which permits leisurely browsing as well as speedy checking of bibliographical references at the shelf. Furthermore, because our books do not circulate, even to members, the reader pressed for time is grateful for the reasonable assurance that he can put his hands on the book he needs with a minimum of effort and time loss.

We are the official depository for publications of the Chemical Market Research Association and the Commercial Chemical Development Association. Inasmuch as many of these meeting papers are not published in periodicals, the two sets of proceedings form a valuable and interesting addition to our library. An up-to-date author and subject index is maintained by the library, so the material is of practical service to chemical market readers and to members of industrial market research departments.

The Society of Cosmetic Chemists has deposited with us its collection of books on chemistry and its applications in the cosmetic field. These books are available for use by the reading public, but may also be circulated to members of the Society of Cosmetic Chemists upon presentation of the proper member credentials.

Our special collection of references to biographical material is culled largely from periodicals, so we have at our fingertips information on a larger number of living chemists than most other formal biographical sources. We note, too, any illustration which may accompany the biography and the resultant "portrait index" is a useful adjunct to the biographical one. At the present time, we have about 9000 separate names in our biography list and an additional 6500 in the portrait list. These two lists will continue to grow. Williams Haynes' gift to us of his very fine collection of 1500 portraits has also proved of inestimable value.

Our list of abbreviations contains interpretations—or translations—of frequently obscure society names and committee or bureau titles as well as full names of commercial products of chemical interest. Throughout the literature today, chemical authors are prone to use the initial letters of a compound instead of the actual compound name, and this practice gives rise to puzzling problems for both reader and librarian. We have almost daily use of this compilation and feel sincerely that its value to us far outweighs the several problems it creates.

Awards in Chemistry

Our compilation of information on prizes and awards in chemistry is continuing. Actually, there seems to be a state of long-standing confusion in the literature as to the year for which many awards are made. An announcement of the award may be made in November of one year; it may be formally presented to the recipient the following February. Some editors call it the award of the year when the announcement was made; others, the award of the year when it was actually presented. Societies differ similarly in their dates; there are subdivisions of some awards, slight variations in the name of an award from one year to the next, and other confusing details. It proves to be a sort of cataloging-reference-research problem to clarify some of the material we find. We include a note of an illustration of the award, the citation, presentation, and acceptance speech where any or all of these are given in printed form. All this necessitates constant revision in our list as new information appears, but the list itself is in current use for answering telephone inquiries and even for occasional photostats. Existing at present on cards, the list cannot be made available outside our own precincts. We are glad, however, to answer telephone and mail inquiries concerning its entries.

We are making a concerted effort to collect printed material on chemical market research, particular emphasis being placed on statistics of interest to the chemical industry. Our collection of the chemical economics handbooks is of tremendous help in the search for statistics. It is in daily use and has proved invaluable to the library staff, the market research worker, and the layman.

Although we actually have only the *Official Gazette of the U. S. Patent Office*, we are still able to help many readers seeking patent information because we are subscribers to the *Uniterm Index to Chemical Patents.*

We also collect information on the history of specific companies, where such is available to us. The history of special industries, such as inkmaking, dental alloy manufacture, cellophane, and various other interesting specialties, is also in demand.

Our collection has been enriched by a gift of books on papermaking, included in which are books of hand-made paper with hand-set type and hand-made bindings. From the same source came a magnificent collection of water-marked papers.

For the past five years, the library and the Library Committee have organized an annual spring symposium on a single topic of current interest. The 1960 subject was market research and two weeks before the meeting date, we were forced to close registration with 250 registrants because of space limitations.

Regular photostat and translation services are available to our readers; prices are standard with others in the city and this department is a busy one. We can also provide a quick positive photostat of easily reproduced material.

BASED on a paper presented before the Division of Chemical Literature, Symposium on Searching the Chemical Literature, 130th Meeting, ACS, Atlantic City, N. J., September 1956. Revised 1960.

Scientific and Technical Collections in The New York Public Library

GEORGE S. BONN
Science & Technology Division, The New York Public Library, New York, N. Y.

Of potential interest to chemists are the science-technology research collections of the library housed in the Science and Technology Division, the Information Division, the Oriental Division, and the Slavonic Division depending on language or publisher (such as academy or learned society). Emphasis is on pure and applied physical science; little or no biological science is represented. Patents form an important part of the main collection. The library does not lend, but a complete photoduplication service is available at cost.

Among the several large libraries in the United States of some bibliographic interest to chemists is the collection of the Astor, Lenox, and Tilden Foundations, the privately endowed Reference Department of The New York Public Library at 5th Avenue and 42nd Street. The total reference collection of almost 4,000,000 volumes, with very few titles duplicated, is one of the large reference collections in the world, financed, incidentally, almost entirely from private funds.

One of the strongest fields of collection in the Reference Department is the combined area of pure and applied physical sciences, mathematics, and industrial technology. Medicine, dentistry, and pharmacy are not extensively represented in the library, and the biological sciences are not as well represented as some of the other physical sciences. A brief statement of the kinds of materials in the various divisions of the library that are of interest to scientists and particularly to chemists may be of interest even to those who do not live in the environs of New York City.

The scientific and technical collections are divided primarily by language, materials in Slavonic or Cyrillic alphabets and in Oriental languages being kept separately from those in English and other West European languages. The biggest concentration of scientific and technical material in the library is in the Science and Technology Division, which houses the publications in English and in other West European languages. Here are the basic standard works dealing with science or technology: advanced textbooks, treatises, monographs, tables, handbooks, Handbücher, encyclopedias, dictionaries, directories, and the indexing and abstracting services. Here also are the periodical and other serial publications of scientific, technical, and professional societies as well as the scientific, technical, and industrial periodicals of private publishers, industries, universities, libraries, pertinent government agencies, and international organizations. Here are microcards of Atomic Energy Commission documents as well as pamphlets, brochures, and special materials on many subjects. Perhaps the largest single section of the Science and Technology Division is the Patents Section in its own separate wing.

Another large segment of science-technology literature is in the main stacks, obtainable through the Main Reading Room of the Library. Here are housed the publications of the general learned societies and the academies, but again only in English and Western European languages. Here also are the biological sciences generally, those that are in the collection at all: materials in food, agriculture, cosmetics, perfumery, and certain other allied areas. Current journals from the societies and academies and in the biological sciences are obtainable in the Periodicals Division. Material on the trade and the statistical aspects of chemical industry is obtainable in the Economics Division.

These general statements cover all science and technology about equally, but of particular interest to chemists may be some of the following information.

Even at the time that the present library was formed in 1895, the collections were sizable in the long runs of learned society and professional society materials, and all of these have been maintained throughout the years. For instance, there are in the library today generally complete files of the serials of most of the important American, English, and continental European learned and professional organizations and institutions.

The complete holdings of the Science and Technology Division amount to about 400,000 volumes, some 100,000 of which are books. The rest is made up of 15,000 to 20,000 sets of scientific and technical periodicals, most of them complete from volume 1 number 1. This division now is receiving 4000 current periodicals, not all in chemistry, of course, but many of interest to chemists. Important Russian, Polish, Czech, and other Slavonic language current periodicals are in the Slavonic Division and Oriental (especially Japanese) scientific periodicals are in the Oriental Division.

Patent and Trade-Mark Literature

Of particular interest to many chemists is the large collection of patents, abstracts of patents, and trade-mark literature that is available in the Patent Section of the division. It is said that this collection is the largest of any public library in the United States and is second only to the essentially complete collection in the U. S. Patent Office. Here are housed complete and current runs of patents of the United States, Sweden, Great Britain, France, Belgium (since they were first published in 1950), Denmark, and Japan (except for a wartime gap). Germany is represented substantially complete, except for an earlier gap of some ten or twelve years. Complete and current abstracts of patents are available from Australia, Canada, Ireland, and New Zealand, and current abstracts from the U.S.S.R. Current patent lists are received from Cuba, Italy, Mexico, the Netherlands, Spain, Switzerland, and Venezuela. Altogether the patent room of the library has holdings of 39 different countries, more or less completely represented.

Photoreproduction

The Reference Department of The New York Public Library offers no lending or interlibrary loan service. However, it does have an efficient and well-equipped Photographic Service Division which handles requests for photostat or other types of photoreproduction from the collections of the Reference Department. Photographs, photostats, and microfilms may be obtained from this division of any material in the library within the limits of copyright and fair use as they have been interpreted over the past years. The service is operated at cost and on a cash basis, usually payable through a deposit account plan which eliminates bookkeeping and other operations that may be necessary for those who make frequent requests and may wish to order by mail or by telephone.

Publications of Reference Department

A few publications of the library may be of some help.

"Guide to the Reference Department" is a 24-page pamphlet describing the entire building and its various services.

"The Photographic Service Division, an Aid to the Use of The New York Public Library," is a 6-page brochure describing the activities of the division and how work may be obtained through it. A somewhat larger publication is "Patent and Trademark Publications," describing in some detail the exact holding of The New York Public Library's patent collection up to the time of publication in 1954. Also available is a small brochure on the Science and Technology Division itself. All these publications are free for the asking, except the patent publication which is available for 50 cents.

The Kresge-Hooker Science Library

WENDELL H. POWERS
Department of Chemistry, Wayne State University, Detroit, Mich.

The history of the Kresge-Hooker Science Library at Wayne State University is briefly reviewed. Some outstanding items of the periodical collection are enumerated, as well as some collectors' items of interest to historians of chemistry. Current subscriptions to scientific periodicals include numerous titles which are not found widely in other libraries in this country. An abbreviated list of such periodicals has been compiled. Close proximity of the Detroit Public Library to the Kresge-Hooker Science Library on Wayne's campus, located in the heart of the city, provides excellent science library facilities for the students of that large urban university, the chemical and engineering industries, and the citizenry of Detroit alike.

The facilities of the Kresge-Hooker Science Library are available not only to the students and faculty of Wayne State University and to scientists in the Detroit area, but also to scientists throughout the United States and abroad through its services of translation, photocopying, microfilming, and interlibrary loan. Of the well over 133,000 items of scientific materials in the collection, about 56,000 are books, 57,000 are volumes of bound periodicals, and the remainder are government documents. The library is now receiving 1435 scientific periodicals. Currently chemistry is the field of science most completely covered. However, further expansion into other fields, such as physics, mathematics, and biology, is well under way.

History of the Library

The Kresge-Hooker Science Library is the result of and a monument to cooperative effort. The present book and periodical collection was formed in 1944 as a merger of two sizable libraries, the Wayne State University science collection and the Samuel C. Hooker science library of over 21,000 volumes. The latter was brought to Detroit in that year from Central College, Fayette, Mo., to which it had been sold after Dr. Hooker's death in 1935. The purchase was made for Wayne State University by means of a grant for that purpose by the Kresge Foundation. Also instrumental in bringing this library to Detroit was an enthusiastic committee of the local section of the American Chemical Society in addition to the administrative officers of Wayne State University. The efforts of all groups were coordinated by the late Neil E. Gordon, who at that time was chairman of the Department of Chemistry at the university. The continued cooperation of the Kresge Foundation resulted in 1953 in the dedication of the magnificent Kresge Science Library Building which had been built to house the combined collections.

The Hooker collection itself was the result of a hobby pursued during the lifetime of Dr. Hooker. His goal was to make his private collection the most complete chemical library in the world. Agents in literary centers both in this country and abroad located many rare books and periodicals for him. He tried especially to make all sets of journals complete.

The Hooker science collection, as acquired by Wayne State University in 1944, augmented and complemented Wayne's science collection exceptionally well. Wayne's science holdings were notably weak in the older literature, in which the Hooker collection was exceptionally strong. The combined collections are now known as the Kresge-Hooker Science Library. This combined collection is also much stronger now in science fields other than chemistry than was the original Hooker collection.

Outstanding Items of Periodical Collection

The selected items listed in Table I attest to Dr. Hooker's success in acquiring complete sets of outstanding scientific periodicals. There are also many more extraordinary items in his collection. The *Philosophical Transactions of the Royal Society of London,* which is complete from 1665, is an excellent example of his zeal and success in assembling such sets. Some of the earlier volumes of this set bear the bookplate of Richard Arkwright, the inventor of the spinning jenny, while others of the same set were owned at one time by Sir William Crookes. Hooker acquired the library of Crookes in 1927. The beginnings of scientific literature are often dated from 1665 when the Royal Society of London initiated the publication of its *Philosophical Transactions,* which except for the years 1679–82 has been continuously published to the present. [In the early days this publication seems to have been a private venture of the secretary of the Royal Society. A change in secretaries led to suspension of publication for a few years (1679–82), though published summaries of the proceedings are available. Publication of the *Transactions* was resumed when the society guaranteed that at least 30 copies would be purchased by members! (2).] Its unbroken history of nearly 300 years makes it the oldest scientific publication currently being published.

The first exclusively chemical periodical was started in 1778 and was edited by Lorenz von Crell. This was the *Chemisches Journal für die Freunde der Naturlehre*. It survived until 1781. In 1784 it resumed publication under the name of *Chemische Annalen für die Freunde der Naturlehre*. The Kresge-Hooker Library is one of the few libraries in the country holding original copies of this set.

Other outstanding periodicals, complete or nearly complete from their inception, are the *Annales de chimie et de physique* from 1789, the *Philosophical Magazine* from 1798, the *Journal de pharmacie et de chimie* from 1809, the *Jernkontorets annaler* from 1817, the *American Journal of Science* from 1818, the *Journal of the Franklin Institute* from 1826, Liebig's *Annalen der Chemie* from 1832, the

Table I. Selected Complete Sets of Periodicals of Interest to Chemists

(1) Académie des Sciences, *Comptes rendus hebdomadaires des séances,* Paris (1835–)
(2) Akademie van Wetenschoppen, *Verhandelingen Afdeeling natuurkunde,* Amsterdam
Eerste sectie (1892/93–)
Tweede sectie (1893–)
(3) *American Chemical Journal,* Baltimore (1879–1913)
(4) American Chemical Society
Proceedings (1876–78)
Journal (1879–)
(5) *American Chemist* (C. F. and W. H. Chandler, eds.), New York (1870–77)
(6) *American Journal of Science* (Silliman), New Haven, Conn. (1818–)[a]
(7) *Analyst,* Cambridge, England (1876–)
(8) *Annalen der Chemie* (Liebig), Leipzig, etc. (1832–)[a]
(9) *Annalen der Physik,* Leipzig (1799–)[a]
(10) *Annales de chimie,* Paris (1914–)
(11) *Annales de chimie et de physique,* Paris (1789–1913)
(12) *Annales de physique,* Paris (1914–)
(13) *Archiv for pharmaci og chemi,* Copenhagen (1894–)[a]
(14) *Arkiv för kemi, mineralogi och geologi,* Stockholm (1903–49)
(15) *Arkiv för kemi,* Stockholm (1949/50–)
(16) *Arkiv för fysik,* Stockholm (1949/50–)
(17) *Arkiv för mineralogi och geologi,* Stockholm (1950–)
(18) *Berichte der deutsche Pharmaceutische Gesellschaft,* Berlin (1891–1923)
(19) *Biochemical Journal,* Cambridge, England (1906–)
(20) *Chemical Abstracts,* Easton, Pa. (1907–)
(21) *Chemical Age,* a consolidation of *Chemical Engineer* and *Chemical Age,* Chicago (1904–25)
(22) *Chemical Engineering,* New York (1902–)
(23) Chemical, Metallurgical, and Mining Society of South Africa, *Proceedings,* Johannesburg (1894–1904)
(24) *Chemical News and Journal of Industrial Science,* London, American Reprint (1867–70)
(25) Chemical Society of London
Annual Reports on the Progress of Science (1904–)
Journal (1847–)
Memoirs and Proceedings (1841–48)
Proceedings (1885–1932)
(26) *Chemisch Weekblad,* Amsterdam (1903–)
(27) *Chemisches Berichte* (*Berichte der deutschen chemischen Gesellschaft*), Heidelberg (1868–)
(28) *Chemisches Annalen für die Freunde der Naturlehre* (Crell), Helmstädt, Leipzig (1784–1803)
(29) *Chemisches Journal für die Freunde der Naturlehre* (Crell), (1778–81)
(30) *La chimica nell' industria . . . .,* Turin (1907–18)
(31) *Edinburgh Philosophical Journal,* Edinburgh (1819–26)
(32) *Electrician, ...* London (1861–64)
(33) Electrochemical Society
Transactions (1902–49)
Journal (1950–)
(34) *Experiment Station Record,* Washington (1889–1946)
(35) Franklin Institute, Philadelphia
Journal (1826–)
Proceedings, Chemical section (1889–94)
(36) *Fysisk Tidsskrift,* Copenhagen (1902/03–)
(37) *Giornale di farmacia,* Trieste (1896–1907)
(38) Great Britain, *Official journal, Patent Office* (1889–)
(39) Institut Pasteur, *Bulletin,* Paris (1903–)
(40) Iron and Steel Institute, London, *Transactions* (1869–70)
(41) *Iron and Steel Magazine, . . .* Boston (1898–1906)
(42) *Jernkontorets annaler,* Bihang, Stockholm (1900–18)
(43) *Jernkontorets annaler,* Stockholm (1817–)[a]
(44) *Journal of Analytical and Applied Chemistry,* Easton, Pa. (1887–93)
(45) *Journal für Chemie und Physik,* Nuremberg (1811–33)
(46) *Journal of the Japanese Biochemical Society* (1925–)
(47) *Journal of Natural Philosophy, Chemistry and Arts* (Nicholson), London (1797–1813)
(48) *Journal de pharmacie,* Paris (1797–99)
(49) *Journal de pharmacie et de chimie,* Paris (1809–1942)
(50) *Journal of the Pharmaceutical Society of Japan* (1881–)[a]

(51) *Journal of Physical Chemistry*, Baltimore (1896–)
(52) *Journal de physique et le radium*, Paris (1872–)[a]
(53) *Journal der Physik*, Leipzig (1790–94)
(54) *Journal für praktische Chemie*, Leipzig (1834–)[a]
(55) *Journal of Science and Annals of Astronomy, Biology, Geology, Industrial Arts, Manufacture and Technology*, London (1864–85)
(56) *Microscope*, Ann Arbor, Detroit, Washington (1881–97)
(57) *Moniteur scientifique de Quesnesville*, Paris (1857–1926)
(58) *Neues Journal de Physik*, Leipzig (1795–97)
(59) *Neues Zeitschrift für Rübenzucher-Industrie*, Berlin (1878–99)
(60) *Nouveautés chimiques* (Poulenc), Paris (1896–1914)
(61) *Philosophical Magazine*, London (1798–)[a]
(62) Physico-Mathematical Society of Japan, Tokyo, *Proceedings* (1884–1944)
(63) *Physikalisch-Chemisches Centralblatt*, Leipzig (1903–09)
(64) *Quarterly Journal of Science, Literature and Art*, London (1816–30)
(65) *Raccolta fisico-chimica italiana*, Venice (1846–48)
(66) *Revue de physique et de chimie et de leurs applications industrielles*, Paris (1896–1901)
(67) Rochester Academy of Science, *Proceedings*, Rochester, N. Y. (1889–)
(68) Royal Institution of Great Britain, *Journal* (1830–31)
(69) Royal Society of Arts, London, *Transactions* (1783–1851)
(70) Royal Society of London
Philosophical Transactions (1665–1886)
Philosophical Transactions, Series A (1887–)
Philosophical Transactions, Series B (1887–)
Proceedings (1880–1905)
Proceedings, Series A (1905–)[a]
Proceedings, Series B (1905–)[a]
(71) Società Chimica Italiana, *Rendiconti*, Rome (1903–18)
(72) Société d'Arcueil, *Mémoires de physique et de chimie*, Paris (1807–17)
(73) Société Chimique de France
Bulletin (1858–)[a]
Leçons de chimie (1860–69)
Repertoire de chimie appliquée, Paris (1858–63)
Repertoire de chimie pure, . . . Paris (1858–63)
(74) Société Scientifique de Bruxelles, *Annales* (1875–)[a]
(75) Sociétés Chimiques Belges, *Bulletin* (1887–)
(76) Society of Chemical Industry, London
Proceedings (1881)
Journal (1882–)[a]
(77) *Sucrerie indigène et coloniale*, Paris (1866–1914)
(78) *Svensk Kemisk Tidskrift* (1889–)[a]
(79) *Technical Repository*, London (1922–27)
(80) *Technology Quarterly and Proceedings of the Society of Arts*, Boston (1887–1908)
(81) *Tijdschrift voor schei- en artzenijbereidkunde*, Leyden (1844–45)
(82) *Tijdschrift voor weteschappelijke Pharmacie*, Vossburg (1849–67)
(83) *Zeitschrift des Vereins deutscher Spiritusfabrikanten*, Leipzig (1857–66)
(84) *Zeitschrift für Zuckerindustrie*, Prague (1872–74)

[a] Nearly complete.

Bulletin de la Société Chimique de France from 1858, and the *Svensk Kemisk Tidskrift* from 1889.

Another outstanding feature is Hooker's remarkably fine collection of yearbooks and review serial sets. Table II is a compilation of some representative *Jahrbuch* and *Jahresbericht* sets. The first publication of this was the *Berlinisches Jahrbuch für die Pharmacie*, lasting from 1795 to 1840. Kresge's set runs from 1795 to 1829. Another very early example of this group is the annual report of Jöns Jacob Berzelius to the Swedish Academy on the progress in chemistry (translated by Wöhler from Swedish into German) and known as the *Jahresbericht über die Fortschritte der Chemie und Mineralogie* (1822–51). Also worthy of special notation are J. Buchner's "*Repertorium für die Pharmacie*" (1815–51) and L. A. Buchner's *Neues Repertorium für die Pharmacie*, which is a continuation of the first for the years 1852–76.

Table II. Representative Yearbook and Review Serial Sets (Complete Sets)

(1) *Berlinisches Jahrbuch für die Pharmacie* (1795–1840)[a]
(2) *Chemisch-technisches Repertorium* (Jacobsen) (1862–1901)
(3) *Jahrbuch für Acetylen und Carbid,* Halle a. S. (1899–1901)
(4) *Jahrbuch der Chemie* (Mayer), Frankfurt-am-Main, Brunswick (1891–1918)
(5) *Jahrbuch der Elektrochemie und angewandten physikalischen Chemie* (Nernst and Borchers), Halle a. S. (1894–1909)[a]
(6) *Jahrbuch der organischen Chemie,* Leipzig (1893–95)
(7) *Jahrbuch der Radioaktivität und Elektronik* (Stark), Leipzig (1904–24)
(8) *Jahresbericht über die Fortschritte der Chemie und Mineralogie* (Berzelius), Tübingen (1822–51)
(9) *Jahresbericht über die Fortschritte der Chemie und verwandter Theile Wissenschaften* (Liebig and Kopp), Giessen, Brunswick (1847–1910)
(10) *Jahresberichte über die Fortschritte auf Gebiete der reinem Chemie* (Staedel), Tübingen (1873–81)
(11) *Jahresbericht über die Forstchritte in der Lehre von den Gahrungs-Organismen* (Koch) (1890–1911.)
(12) *Jahresberichte über die Fortschritte der Tierchemie, oder der physiologischen und pathologischen Chemie* (Maly), Wiesbaden (1871–1919)
(13) *Neues Jahrbuch für Pharmacie und verwandte Fächer* (Walz, Winckler, Vorwerk), Speyer, Heidelberg (1854–73)
(14) *Neues Repertorium für die Pharmacie* (L. A. Buchner), Munich (1852–76)
(15) *Oesterreichische Jahreshefte für Pharmazie und verwandte Wissensweige,* Vienna (1902–14)
(16) *Repertorium der analytischen Chemie,* Hamburg (1881–87)
(17) *Repertorium für die Pharmacie* (J. Buchner), Nuremberg (1815–51)
(18) *Repertorium der Physik* (Carl), Munich (1865–91)
(19) *Repertorium der Physik* (Dove), Berlin (1837–49)
(20) *Technisch-chemisches Jahrbuch* (Biederman), Berlin (1878–1905)[a]
(21) *Vierteljahresschrift über die Fortschritte auf Gebiete der Chemie der Nahrungs- und Genussmittel,* Berlin (1886–97)

[a] Nearly complete.

Current subscriptions to scientific periodicals include many titles which are not found widely in other libraries in the United States. From the 1956 "List of Periodicals Abstracted by *Chemical Abstracts*" an abbreviated list of such journals has been compiled (Table III). In this list are found periodicals which are available in but ten or less American libraries, of which the Kresge-Hooker Science Library is one.

A complete list of all volumes of periodicals and journals owned by the Kresge Library was published in sections in the *Record of Chemical Progress* during the years 1954–56. A limited number of reprints are available and may be obtained free by writing to the author in care of the Kresge-Hooker Science Library, Wayne State University, Detroit 2, Mich.

Cooperation between Kresge-Hooker and Detroit Public Library

The Kresge Library is currently receiving about 1300 of the periodicals listed in the 1956 "List of Periodicals" and its 1957, 1958, and 1959 supplements. Together with the Technology Department of the Detroit Public Library, which is situated only one city block away, there are available some 1720 different periodicals found in the *Chemical Abstracts* list. Whereas a certain amount of duplication between these two cooperating libraries is desirable and necessary, a serious attempt is made to keep it at a minimum—for example, the Kresge Library purposely is not accumulating vast holdings of government documents, including patents, because the Detroit Public Library is a "depository library" and consequently receives from the Superintendent of Documents all publications of the National Government, including complete files of the Annual Reports of the U.S. Patent

Table III. Current Periodicals Available at the Kresge-Hooker Science Library and Found in But Ten or Less Libraries in the United States

(According to the 1956 "List of Periodicals Abstracted by *Chemical Abstracts*")

	No. of Libraries
(1) *Archiv for Pharmaci og Chemi* (1894–)	7
(2) *Australian Sugar Journal* (1946–)	9
(3) *Bollettino chimico farmaceutico* (1875–)	7
(4) *Bulletin de la société des sciences de Nancy* (1945–)	5
(5) *Bulletin de la société scientifique d'hygiène alimentaire et d'alimentation rationnelle de l'homme* (1904–)	9
(6) *Chemische en pharmaceutische techniek* (1945–53, 1956–)[a]	6
(7) *Dansk Patenttidende* (1948–)	2
(8) *Dansk Tidsskrift for Farmaci* (1927–)	7
(9) *Deutsche Lebensmittel-Rundschau* (1939–)	7
(10) *Deutsche Zeitschrift für Verdauungs- und Stoffwechselkrankheiten, einschiesslich Theorie und Praxis de Krankenernahrung* (1939–)	8
(11) *Finnish Paper and Timber* (1950–)	10
(12) *Folia Pharmacologica Japonica* (*Nippon Yakurigaku Zasshi*), (1925–)	6
(13) *Fysisk Tidsskrift* (1902–)	10
(14) *Industrie céramique* (1946–)	6
(15) *Ingénieur chimiste* (1912–)	4
(16) *Ion* (1947–)	9
(17) *Journal of the Birmingham Metallurgical Society* (1946–)	10
(18) *Journal of the Fuel Society of Japan* (*Nenryô Kyôkaishi*) (1922–)	8
(19) *Journal of the Iron and Steel Institute* (*Japan*) (*Tetsu to Hagane*) (1917–)	2
(20) *Journal of the Japanese Association of Mineralogists, Petrologists and Economic Geologists* (*Ganseki Kôbutsu Kôshô Gakkaishi*) (1929–)	4
(21) *Journal of the Japanese Biochemical Society* (*Seikagaku*) (1925–)	5
(22) *Journal of Japanese Chemistry* (*Kagaku no Ryôiki*) (1947–)	6
(23) *Journal of the Missouri Water and Sewerage Conference* (1941–)	4
(24) *Journal of the New Zealand Institute of Chemistry* (1946–)	8
(25) *Journal des Usines à Gaz* (1922–35, 1946–)[a]	5
(26) *Kemisk Maanedsblad* (1951–)	1
(27) *Magyar Kémiai Folyóirat* (1895–)	4
(28) *Magyar Kémikusok Lapja* (1949–)	5
(29) *Mémorial des services chimique de l'état* (Paris) (1948–)	8
(30) *Metropolitan Detroit Science Review* (1940–)	4
(31) *Mitteilungen aus dem Gebiete der Lebensmitteluntersuchung und Hygiene* (1910–)	7
(32) *Norsk Skogindustri* (1947–)	8
(33) *Octrooiraad Nederland* (1947–)	1
(34) *Paperi ja Puu* (*Soumen Puutalous*) (1950–)	10
(35) *Papeterie, La* (1951–)	7
(36) *Praktische Chemie* (1950–)	7
(37) *Przeglad Techniczny* (1949–)	3
(38) *Revue du nickel* (1946–)	2
(39) *Revue technique des industries du cuir* (1947–)	7
(40) *Rivista dell'istituto sieroterapica italiano* (1952–)	8
(41) *Rivista italiana essenze, profumi, piante officinali, oli vegetali, saponi* (1946–)	6
(42) *South African Sugar Journal* (1946–)	10
(43) *Svensk Farmaceutisk Tidskrift* (1897–)	7
(44) *Svensk Trävaru-Tidning* (1946–)	6
(45) *Teknisk Ukeblad* (1940–)	9
(46) *Textile Mercury and Argus* (1945–)	9
(47) *Textile Weekly* (1947–)	7
(48) *Wochenblatt für Papierfabrikation* (1930–43, 1956–)	8
(49) *World's Paper Trade Review* (1946–)	9

[a] Holdings complete for years listed.

Office, the *Official Gazette*, Decisions of the Commissioner of Patents, and the Annual Index.

The Detroit Public Library is also a depository library for the U.S. Atomic Energy Commission and thus gets all original unclassified and microcard material from that commission. Canadian and British materials in this field are also made available through the Atomic Energy Commission.

The Technology Department of the Detroit Public Library receives about 60% of the periodicals indexed by the *Engineering Index* and is especially strong in the engineering fields related to the automobile industry. It held in 1956 between 6000 and 8000 books and between 5000 and 6000 volumes of periodicals pertaining to the automobile industry. Also included were over 100,000 volumes of automobile trade literature and catalogs, in addition to over 100,000 photographs of motor vehicles.

The Farmington Plan

The Farmington Plan is an experiment in specialization by voluntary agreement among American research libraries. Its objective is to make sure that at least one copy of each new foreign book and pamphlet, which might reasonably be expected to interest a research worker in the United States, will be acquired by an American library and that it will be promptly listed in the Union Catalog at the Library of Congress and thus made available throughout the country by interlibrary loan or photographic reproduction. Wayne State University, through its Kresge-Hooker Science Library division, cooperates in the plan and has as its responsibility the acquisition of foreign literature on "Chemical Technology, including Engineering, Manufacturing and Technology" (with the exception of a few minor aspects in sugar technology). These areas are included in the Library of Congress Classification Numbers (TP: 1–373, 415–9999).

The Detroit Public Library also cooperates in the plan and has as its responsibility the acquisition of foreign literature on the "Engineering and Technology of Motor Vehicles and Cycles," again with certain minor exceptions. This area is included in the Library of Congress Classification Numbers (TL: 1–499).

Since 1948, when the Kresge-Hooker Library first cooperated in this plan, approximately 90 titles per year have been received. The majority of these works have come from France, Germany, and Italy, although over 100 countries are covered by the plan.

Midwest Inter-Library Corp.

Wayne State University has been a member of the Midwest Inter-Library Corp. since 1951. Nineteen other research libraries in the Midwest belong to this cooperative organization, established for the purpose of storing, cataloging, and making available to each other its less-used research materials. Each member institution selects materials from its library which are of too great value to be discarded, but are not used frequently, and deposits them with the Inter-Library Center in Chicago. By thus combining these resources, more adequate research materials have been provided for the needs of midwestern scholarship and research; and materials now available can thus be more efficiently and economically used.

Collectors Items of Historical Interest to Chemists

The library has many items of value to chemists interested in the history of their science. Most of these were acquired by Dr. Hooker himself and came to Wayne as part of that collection. A partial chronological list of these items is given in Table IV. Mention should be made of a few of these, especially Berzelius'

"Lehrbuch der Chemie" (item 31 in Table IV). The book, by this very influential chemist of his day, went through five editions between 1808 and 1848, and was the standard chemical reference book during that period. Another book of great importance to the development of chemistry was Thomas Thomson's "A System of Chemistry" (*28*). In this book, he was the first to advocate, ardently, Dalton's atomic theory and thereby did much to make Dalton's ideas well known to other chemists (*4*).

Table IV. Collectors' Items of Interest to Historians of Chemistry

(1) Plinius Secundus, "The History of the World," English translation, London, 1634.
(2) Francis Bacon, "Sylva Sylvarum," London, 1664.
(3) Robert Boyle, "Tentamina Quaedam Physiologica," Amsterdam, 1667.
(4) Descartes, "Epistolae," Amsterdam, 1668.
(5) Thomas Sprat, "History of the Royal Society of London," 2nd ed., 1702.
(6) Thomas Birch, "The Life of the Honorable Robert Boyle," London, 1744.
(7) T. Cavallo, "A Complete Treatise on Electricity," London, 1745 (2 of 3 volumes).
(8) Plache, "Le Spectacle de la Nature," Paris, 1749 (8 volumes).
(9) . . . "Nouveau Dictionnaire Universale des Arts et des Sciences," 1753–4 (2 volumes).
(10) Wm. Watson, "A Sequel to the Experiments and Observations Tending to Illustrate the Nature and Properties of Electricity," London, 1766.
(11) Nollet, "Leçons de physique expérimentale," Paris, 1767 (6 volumes).
(12) M. Monnet, "Traité de la Dissolution des Métaux," Amsterdam, 1775.
(13) John Pringle, "Six Presidential Discourses before Royal Society," London, 1783.
(14) Richard Watson, "Chemical Essays," 5th ed., London, 1789.
(15) . . . "Vocabulary and Tables of the Old and New Nomenclatures of the Names of All the Subjects of Chemical Science," Edinburgh, 1796.
(16) J. Gehler, "Physikalisches Wörterbuch," Leipzig, 1789–99 (5 volumes).
(17) Scherer, ed., *Allgemeines Journal der Chemie*, 1798–1801.
(18) Gehlen, ed., *Neues allgemeines Journal der Chemie*, 1803–06.
(19) John Imison, "Elements of Science and Art," London, 1803 (2 volumes).
(20) Frederick Accum, "A System of Theoretical and Practical Chemistry," London, 1803.
(21) J.-A. Chaptal, "Chimie Appliqueé aux Arts," Paris, 1804 (4 volumes).
(22) A. F. Fourcroy, "Elements of Chemistry and Natural History," Edinburgh, 1800 (2 of 3 volumes).
(23) C. L. Berthollet, "Essai de Statique Chimique," Paris, 1803 (2 volumes).
(24) C. L. Berthollet, "Researches into the Laws of Chemical Affinity" (translated by M. Farrell), London, 1804.
(25) Wm. Nicholson, "British Encyclopedia or Dictionary of Arts and Sciences," London, 1809 (6 volumes).
(26) A. F. Fourcroy, "Système des Connaissances Chimique," Paris, 1809–11 (11 volumes).
(27) Columbian Chemical Society of Philadelphia, Memoirs, 1813.
(28) Thomas Thomson, "A System of Chemistry," Philadelphia, 1818 (4 of 5 volumes).
(29) Wm. T. Brande, "Manual of Chemistry," London, 1821.
(30) Amos Eaton, "Philosophical Instructor," Albany, N. Y., 1824.
(31) J. Berzelius, "Lehrbuch der Chemie," 3rd ed., Dresden and Leipzig, 1833–41 (10 volumes).
(32) M. C. Gerhardt, "Précis de Chimie Organique," 1844–45 (2 volumes).
(33) L. Gmelin, "Handbuch der Chemie," 4th ed. (English translation by Watts), 1848–72 (19 volumes).
(34) F. K. Beilstein, "Handbuch der organischen Chemie," 1st ed., 1880–2 (2 volumes).

Another set of books used extensively in America when scientific chemistry was just beginning is A. F. Fourcroy's "Elements of Chemistry and Natural History" (item 22). In it Fourcroy advocates the antiphlogiston theory of Lavoisier, although ironically it was largely through Fourcroy's relentless fury that Lavoisier was guillotined. Fourcroy's object to crush Lavoisier eventually was accomplished, although earlier (in 1787) Fourcroy, Lavoisier, de Morveau, and Berthollet had labored together to purge the nomenclature of chemistry from its earlier cumbersome and mythical terms (*3*). C. L. Berthollet himself is represented in the collection as the author of two early works. The first is the "Essai de Statique Chimique" (item 23). In it Berthollet challenges the Law of Constant Proportions and also here publishes his ideas about affinity. The second work is the Farrell translation of Berthollet's "Researches into the Laws of Chemical Affinity" (item 24).

A textbook of great appeal to early American chemists is that of Frederick Accum, entitled "A System of Theoretical and Practical Chemistry" (item 20). Several early American chemists—Benjamin Silliman of Yale, James Freeman Dana of Dartmouth, John Gorham of Harvard—studied in his laboratory in London (*1*). One of the early American textbooks used in training medical students was that of Amos Eaton, a professor of natural philosophy and chemistry in the Vermont Academy of Medicine. His book is entitled "Philosophical Instructor" (item 30).

Kresge-Hooker Science Library Associates

A good chemical library is expensive, not only to acquire, but also to maintain. To help maintain the excellent quality of the Kresge-Hooker Library an organization was formed several years ago, currently known as the Kresge-Hooker Science Library Associates. Its purpose is to foster the development and use of the library and to help make its resources and facilities available to scientific scholarship. Substantial grants have been obtained from industry and individuals to be used for the purchase of periodicals and books. For the continued expansion of the library's holding in chemical literature and the literature of the other sciences as well, further grants and support from industry are urgently needed. The associates hope to obtain such support for the library through increased membership in their society. The membership fees are used for library development. Members are then entitled to use the library's translation and photocopying services at reduced rates.

Literature Cited

(1) Browne, C. A., *Chymia* **1**, 9 (1948).
(2) Downes, H. R., "Chemistry of Living Cells," p. 10, Harper, New York, 1955.
(3) Smith, E. F., "Old Chemistries," p. 24, McGraw-Hill, New York, 1927.
(4) *Ibid.*, p. 58.

Based on paper presented before Division of Chemical Literature, Symposium on Searching the Chemical Literature, 130th Meeting, ACS, Atlantic City, N. J., September 1956. Revised 1960.

Chemical Literature in the John Crerar Library and Other Chicago Libraries

HERMAN H. HENKLE

86 East Randolph St., Chicago 1, Ill.

Cooperation and division of fields in the development of research collections are long-standing traditions in Chicago. The John Crerar Library, Chicago's principal scientific library, gives special attention to building complete files of all the leading chemical periodicals and indexing and abstracting services. For more than a decade a program has aimed at complete coverage of world chemical literature of research value. The Chicago Chemical Library Foundation, sponsored by local organizations of chemists, obtained substantial grants from industry and developed a 10-year program for expanding library resources. Annual grants to Crerar Library have made possible extensive coverage of foreign language books and greatly improved coverage of foreign periodicals. Other important collections are located in the University of Chicago and Northwestern University libraries and in libraries of industrial firms. The Midwest Inter-Library Center (sponsored by 20 research institutions in the Midwest) makes available current subscriptions of all periodicals indexed in *Chemical Abstracts*, which are not in the collections of the cooperating libraries.

Chicago is fortunate in having the library resources to make it one of the principal centers in the world of literature research in chemistry. Initially this was due to the founding of The John Crerar Library. Beginning in 1947, the chemists in Chicago, working individually and through their local professional organizations, have been responsible for major advances in the growth of chemical library collections, through their support of Crerar Library. And in 1958, the Midwest Inter-Library Center initiated a program designed to develop supplementary library resources in chemistry which will be of great importance not only regionally, but nationally as well.

The John Crerar Library

The John Crerar Library was chartered in the State of Illinois late in 1894, and formally established by the Board of Directors in January 1895. Its founding as a free public library was made possible by funds left under the will of John Crerar (1827–1889) (*1*), who accumulated a substantial fortune through successful business enterprises including banking, insurance, and railroads, especially the manufacture and sale of railroad supplies. He had as close personal friends such nationally known men as Marshall Field, George A. Armour, and Robert T. Lincoln, and many of the leading men of Chicago. From among these, he designated in his will the 13 men who became the first Board of Directors of the library which bears his name.

During 1894, the trustees of the Crerar estate, and the first directors of the new library, made an extensive study of the subject areas in which Crerar Library could most effectively supplement the libraries then existing in Chicago. On the basis of a preliminary report of the library resources of Chicago, the trustees expressed themselves as "disposed to recommend to the Directors that The John Crerar Library should be a reference library, embracing such departments as are not fully occupied by any other existing library in Chicago, and the number of departments created be limited to such as the funds for the use of the library can render complete and unique, each of its kind." In the light of this general objective, and particularly in view of the existence of the Newberry Library, already established in Chicago, the directors decided to establish Crerar as a library of science and technology.

The first librarian, Clement Walker Andrews, was a chemist. At the time of his appointment he held the positions of librarian and instructor in chemistry at the Massachusetts Institute of Technology. Under his leadership, a committee of the Crerar, Newberry, and Chicago Public libraries formalized a plan for division of fields among the public libraries in Chicago. Crerar was designated as having exclusive responsibility for the natural sciences (including chemistry), engineering, agriculture, domestic economy, chemical technology, manufactures, mechanic trades, building, landscape architecture, and photography. To these was added medicine, by transfer from Newberry to Crerar in 1906.

The development of collections for Crerar Library began in earnest early in 1896, and chemistry received due attention from the beginning. It was appropriate that the first book accessioned which was classified in chemistry should be the classic bibliography by H. C. Bolton: "Select Bibliography of Chemistry, 1492–1892." Other current books accessioned during that first year included such special works as Plattner's "Manual of Qualitative Analysis with the Blowpipe" (1892), Comey's "Dictionary of Chemical Solubilities, Inorganic" (1896), the second edition of Watt's "Dictionary of Chemistry" (1890–94), and Victor Meyer's "Chemical Problems of Today"—i.e., of 1891. Among the numerous books classified under chemical technology during that first year was one on a subject still of both professional and personal interest to chemists—"Drinks of the World" (1892), by Mew and Ashton.

The emphasis on complete files of scientific journals and of the standard bibliographies of science, which has characterized Crerar throughout its history, was reflected in the accessions records for the year 1896. Complete files of numerous important chemical journals from their beginnings through 1895 were acquired during that first year. Some of these were: *Annales de chimie* (1790–1816) and its successor, *Annales de chimie et de physique* (1816+), and *Jahrbuch für Mineralogie* (later *Neues Jahrbuch*, 1830+). There were *Chemical News and Journal of Physical Science* (1861+), *American Chemical Journal* (1879+), *Journal of the Chemical Society* (London, 1849+), *Proceedings* of the Society of Chemical Industry (1882+), *Zeitschrift für physikalische Chemie* (1887+), and *Jahresbericht über die Fortschritte der Chemie* (1849+), as well as others of the German *Jahresberichten* and *Jahrbücher* of the period. And the new journals, such as *Zeitschrift für Elektrochemie* (1894+), with birthdays contemporary with the founding of Crerar Library were added to the current subscription list along with the older established journals. There were, and continue to be, some exceptions to the tradition of volume-one-plus. Mr. Andrews was able to obtain only volume 6 (1873) through 1895 of the *Berichte der deutschen chemischen Gesellschaft*. The early gap had to be made up later.

The policy of building up back files of journals, however, led to the rapid growth of the collections during the early years of the library. By the end of the 32 years in which Mr. Andrews served as librarian, the collections had grown to approximately half a million volumes and some 300,000 pamphlets; and they have continued to grow to a total approximating one million volumes and pamphlets. Of these, more than 50,000 volumes are classified in chemistry and chemical technology. Periodicals and other serial publications received by the library now number more than 10,000 titles.

The strength of the Crerar collections in chemistry is not measured by the volumes classified as devoted primarily to chemistry. The widespread importance of chemistry in all branches of science and technology and the fact that the scope of the Crerar acquisitions policy includes all of the basic sciences and their applications in engineering, agriculture, and medicine led to fortification of the strength of the chemistry collection by the large amount of chemical literature scattered throughout the publications classified in other disciplines. There are, for example, several hundred medical journals regularly indexed by *Chemical Abstracts*, most of which are in Crerar. Freyder (*8*) has discussed the chemical interest of medical periodicals.

Crerar Services

Crerar Library was established as a "reference" library, as opposed to a lending library, in science and technology. It was one of the first libraries in the United States to establish photocopying service in lieu of interlibrary loans. This service was first established in 1912 and has been available almost continuously since that date. For a period of years the service was available through the cooperation of a local copying service, but in recent years all such work has been done in the library's own photoduplication laboratory. Both photoprints and microfilm are available, under the principle of reimbursement to the library for the actual costs of the service. Details of the service are described in a brochure available on request from the library's Photoduplication Service.

Literature searching and current reporting services are available through Crerar's Research Information Service, established in 1947 (*5*). Staffed by "literature chemists" and other technically qualified personnel, Research Information Service will prepare bibliographies and abstracts tailored to the particular needs or interests of a company's research and development. These may be retrospective in character, or be devoted to periodic reports of relevant literature appearing in the new books and periodicals received by the library. The new acquisitions are perused daily in the interest of this service and for identification of papers to be included in abstract services prepared in Crerar Library. Two of these are of interest to special groups of chemists. The first is *Crerar Metals Abstracts,* which provides prompt and comprehensive reporting service on new literature relating to titanium, zirconium, hafnium, molybdenum, vanadium, and the rare earths. The second is *ABT: Abstracts of Bioanalytic Technology,* a quarterly journal prepared by Research Information Service and published by the American Association of Bioanalysts.

Two types of translation service are offered by Crerar Library. The first, growing rapidly in scope, is the SLA (Special Libraries Association) Translations Center. This is a national cooperative depository of translations of scientific and technical papers maintained by Crerar Library under contract with the association. Translations in the center, numbering 50,000 by 1960, are obtainable in photocopies through Photoduplication Service at Crerar Library, or on loan.

Information on translations available in the center may be obtained from the following publications:

SLA Author List of Translations, 1953.
SLA Author List of Translations, Supplement, 1954.
Bibliography of Translations of Russian Scientific and Technical Literature, originally published by The Library of Congress in 39 issues, 1953–1956.
Translation Monthly, published by Crerar Library for Special Libraries Association. Volumes 1 and 2 (1955 and 1956) included translations of papers from languages other than Russian; volumes 4 and 5 (1957 and 1958) included translations from all foreign languages. This publication was discontinued in December 1958.
Technical Translations, published semimonthly, beginning January 1959, by the U. S. Office of Technical Service, with the cooperation of the SLA Translations Center. All translations newly acquired in the SLA Center and in the OTS depository at The Library of Congress are announced in this journal.

Technical Translations is available on subscription from the Superintendent of Documents, Washington, D. C. All of the other publications are kept in print and may be purchased from the SLA Translations Center, The John Crerar Library, Chicago, Ill.

When translations are not included in the SLA Center, limited translation service may be obtained through Crerar's Research Information Service, or by referral to other translating agencies.

Chicago Chemical Library Foundation

In 1944, the Chicago Section of the American Chemical Society and the Chicago Chemists' Club set up a joint library committee to study the scientific literature needs of the Chicago area. As a result of the work of this committee, a decision was made in November 1946 to establish the Chicago Chemical Library Foundation (*3, 10*). In the constitution and bylaws of the CCLF adopted December 31, 1947, the object of the foundation is stated as follows (*4*):

The object of the Foundation is to assist in providing in the Chicago area a more complete collection of technical literature than presently exists, to assist in maintaining the same, and to assist in making the same available to the public. More specifically, it is the object of the Foundation to raise funds for the purchase of publications of professional use to chemists, to select publications which are available for purchase and which desirably may be added to the collection of The John Crerar Library and other libraries of non-profit organizations in the Chicago area, to purchase such publications and to present the same as gifts to such libraries.

In the initial planning, the object of the foundation was more broadly stated and is best quoted in full from the Progress Report, now out of print, which was issued by CCLF in 1951 (*4*).

> The object of the Foundation was to provide the Chicago area with a more complete collection of technical literature than existed at the time of the group's formation. The technical collections of any organization in the area, provided they were freely open to the public, were to be supplemented. Duplication of holdings simply for the sake of centralizing all chemical literature in one library was considered wasteful and was to be avoided. In addition, the Foundation did not propose to subsidize any institution. Its funds were to supplement where regular budgets were inadequate.
>
> The largest and most accessible collection proved to be that of The John Crerar Library. Its holdings were so extensive that, for all practical purposes, publications not located there were not held by any other library in the area. Accordingly, the activity of the Foundation has centered on filling in and augmenting the book and periodical holdings of this library with emphasis on chemistry and chemical technology . . .

The Board of Trustees of the foundation consists of five chemists, two selected by each of the sponsoring organization and one elected by the four members representing the sponsoring organizations. There are two standing committees, the Finance Committee, which is responsible for devising ways and means for obtaining and investing funds, and the Library Committee, whose function "is to continue to survey the needs of the Crerar Library, to evaluate the periodicals and books needed or desired by Crerar that cannot be covered in its regular budget, and to make recommendations to the Foundation's Trustees for appropriations to cover purchasing such publications" (*4*).

One of the first activities of the Library Committee was the preparation of a list of current periodicals to be added to those already received by Crerar Library. The first list authorized by the CCLF Trustees included 120 titles and many have been added since that time, including some of the scientific Russian journals published in English translation.

The following quotation from the 1951 Progress Report describes the program for acquiring current books on chemistry from CCLF grants to Crerar Library (*4*):

> The initial selection of books was based on the list of chemical and other technical books reprinted for the Alien Property Custodian, under the license issued to Edwards Bros., Ann Arbor, Michigan, and listed in their Catalog 6. Eighty percent of these were already available at Crerar. The Library Committee prepared a list from the remaining twenty percent. Later, since the Alien Property Custodian's authorizations already represented a selective list, it was decided that all of the books in the remaining twenty percent should be purchased. Some additional books from other Alien Property Custodian lists were also selected and approved for purchase.
>
> The Trustees have allocated Foundation funds and have authorized Crerar to purchase current foreign language books under a program similar to the Farmington Plan. This is a cooperative program in which library members of the Association of Research Libraries, and certain other libraries, agree to purchase every new book of research value on designated subjects from designated countries. Under this plan, Crerar Library is attempting to acquire all important foreign language books on chemical subjects. Principal emphasis has been on books from Western European countries, but books from Russia and from Central European countries are purchased when available. A beginning has been made toward purchasing books from South and Central American countries as well.

Through cooperation of the CCLF Library Committee and Crerar Library, books listed in *Chemical Abstracts* are checked against Crerar holdings. Those already acquired by Crerar are normally found to be from 60 to 75% of all *CA* book titles. Titles not yet acquired are reviewed by the Library Committee and book selectors on the Crerar Library staff for choice of additional books to be acquired by the library. On several occasions the CCLF trustees have approved special appropriations for this purpose.

As the first decade of the CCLF program came to a close, the trustees decided to continue seeking industrial support for this special aid to chemical research, giving assurance that the strong chemical library resources developed in Chicago will be maintained. It is difficult to ascertain when a library has reached the optimum coverage of literature of a particular field. Inventories of chemical periodicals in Crerar have shown approximately 60% of the titles indexed by *Chemical Abstracts* (*2*). A recent check of photocopy orders filled by Crerar indicates that the actual proportion of currently used chemical literature in the library is much higher than 60%. Analysis of photo orders from ten large chemical companies outside of Illinois, for a 6-month period, showed that copies of 1016 journal articles were requested. Of these the library was able to supply 87.9% from its own collections. Each of the ten companies is located near one or more good libraries and, it may be assumed, is able to get a large proportion of its needed literature at home. This assumption is supported by the fact that relatively few of the articles requested are in the more common chemical journals. The conclusion can be drawn that the percentage of the total current chemical literature in Crerar is substantially above the 87.9% of photo orders filled.

Oliver Wendell Holmes is quoted by Wilson (*10*) as saying: "Every library should be complete in something, if it were only the history of pinheads." Thanks to the constructive cooperation of the chemists of Chicago, Crerar Library has taken long strides toward becoming complete in chemistry, although there is still some margin not included. From the present high percentage of coverage, however, final completeness can probably be most economically attained through regional action.

The Midwest Inter-Library Center's Program

The objective of complete coverage on a regional basis of all periodicals currently indexed by *Chemical Abstracts* has been adopted by the Midwest Inter-Library Center.

The incorporation and formal organization of the Midwest Inter-Library Corp. early in 1949 were the culmination of years of discussion and planning for the development of a regional library in the Midwest. Grants of $750,000 from the Carnegie Corp. and $250,000 from the Rockefeller Foundation made possible the construction and equipment of a building to serve as the Midwest Inter-Library Center, which by decision of the MILC Corp. was located in Chicago. Twenty research libraries in ten midwestern states are affiliated with the center (*6, 7, 9*).

Among the cooperative programs sponsored by MILC are several which are designed to strengthen the library resources for research in the Midwest. One of these is a program designed to assure location of at least one copy of every periodical indexed by *Chemical Abstracts* in one of the MILC-affiliated libraries or in the center's own collections. Because of its primary interest in chemistry, Crerar Library initiated the project by identifying in the 1951 *CA* list those periodicals not recorded as being held by at least one MILC-affiliated library.

A report submitted to the MILC libraries in June 1954 showed that 1583 periodicals were not recorded as being in any of the sixteen libraries then affiliated with MILC. The *MILC Newsletter* issued July 31, 1955, reflects actions taken as a result of this report (9).

During the spring, member libraries have checked copies of the 255-page *Chemical Abstracts* periodical list (of 1951) against their own records to determine how many of the 1,583 periodicals recorded as not being in any MILC library were in fact being received. Tabulation of results on a master copy of the list provided the following data concerning these 1,583 titles:

Titles actually found to be in one or more MILC library	651
Titles not found to be in any MILC library	932
	1,583

Of the 651 titles found to be in MILC libraries, 357 were found to be coming to one library only, and 116 coming to two libraries.

. . . the next steps which have been agreed upon are: (1) The Center will ask those libraries which appear to be receiving titles that are unique within the MILC group to recognize that they are assuming a regional level of responsibility for such titles and to double check that subscriptions are in good order—that there might be reasonable assurance that the periodicals are in fact being received regularly. (2) That the Center will ask those libraries which offered to subscribe to certain titles not being received by any member to proceed to enter subscriptions to specified journals immediately. And (3) that the remaining 864 periodicals (a number derived by eliminating dead titles, etc.), not now being received by any MILC library, would comprise a group for ultimate subscription by The Center itself, but that the placing of subscriptions would be postponed until fiscal year 1956/57.

With grant support from the National Science Foundation, this acquisitions program was initiated; and by the end of 1960, some 1235 journals indexed in *Chemical Abstracts*, but not received by any of the twenty cooperating libraries, were being subscribed for by MILC. The continued objective of the program is to assure complete coverage of chemical literature among the research libraries of the Midwest.

Other Chicago Libraries

Reference has been made above to three Chicago area libraries other than Crerar and MILC—those in the University of Chicago, Northwestern University, and Illinois Institute of Technology. The University of Chicago Library, in particular, is an important center of chemical literature. To these larger libraries should be added a considerable number of company libraries, many of which, because of their more highly specialized interests, have some periodicals which are not located in other libraries of the area. Perhaps more important than any other one factor is the great chemical strength of Chicago area libraries, is the spirit of cooperation among these libraries which supports the efforts of the Chicago Chemical Library Foundation and the Midwest Inter-Library Center in their intensive programs to bring comprehensive coverage of chemical literature to the Midwest.

Literature Cited

(1) Bay, J. C., "The John Crerar Library, 1895–1944," Chicago, Ill., 1945.
(2) *Chemical Abstracts*, Columbus, Ohio, "List of Periodicals Abstracted by *Chemical Abstracts* with Key to Library Files and Other Information," 1951.
(3) *Chem. Bull.* **34** (3), 15–16 (1947).
(4) Chicago Chemical Library Foundation, Chicago, Ill., "Progress Report," 1951.
(5) John Crerar Library, "For Economy in Research," Research Information Service, John Crerar Library, Chicago, Ill., 1961.

(6) Esterquest, R. T., *College and Research Libraries* **15**, 47–94 (January 1954); Midwest Inter-Library Center, "Acquisition Policy and Program," 1950–53.
(7) Esterquest, R. T., *Library J.* **76**, 2031–5 (1951).
(8) Freyder, M., ADVANCES IN CHEM. SER., No. **16**, 42–6 (1956).
(9) Midwest Inter-Library Center, Annual Reports, and *Newsletter* No. **63** (July 31, 1955).
(10) Wilson, L. D., *Chem. Eng. News,* **25**, 776, 819 (1947).

BASED on paper presented to Division of Chemical Literature, Symposium on Searching the Chemical Literature, 130th Meeting, ACS, Atlantic City, N. J., September 1956. Revised 1960

INDEX

D

E

F

G

H

K

L

M

N

Q

R

— Notes —

— Notes —

— Notes —

— Notes —

— Notes —

— *Notes* —

— Notes —

— Notes —

— *Notes* —

— Notes —

— Notes —

— *Notes* —

— Notes —

— Notes —

— Notes —

— Notes —

HETERICK MEMORIAL LIBRARY
016.54 A51s 1961 onuu
American Chemical S/Searching the chemic
3 5111 00103 1206